P9-DMJ-887

TEST ITEMS, VOLUME I, FOR STEWART'S
CALCULUS
THIRD EDITION

JAMES STEWART
McMaster University

with contributions from

EDWARD SPITZNAGEL
JOAN THOMAS
ENGINEERING PRESS
LAUREL TECHNICAL SERVICES

Brooks/Cole Publishing Company

 An International Thomson Publishing Company

Pacific Grove · Albany · Bonn · Boston · Cincinnati · Detroit · London · Madrid · Melbourne
Mexico City · New York · Paris · San Francisco · Singapore · Tokyo · Toronto · Washington

COPYRIGHT© 1995 by Brooks/Cole Publishing Company
A division of International Thomson Publishing Inc.

I(T)P The ITP logo is a trademark under license.

For more information, contact:

BROOKS/COLE PUBLISHING COMPANY
511 Forest Lodge Road
Pacific Grove, CA 93950
USA

International Thomson Publishing Europe
Berkshire House 168-173
High Holborn
London WC1V 7AA
England

Thomas Nelson Australia
102 Dodds Street
South Melbourne, 3205
Victoria, Australia

Nelson Canada
1120 Birchmount Road
Scarborough, Ontario
Canada M1K 5G4

International Thomson Editores
Campos Eliseos 385, Piso 7
Col. Polanco
11560 México D. F. México

International Thomson Publishing GmbH
Königswinterer Strasse 418
3227 Bonn
Germany

International Thomson Publishing Asia
221 Henderson Road
#05-10 Henderson Building
Singapore 0315

International Thomson Publishing Japan
Hirakawacho Kyowa Building, 3F
2-2-1 Hirakawacho
Chiyoda-ku, Tokyo 102
Japan

All rights reserved. Instructors of classes using *Calculus,* 3rd edition, by James Stewart, as a textbook may reproduce material from this publication for classroom use. Otherwise, the text of this publication may not be reproduced, stored in a retrieval system, or transcribed, in any form or by any means—electronic, mechanical, photocopying, recording, or otherwise—without the prior written permission of the publisher, Brooks/Cole Publishing Company, Pacific Grove, California 93950.

Some of the problems and solutions contained herein are taken from *Calculus I Exam File, Calculus II Exam File, and Calculus III Exam File,* published by Engineering Press, Inc. These problems and solutions are used by permission of Engineering Press, Inc., the copyright owner.

The following professors contributed to the above mentioned volumes: D. R. Arterburn, New Mexico Institute of Mining and Technology; Bill Bompart, Augusta College; Peter Braunfeld, University of Illinois at Urbana-Champaign; Frances Burford, Galveston College; William E. Demmon, University of Wisconsin Center–Manitowoc; Mary Elick, Missouri Southern State College; Constance M. Elson, Ithaca College; Billy Finch, University of Florida; Joe Flowers, Northeast Missouri State University; Michael E. Frantz, University of LaVerne; Biswa N. Gosh, Hudson County College; LeRoy P. Hammerstrom, Eastern Nazarene College; John H. Jenkins, Embry-Riddle Aeronautical University; Anya M. Kroth, West Valley College; Ann F. Landry, Dutchess Community College; David H. Lankford, Bethel College; Eric M. Lederer, University of Colorado at Denver and Red Rocks Community College; John Martin, Santa Rosa Junior College; Varoujan Mazmanian, Stevens Institute of Technology; Thomas A. Metzger, University of Pittsburgh; Alejandro Perez, Laredo Junior College; Calvin E. Piston, John Brown University; John Putz, Alma College; Michael Schneider, Belleville Area College; Walter S. Sizer, Moorhead State University; Alan Stickney, Wittenberg University; Joseph F. Stokes, Western Kentucky University; Norman Sweet, State University College; Bill W. Vannatta, Temple Junior College; Robert P. Webber, Longwood College; Joseph E. Wiest, West Virginia Wesleyan College.

Printed in the United States of America

5   4   3   2   1

ISBN 0-534-21810-5

Preface

These Test Items supplement Chapters 0 through 10 of Calculus, 3rd Edition, by James Stewart. The Test Items provide a set of test questions and answers for each section. The questions are rated easy, medium or hard. These Test Items also include problems designed to be solved using a graphing utility or calculators. Such problems are denoted by $\boxed{\text{G}}$ icon (for graphing) or by the $\boxed{\text{C}}$ icon (for calculators).

Electronic versions of these Test Items are available on EXP-TEST™ and Exam Builder™. The electronic versions allow you to select and add your own questions to create exams.

Contents

Contents (Continued)

Contents (Continued)

Contents (Continued)

Calculus, 3rd Edition
by James Stewart
Review and Preview, Section 1
Functions and Their Graphs

1. Find the largest value in the domain of the function $f(x) = 7 - 2x$, $-1 \le x \le 6$.

   A) 9   B) 6   C) 1   D) 2

   E) -1 F) -7 G) 7   H) -2

   Answer: 6 (easy)

2. Find the largest value in the range of the function $f(x) = 7 - 2x$, $-1 \le x \le 6$.

   A) 7   B) 1   C) 9   D) -7

   E) -2 F) 2   G) 6   H) -1

   Answer: 9 (easy)

3. Find the smallest value in the domain of the function $f(x) = \sqrt{2x - 5}$.

   A) 2   B) 5/2   C) 5   D) 2/5

   E) -2 F) 1   G) 0   H) -5

   Answer: 5/2 (easy)

4. Find the largest value in the range of the function $f(x) = 3 - 2x^2$.

   A) $-2/3$ B) 2/3   C) 3   D) -2

   E) -3 F) $-3/2$ G) 2   H) 3/2

   Answer: 3 (medium)

5. The domain of the function $f(x) = \sqrt{1 - x - x^2}$ is a closed interval $[a, b]$. Find its length $b - a$.

   A) $\sqrt{10}/2$ B) $\sqrt{2}/2$ C) $\sqrt{3}$ D) $\sqrt{5}$

   E) $\sqrt{5}/2$ F) $\sqrt{10}/3$ G) $\sqrt{2}$ H) $\sqrt{3}/2$

   Answer: $\sqrt{5}$ (medium)

6. Find the smallest value in the range of the function $f(x) = |2x| + |2x + 3|$.

   A) 2   B) 3   C) 5   D) 1/2

   E) 3/2   F) 5/2   G) 0   H) 1

   Answer: 3 (medium)

7. Find the smallest value in the domain of the function $f(x) = \sqrt{\frac{x}{\pi - x}}$.

A)0   B)$\pi - 2$ C)$\pi/2$ D)$\pi - 1$
E)$-\pi$ F)$1 - \pi$ G)$-\pi/2$ H)π

Answer: 0 (medium)

8. A rectangle has an area of $16 \ m^2$. Express the perimeter of the rectangle as a function of the length of one of its sides.

Answer: Let the length and width of the rectangle be l and w respectively. Then the area is

$lw = 16$, so that $w = 16/l$. The perimeter is $P = 2l + 2w$, so $P(l) = 2l + 2(16/l) = 2l + 32/l$, and the domain of P is $l > 0$, since lengths must be positive quantities.

(medium)

9. Express the surface area of a cube as a function of its volume.

Answer: Let the volume of the cube be V and the length of an edge be l. Then $V = l^3$ so

$l = \sqrt[3]{V}$, and the surface area will be $S(V) = 6\left(\sqrt[3]{V}\right)^2 = 6V^{2/3}$, with domain $V > 0$.

(medium)

10. Find the range of the function $f(x) = 3x - 12$, $-2 \leq x \leq 6$.

A) $[-20, -18]$ B) $(-20, -18)$ C) $[0, 6]$ D) $[6, \infty]$
E) $[-18, 6]$ F) $(-18, 6)$ G) $[-6, 18]$ H) $\mathbf{R}$

Answer: $[-18, 6]$ (easy)

11. Find the domain of the function $f(x) = \frac{1+x}{1-x}$.

A)$(-\infty, -1), (-1, \infty)$ B)$(-\infty, 1), (1, \infty)$ C)$(-\infty, -1)$
D)$(-1, \infty)$ E)$(-\infty, 1)$ F)$(1, \infty)$
G)$(-1, 1)$ H)$\mathbf{R}$

Answer: $(-\infty, 1), (1, \infty)$ (medium)

12. Find the domain of the function $f(x) = \sqrt{x^2 - 9} - 3$.

A)$(-3, \infty)$ B)$[3, \infty)$ C)$(-3, 3)$
D)$[-3, 3]$ E)$(-\infty, 3), (3, \infty)$ F)$(-\infty, -3], [-3, \infty)$
G)$[3, \infty)$ H)$\mathbf{R}$

Answer: $(-\infty, -3], [3, \infty)$ (medium)

13. Find the range of the function $f(x) = |x - 1| + x - 1$.

A) $[1, \infty)$ B) $(1, \infty)$ C) $[0, \infty)$ D) $(0, \infty)$
E) $[-1, \infty)$ F) $(-1, \infty)$ G) $[0, 1]$ H) $\mathbf{R}$

Answer: $[0, \infty)$ (medium)

14. Let $f(x) = \sqrt{x^2 + 9}$ and let $g(x) = \sqrt{x}$. Find the value of $(f + g)(x)$ when $x = 4$.

A) 8   B) 6   C) 2   D) 5
E) 9   F) 7   G) 3   H) 4

Answer: 7 (easy)

15. Find the range of the function $f(x) = \frac{1}{x} - x$.

A) $(0, \infty)$ B) $(-\infty, 0)$ C) $(1, \infty)$ D) $(-\infty, 1)$
E) $\{0\}$ F) $(-\infty, 0), (0, \infty)$ G) $(-\infty, 1), (1, \infty)$ H) $\mathbf{R}$

Answer: $\mathbf{R}$ (medium)

16. Let $f(x) = \sqrt{x^2 + 4}$ and $g(x) = -\sqrt{x^2 - 4}$. Find the domain of $(g \circ f)(x)$.

A) $(-\infty, 0]$ B) $(2, \infty)$ C) $(-\infty, -2)$ D) $(-\infty, 2), (2, \infty)$
E) $[-2, \infty)$ F) $(-\infty, -2]$ G) $(-\infty, -2], [2, \infty)$ H) $\mathbf{R}$

Answer: $\mathbf{R}$ (medium)

17. Let $f(x) = \sqrt{x^2 - 4}$ and $g(x) = \sqrt{x + 1}$. Find the domain of $(\frac{g}{f})(x)$.

A) $(-\infty, -2], [2, \infty)$ B) $(\infty, -2), (2, \infty)$ C) $(-1, \infty)$
D) $[-1, \infty)$ E) $[2, \infty)$ F) $(2, \infty)$
G) $(-1, 2)$ H) $\mathbf{R}$

Answer: $(\infty, -2), (2, \infty)$ (medium)

18. Determine whether $f(x) = x - \frac{1}{x}$ is odd, even, or neither.

Answer: odd (easy)

19. Determine whether $f(x) = \frac{x^2 + 1}{x}$ is odd, even, or neither.

Answer: odd (easy)

20. Let $f(x) = 2x + 3$ and let $g(x) = 2 - 3x$. Find the value of $(fg)(x)$ when $x = 1$.

A) 1   B) 7   C) -1 D) 5
E) -5 F) 3   G) 9   H) -3

Answer: -5 (easy)

21. Let $f(x) = x + 3$ and let $g(x) = 2x$. Find the value of $(f \circ g)(x)$ when $x = 1$.

A) 9   B) -5 C) -1 D) 5
E) 7   F) 3   G) -3 H) 1

Answer: 5 (easy)

22. Let $f(x) = x^2$ and let $g(x) = 2x$. Find the value of $(g \circ f)(x)$ when $x = 3$.

A) 36   B) 144   C) 48   D) 72
E) 18   F) 4   G) 9   H) 6

Answer: 18 (medium)

23. Let $f(x) = x^2 - 1$. Find the value of $(f \circ f \circ f)(x)$ when $x = 2$.

A) 45   B) 65   C) 27   D) 63
E) 8   F) 91   G) 21   H) 3

Answer: 63 (medium)

24. Let $f(x) = 2x$ and let $(f \circ g)(x) = x^2$. Find the value of $g(4)$.

A) 6   B) 2   C) 16   D) 8
E) 0   F) 1   G) 12   H) 4

Answer: 8 (medium)

25. Let $f(x) = 2x$ and let $(g \circ f)(x) = x^2$. Find the value of $g(4)$.

A) 4   B) 2   C) 16   D) 12
E) 8   F) 1   G) 0   H) 6

Answer: 4 (medium)

Review and Preview, Section 2
Types of Functions; Shifting and Scaling

26. Relative to the graph of $y = x^2$, the graph of $y = (x - 2)^2$ is changed in what way?

A) shifted 2 units up   B) compressed vertically by the factor 2
C) compressed horizontally by the factor 2   D) shifted 2 units to the left
E) shifted 2 units to the right   F) shifted 2 units down
G) stretched vertically by the factor 2   H) stretched horizontally by the factor 2

Answer: shifted 2 units to the right (easy)

27. Relative to the graph of $y = x^2$, the graph of $y = x^2 - 2$ is changed in what way?

A) shifted 2 units down   B) stretched horizontally by the factor 2
C) shifted 2 units to the right   D) stretched vertically by the factor 2
E) compressed horizontally by the factor 2   F) compressed vertically by the factor 2
G) shifted 2 units up   H) shifted 2 units to the left

Answer: shifted 2 units down (easy)

28. Relative to the graph of $y = x^3$, the graph of $y = 2x^3$ is changed in what way?

A) compressed horizontally by the factor 2
B) shifted 2 units down
C) stretched vertically by the factor 2
D) stretched horizontally by the factor 2
E) shifted 2 units up
F) compressed vertically by the factor 2
G) shifted 2 units to the right
H) shifted 2 units to the left

Answer: stretched vertically by the factor 2 (easy)

29. Relative to the graph of $y = x^2 + 2$, the graph of $y = 4x^2 + 2$ is changed in what way?

A) compressed vertically by the factor 2
B) stretched horizontally by the factor 2
C) compressed horizontally by the factor 2
D) shifted 2 units up
E) shifted 2 units to the right
F) stretched vertically by the factor 2
G) shifted 2 units to the left
H) shifted 2 units down

Answer: compressed horizontally by the factor 2 (medium)

30. Relative to the graph of $y = \sin x$, the graph of $y = \sin(x - 3)$ is changed in what way?

A) compressed horizontally by the factor 3
B) shifted 3 units to the right
C) compressed vertically by the factor 3
D) shifted 3 units up
E) shifted 3 units to the left
F) stretched vertically by the factor 3
G) shifted 3 units down
H) stretched horizontally by the factor 3

Answer: shifted 3 units to the right (medium)

31. Relative to the graph of $y = x^2$, the graph of $y = 4x^2$ can be thought of as expanded vertically by the factor 4. In what other way can it be thought of as being changed?

A) shifted 2 units down
B) shifted 4 units down
C) stretched horizontally by the factor 2
D) compressed horizontally by the factor 4
E) shifted 2 units up
F) shifted 4 units up
G) compressed horizontally by the factor 2
H) stretched horizontally by the factor 4

Answer: compressed horizontally by the factor 2 (medium)

32. Relative to the graph of $y = \sin x$, where x is in radians, the graph of $y = \sin x$, where x is in degrees, is changed in what way?

A) stretched vertically by the factor $180/\pi$
B) compressed horizontally by the factor $180/\pi$
C) compressed horizontally by the factor $90/\pi$
D) stretched horizontally by the factor $90/\pi$
E) compressed vertically by the factor $90/\pi$
F) stretched vertically by the factor $90/\pi$
G) stretched horizontally by the factor $180/\pi$
H) compressed vertically by the factor $180/\pi$

Answer: stretched horizontally by the factor $180/\pi$ (hard)

33. Classify the function $f(x) = \frac{x^2+x}{x}$.

A) power function   B) root function   C) polynomial function
D) rational function   E) algebraic function   F) trigonometric function
G) exponential function   H) logarithmic function

Answer: rational function (easy)

34. Classify the function $f(x) = x^{\frac{3}{2}} + 2x^{\frac{1}{2}} + 4$.

A) power function   B) root function   C) polynomial function
D) rational function   E) algebraic function   F) trigonometric function
G) exponential function   H) logarithmic function

Answer: algebraic function (easy)

35. Classify the function $f(x) = \sin(5)\, x^2 + \sin(3)\, x$.

A) power function   B) root function   C) polynomial function
D) rational function   E) algebraic function   F) trigonometric function
G) exponential function   H) logarithmic function

Answer: polynomial function (easy)

Review and Preview, Section 3
Graphing Calculators and Computers

36. $\boxed{G}$ Determine an appropriate viewing rectangle for the graph of the function $f(x) = 6x^2 + x - 10$.

A) $[-50, 50] \times [-50, 50]$ B) $[0, 10] \times [0, 10]$ C) $[-5, 10] \times [-10, 50]$
D) $[-5, 5] \times [-5, 5]$ E) $[-5, 5] \times [-10, 10]$ F) $[-50, 10] \times [-10, 100]$
G) $[-5, 50] \times [-5, 10]$ H) $[-10, 10] \times [-5, 5]$

Answer: $[-5, 5] \times [-10, 10]$ (easy)

37. $\boxed{G}$ Determine an appropriate viewing rectangle for the graph of the function $f(x) = \sqrt[3]{21 - x^2}$.

A) $[-4, 4] \times [0, 5]$ B) $[-10, 10] \times [0, 5]$ C) $[-100, 100] \times [-5, 5]$
D) $[-10, 10] \times [-5, 5]$ E) $[0, 10] \times [0, 10]$ F) $[-5, 5] \times [-3, 3]$
G) $[-50, 50] \times [-10, 10]$ H) $[-1, 1] \times [-1, 1]$

Answer: $[-10, 10] \times [-5, 5]$ (easy)

38. $\boxed{G}$ Determine an appropriate viewing rectangle for the graph of the function $f(x) = \frac{3x}{x^4+75}$.

A) $[-10, 10] \times [-10, 10]$ B) $[-1, 1] \times [-1, 1]$ C) $[-10, 10] \times [-1, 1]$
D) $[-100, 100] \times [-1, 1]$ E) $[-100, 100] \times [-10, 10]$ F) $[-5, 5] \times [-5, 5]$
G) $[-5, 5] \times [-0.5, 0.5]$ H) $[-1, 1] \times [-10, 10]$

Answer: $[-10, 10] \times [-1, 1]$ (easy)

39.   **G** Determine an appropriate viewing rectangle for the graph of the function $f(x) = 4 \cos 50x$.

A) $[-10, 10] \times [-10, 10]$ B) $[-5, 5] \times [-5, 5]$ C) $[-100, 100] \times [-5, 5]$
D) $[0, 0.5] \times [0, 5]$ E) $[-0.5, 0.5] \times [-1, 1]$ F) $[-0.5, 0.5] \times [-5, 5]$
G) $[-5, 5] \times [-1, 1]$ H) $[-1, 1] \times [-1, 1]$

Answer: $[-0.5, 0.5] \times [-5, 5]$ (easy)

40.   **G** Determine an appropriate viewing rectangle for the graph of the function $f(x) = 4x - |3x^2 - 10|$.

A) $[-5, 5] \times [-5, 2]$ B) $[-50, 20] \times [-50, 10]$ C) $[-2, 5] \times [-1, 10]$
D) $[-10, 10] \times [-500, 500]$ E) $[-10, 10] \times [-500, 5]$ F) $[-2, 5] \times [-15, 10]$
G) $[-10, 5] \times [1, 10]$ H) $[0, 10] \times [-2, 5]$

Answer: $[-2, 5] \times [-15, 10]$ (easy)

41.   **G** Determine the appropriate functions of x needed in order to graph the equation $4y^2 - x^2 - 2x = 1$.

Answer: $y = \frac{x+1}{2}, y = -\frac{x+1}{2}$ (medium)

42.   **G** Determine the appropriate functions of x needed in order to graph the ellipse $2y^2 + x^2 = 1$.

Answer: $y = \frac{\sqrt{1-x^2}}{\sqrt{2}}, y = -\frac{\sqrt{1-x^2}}{\sqrt{2}}$ (medium)

43.   **G** Determine the number of real solutions of the equation $5x^4 - 3x^2 = 10x^5 + x^3 - 5$.

A) 0   B) 1   C) 2   D) 3
E) 4   F) 5   G) 6   H) 7

Answer: 1 (medium)

44.   **G** Determine the number of solutions of the equation $8 \sin 2x - 1 = x$.

A) 0   B) 3   C) 4   D) 7
E) 9   F) 10   G) 11   H) 12

Answer: 9 (medium)

45.   **G** Find the difference of the largest and smallest solutions of the equation $5x^4 + x^2 - 1 = 2^x$ rounded to two decimal places.

A) 2.50   B) 2.20   C) 2.10   D) 1.70
E) 1.10   F) 1.20   G) 1.30   H) 1.50

Answer: 1.50 (medium)

46.	$\boxed{\text{G}}$ Find the difference of the largest and smallest solutions of the equation $-x^2 + 8x + 5 = \sin x$ rounded to two decimal places.

A) 9.14	B) 8.29	C) 0.65	D) 8.91
E) 6.15	F) 3.14	G) 10.11	H) 11.21

Answer: 9.14 (medium)

47.	$\boxed{\text{G}}$ Find apporoximate values of all real solutions of the equation $x^5 + 8x^3 + 2x^2 + 1 = 0$.

A) .587	B) −.587	C) −0.35	D) −.587, −0.35
E) .587, −0.35	F) 0.35	G) 0.35, −2.31	H) 0.35, .587

Answer: −.587 (medium)

Review and Preview, Section 4
Principles of Problem Solving

48.	The solution set of the inequality $|x| + |x - 1| \le 5$ is an interval of the form $[a, b]$. Find the value of $b - a$ (that is, the length of the interval).

A) 6	B) 7/5	C) 3/2	D) 7/3
E) 3	F) 5/2	G) 4	H) 5

Answer: 5 (hard)

49.	Find the larger of the two roots of the equation $\left|\frac{2x-1}{x+1}\right| = 3$.

A) − 4/3	B) − 3/4	C) − 2/3	D) − 5/4
E) − 3/5	F) − 5/2	G) − 2/5	H) − 3/2

Answer: − 2/5 (hard)

50.	Given $|x - 4| = 2x + 1$ find the value of x.

A) − 1	B) − 5	C) 5	D) 1
E) 0	F) 2	G) − 2	H) 3

Answer: 1 (medium)

51.	Find the final digit in the number 563^{563}.

A) 1	B) 2	C) 3	D) 4
E) 6	F) 7	G) 8	H) 9

Answer: 7 (medium)

52. Find the final digit in the number 312^{1997}.

A) 1   B) 2   C) 3   D) 4
E) 6   F) 7   G) 8   H) 9

Answer: 2 (medium)

53. Bob can paint the house in 6 days. Sue can pain the house in 4 days. Find the number of days it takes them to paint the house together.

A) $3\frac{1}{2}$ days   B) $3\frac{1}{3}$ days   C) $3\frac{1}{5}$ days   D) 3 days
E) $2\frac{2}{3}$ days   F) $2\frac{2}{5}$ days   G) $2\frac{1}{2}$ days   H) 2 days

Answer: $2\frac{2}{5}$ days (medium)

54. Working together, Mark and Lisa did the job in 5 hours. Working alone, it takes Mark 8 hours. Find the amount of time it takes Lisa to do the job by herself.

A) 11 hours   B) 12 hours   C) $12\frac{1}{2}$ hours   D) $12\frac{4}{5}$ hours
E) 13 hours   F) $13\frac{1}{3}$ hours   G) $13\frac{1}{2}$ hours   H) $13\frac{3}{5}$ hours

Answer: $13\frac{1}{3}$ hours (medium)

55. The sum of two numbers is $1\frac{5}{6}$ and their product is $\frac{1}{2}$. find the square of the difference.

A) $1\frac{13}{36}$ B) $2\frac{11}{25}$ C) $1\frac{11}{36}$ D) 2
E) 1   F) $2\frac{11}{36}$ G) $2\frac{17}{36}$ H) none of the above

Answer: $1\frac{13}{36}$ (medium)

56. The sum of two numbers is $1\frac{5}{12}$ and their product is $\frac{1}{2}$. find the square of the difference.

A) $\frac{25}{144}$ B) $\frac{49}{144}$ C) $1\frac{1}{144}$ D) $1\frac{25}{144}$
E) $\frac{1}{144}$ F) $\frac{1}{36}$ G) $\frac{121}{144}$ H) none of the above

Answer: $\frac{1}{144}$ (medium)

57. If $f_0 = \frac{1}{1-x}$ and $f_{n+1} = f_0 \circ f_n$ for $n = 0, 1, 2, \ldots$, find $f_{101}(2)$.

A) 1   B) 2   C) 202   D) -1
E) $\frac{1}{100}$ F) $\frac{1}{2}$ G) 32   H) none of the above

Answer: $\frac{1}{2}$ (medium)

Calculus, 3rd Edition
by James Stewart
Chapter 1, Section 1
The Tangent and Velocity Problems

1. For the curve $y = x^2$, find the slope of the tangent line at the point $(3, 9)$.

   A) 2   B) 1   C) 3   D) 6
   E) 5   F) 9   G) 4   H) 8

   Answer: 6 (easy)

2. For the curve $y = x^2$, find the slope M_{PQ} of the secant line through the points $P = (1, 1)$ and $Q = (2, 4)$.

   A) 8   B) 2   C) 5   D) 4
   E) 1   F) 9   G) 3   H) 6

   Answer: 3 (easy)

3. For the curve $y = \sqrt{x} + x$, find the slope M_{PQ} of the secant line through the points $P = (1, f(1))$ and $Q = (4, f(4))$.

   A) 2   B) 1   C) 2/3   D) 3/2
   E) 4/3   F) 3/4   G) 1/2   H) 3

   Answer: 4/3 (medium)

4. The displacement in meters of a particle moving in a straight line is given by $s = t^2 + t$, where t is measured in seconds. Find the average velocity in meters per second over the time period $[1, 2]$.

   A) 5   B) 3   C) 8   D) 1
   E) 4   F) 6   G) 2   H) 9

   Answer: 4 (medium)

5. If a ball is thrown into the air with a velocity of 80 ft/s, its height after t seconds is given by $y = 80t - 16t^2$. Find the average velocity in ft/s for the time period beginning when $t = 1$ and lasting 2 seconds.

   A) 20   B) 40   C) 30   D) 10
   E) 81   F) 36   G) 32   H) 16

   Answer: 16 (hard)

Chapter 1, Section 2
The Limit of a Function

6. Find the value of the limit $\lim\limits_{x \to 2} (x^2 + 2)$.

   A) 12   B) 3   C) 2   D) 6
   E) 9   F) 4   G) 8   H) 10

   Answer: 6 (easy)

Use the graph below for the following questions:

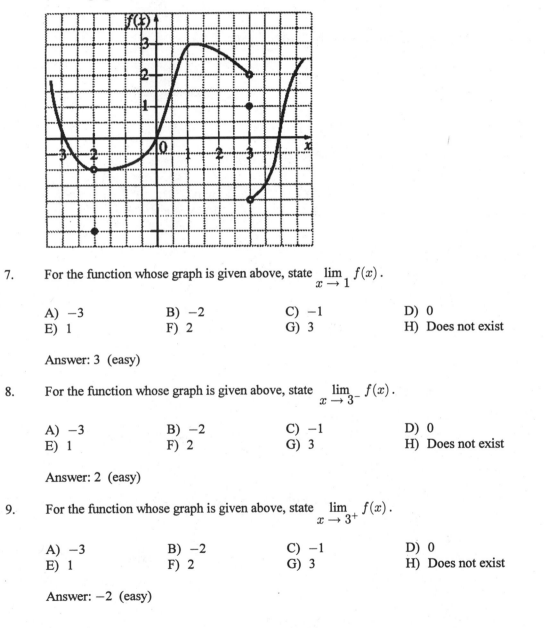

7. For the function whose graph is given above, state $\lim\limits_{x \to 1} f(x)$.

   A) −3   B) −2   C) −1   D) 0
   E) 1   F) 2   G) 3   H) Does not exist

   Answer: 3 (easy)

8. For the function whose graph is given above, state $\lim\limits_{x \to 3^-} f(x)$.

   A) −3   B) −2   C) −1   D) 0
   E) 1   F) 2   G) 3   H) Does not exist

   Answer: 2 (easy)

9. For the function whose graph is given above, state $\lim\limits_{x \to 3^+} f(x)$.

   A) −3   B) −2   C) −1   D) 0
   E) 1   F) 2   G) 3   H) Does not exist

   Answer: −2 (easy)

10. For the function whose graph is given above, state $\lim\limits_{x \to 3} f(x)$.

A) -3 B) -2 C) -1 D) 0
E) 1   F) 2   G) 3   H) Does not exist

Answer: Does not exist (easy)

11. For the function whose graph is given above, state $f(3)$.

A) -3 B) -2 C) -1 D) 0
E) 1   F) 2   G) 3   H) Does not exist

Answer: 1 (easy)

12. For the function whose graph is given above, state $\lim\limits_{x \to -2^-} f(x)$.

A) -3 B) -2 C) -1 D) 0
E) 1   F) 2   G) 3   H) Does not exist

Answer: -1 (easy)

13. For the function whose graph is given above, state $\lim\limits_{x \to -2^+} f(x)$.

A) -3 B) -2 C) -1 D) 0
E) 1   F) 2   G) 3   H) Does not exist

Answer: -1 (easy)

14. For the function whose graph is given above, state $\lim\limits_{x \to -2} f(x)$.

A) -3 B) -2 C) -1 D) 0
E) 1   F) 2   G) 3   H) Does not exist

Answer: -1 (easy)

15. For the function whose graph is given above, state $f(-2)$.

A) -3 B) -2 C) -1 D) 0
E) 1   F) 2   G) 3   H) Does not exist

Answer: -3 (easy)

16. $\boxed{\text{C}}$ Evaluate the function $f(x) = \frac{x-2}{x^3-8}$ at values near 2. Use the results to guess the value of $\lim\limits_{x \to 2} \frac{x-2}{x^3-8}$.

A) $\frac{1}{2}$ B) $\frac{1}{4}$ C) $\frac{1}{8}$ D) $\frac{1}{12}$
E) 1   F) 2   G) -1 H) does not exist

Answer: $\frac{1}{12}$ (medium)

17. **C** Evaluate the function $f(x) = \frac{x+2}{x^3-8}$ at values near 2. Use the results to guess the value of $\lim\limits_{x \to 2} \frac{x+2}{x^3-8}$.

A) $\frac{1}{2}$ B) $\frac{1}{4}$ C) $\frac{1}{8}$ D) $\frac{1}{12}$

E) 1   F) 2   G) -1 H) does not exist

Answer: does not exist (medium)

18. **C** Evaluate the function $f(x) = \frac{4-x^2}{x^2+3x-10}$ at values near 2. Use the results to guess the value of $\lim\limits_{x \to 2} \frac{4-x^2}{x^2+3x-10}$.

A) $-\frac{2}{5}$ B) $-\frac{3}{7}$ C) $-\frac{3}{5}$ D) $-\frac{1}{5}$

E) $-\frac{4}{7}$ F) $-\frac{2}{7}$ G) $-\frac{4}{7}$ H) does not exist

Answer: $-\frac{4}{7}$ (medium)

19. **G** Graph the function $y = \frac{x+2}{x^4-16}$ to guess the value of $\lim\limits_{x \to -2} \frac{x+2}{x^4-16}$.

A) $-\frac{1}{16}$ B) $\frac{1}{16}$ C) $-\frac{1}{8}$ D) $\frac{1}{8}$

E) $-\frac{1}{32}$ F) $\frac{1}{32}$ G) -1 H) does not exist

Answer: $-\frac{1}{32}$ (medium)

20. **G** Graph the function $y = \frac{3^x-1}{x}$ to guess the value of $\lim\limits_{x \to 0} \frac{3^x-1}{x}$ to two decimal places.

A) 1.00   B) 1.90   C) -1.10 D) 1.10

E) -1.00 F) 2.10   G) -1.90 H) does not exist

Answer: 1.10 (medium)

Chapter 1, Section 3
Calculating Limits Using the Limit Laws

21. Find the value of the limit $\lim\limits_{x \to 1} \left(x^{17} - x + 3\right)$.

A) -4 B) 3   C) -2 D) 1

E) -8 F) 2   G) 0   H) -16

Answer: 3 (easy)

22. Find the value of the limit $\lim\limits_{x \to 2} \frac{x^3-8}{x-2}$.

A) 8   B) 4   C) 12   D) 2

E) 6   F) 1   G) 0   H) 3

Answer: 12 (medium)

23. Find the value of the limit $\lim\limits_{x \to 2^+} \frac{|x-2|}{x-2}$.

A) 4   B) -4 C) 1/2   D) -2
E) -1 F) 2   G) 1   H) $-1/2$

Answer: 1 (medium)

24. Find the value of the limit $\lim\limits_{x \to 2^-} \frac{|x-2|}{x-2}$.

A) 1   B) -2 C) 1/2   D) -4
E) -1 F) 4   G) $-1/2$ H) 2

Answer: -1 (hard)

25. Find the value of the limit $\lim\limits_{x \to 1} \frac{x-1}{\sqrt{x}-1}$.

A) $\sqrt{2}$ B) 1   C) -1 D) $-\sqrt{2}$
E) 2   F) -4 G) 4   H) -2

Answer: 2 (medium)

26. Find the value of the limit $\lim\limits_{x \to 1} \frac{\sqrt[3]{x}-1}{\sqrt{x}-1}$.

A) 1   B) 0   C) 2/3   D) $\sqrt{2/3}$
E) $\sqrt{3/2}$ F) 3/2   G) $\sqrt{3-1}$ H) $\sqrt{2-1}$

Answer: 2/3 (hard)

27. Let $f(x) = 2x - 1$ if x is rational; $= 1$ if x is irrational. Find the value a for which $\lim\limits_{x \to a} f(x)$ exists.

A) 1/2   B) -2 C) 2   D) $-1/2$
E) 3/4   F) $-3/4$ G) -1 H) 1

Answer: 1 (medium)

28. Find the value of the limit $\lim\limits_{x \to 1^+} \frac{x^2+x-2}{|x-1|}$.

A) -3 B) 1   C) 2   D) 0
E) 3   F) 1/2   G) -2 H) does not exist

Answer: 3 (hard)

29. Find the value of the limit $\lim\limits_{x \to 4^-} \frac{|x-4|}{x-4}$.

A) ∞ B) 1   C) 0   D) -1
E) 2   F) -3 G) 4   H) does not exist

Answer: -1 (medium)

30. Find the value of the limit $\lim\limits_{x \to -2} \left[\frac{1}{x+2} + \frac{4}{x^2-4} \right]$.

A) -4 B) -2 C) $-1/2$ D) $-1/4$
E) $1/4$ F) $1/2$ G) 2 H) 4

Answer: $-1/4$ (hard)

31. Find the value of the limit $\lim\limits_{x \to 1} \frac{x^3-1}{x^2-1}$.

A) $1/3$ B) $1/6$ C) $1/2$ D) $3/2$
E) 1 F) $1/4$ G) 2 H) 3

Answer: $3/2$ (hard)

32. Find the value of the limit $\lim\limits_{x \to 1} \frac{|x|-x}{x-1}$.

A) 2 B) $1/2$ C) $-1/2$ D) 1
E) -1 F) $-1/4$ G) $1/4$ H) 0

Answer: 0 (hard)

33. Find the value of the limit $\lim\limits_{x \to 0^-} x \sin \frac{1}{x}$.

A) $-\infty$ B) $-1/2$ C) 1 D) -1
E) 0 F) $\sin 1$ G) $1/2$ H) does not exist

Answer: 0 (medium)

34. Find the value of the limit $\lim\limits_{x \to 3^-} \frac{|x-3|}{x-3}$.

A) -4 B) -2 C) -1 D) 0
E) 2 F) 4 G) 6 H) does not exist

Answer: -1 (medium)

35. Find the value of the limit $\lim\limits_{h \to 0} \frac{(h-2)^2-4}{h}$.

A) 2 B) 1 C) -2 D) -4
E) $1/2$ F) 4 G) -1 H) $-1/2$

Answer: -4 (medium)

36. Find the value of the limit $\lim\limits_{h \to 0} \frac{(h+2)^2-4}{h}$.

A) 1 B) 2 C) -1 D) -4
E) 4 F) $-1/2$ G) $1/2$ H) -2

Answer: 4 (medium)

37. Find the value of the limit $\lim\limits_{x \to 3} \frac{1/x - 1/3}{x - 3}$.

A) 1/12   B) 1/6   C) $-1/6$ D) 1/3
E) $-1/9$ F) $-1/12$ G) $-1/3$ H) 1/9

Answer: $-1/9$ (hard)

38. Find the value of the limit $\lim\limits_{x \to -1} \frac{x^2 + 2x + 1}{x^2 - x - 2}$.

A) 1   B) 2   C) -2 D) 0
E) -1 F) 1/2   G) $-1/2$ H) does not exist

Answer: 0 (medium)

39. Find the value of the limit $\lim\limits_{x \to 1} \frac{x-1}{x^4-1}$.

A) 0   B) 2   C) 4   D) 8
E) 1/4   F) 1/8   G) 1/32   H) 1/64

Answer: 1/4 (medium)

40. Find the value of the limit $\lim\limits_{x \to 1} \frac{x^4-1}{x-1}$.

A) 0   B) 1   C) 2   D) 3
E) 4   F) 5   G)   H) does not exist

Answer: 4 (medium)

41. Find the value of the limit $\lim\limits_{x \to 4} \frac{x-4}{\sqrt{x}-2}$.

A) 0   B) 2   C) 4   D) 8
E) 1/4   F) 1/8   G) 1/32   H) 1/64

Answer: 4 (hard)

42. Find the value of the limit $\lim\limits_{x \to 2} \frac{x^2+x-6}{x^2-5x+6}$.

A) -5 B) -3 C) -1 D) 0
E) 1   F) 3   G) 5   H) 6

Answer: -5 (medium)

43. Find the value of the limit $\lim\limits_{x \to 2} \frac{x-2}{x^4-16}$.

A) 0   B) 2   C) 4   D) 8
E) 1/4   F) 1/8   G) 1/32   H) 1/64

Answer: 1/32 (medium)

Chapter 1, Section 4
The Precise Definition of Limit

44. How close to 7 do we have to take x so that $3x + 4$ is within a distance of 0.2 from 25 ?

    A) 1/21   B) 1/10   C) 1/15   D) 1/14
    E) 1/28   F) 1/7   G) 1/25   H) 1/5

    Answer: 1/15 (medium)

45. In using the ϵ, δ definition to prove that $\lim\limits_{x \to 2} (2x - 1) = 3$, when ϵ is $1/2$, what is the largest value that δ can have?

    A) 3/8   B) 7/8   C) 5/8   D) 3/4
    E) 1/8   F) 1   G) 1/4   H) 1/2

    Answer: 1/4 (medium)

46. In using the ϵ, δ definition to prove that $\lim\limits_{x \to 0} x^2 = 0$, when ϵ is $1/4$, what is the largest value that δ can have?

    A) 1/2   B) 4   C) 1/4   D) 1
    E) 1/16   F) 2   G) 0   H) 1/8

    Answer: 1/2 (medium)

47. In using the ϵ, δ definition to prove that $\lim\limits_{x \to 1} x^2 = 1$, when ϵ is 1, what is the largest value that δ can have?

    A) 2   B) 1/2   C) $\sqrt{2} - 1$ D) 1/4
    E) $\sqrt{2}/2$ F) 1   G) $\sqrt{2}$ H) $\sqrt{2} + 1$

    Answer: $\sqrt{2} - 1$ (hard)

48. In using the ϵ, δ definition to prove that $\lim\limits_{x \to 1} \sqrt{x} = 1$, when ϵ is 1, what is the largest value that δ can have?

    A) $\sqrt{2}$ B) 1/2   C) $\sqrt{3}$ D) $\sqrt{3}/3$
    E) 1   F) 2   G) $\sqrt{2}/2$ H) 3

    Answer: 1 (hard)

49. For what value of x does the function $(x - 1)^2/(x^2 - 1)$ fail to have a limit?

    A) 2   B) $-1/2$ C) 1   D) $\sqrt{2}$
    E) 1/2   F) 0   G) -2 H) -1

    Answer: -1 (medium)

50. Use the ϵ, δ definition of a limit to prove $\lim\limits_{x \to a} c = c$.

Answer: Given $\epsilon > 0$, we need $\delta > 0$ so that if $|x - a| < \delta$ then $|c - c| < \epsilon$. But $|c - c| = 0$,
so this will be true no matter what δ we pick. (medium)

51. Use the ϵ, δ definition of a limit to prove $\lim\limits_{x \to 4} (5 - 2x) = -3$.

Answer: Given $\epsilon > 0$, we need $\delta > 0$ so that if $|x - 4| < \delta$, then $|(5 - 2x) - (-3)| < \epsilon$
$\Leftrightarrow |-2x + 8| < \epsilon \Leftrightarrow 2|x - 4| < \epsilon \Leftrightarrow |x - 4| < \frac{\epsilon}{2}$. So choose $\delta = \frac{\epsilon}{2}$.
Then $|x - 4| < \delta \Rightarrow |(5 - 2x) - (-3)| < \epsilon$. Thus $\lim\limits_{x \to 4} (5 - 2x) = -3$ by the definition
of a limit. (medium)

52. Use the ϵ, δ definition of a limit to prove $\lim\limits_{x \to 0} |x| = 0$.

Answer: Given $\epsilon > 0$, we need $\delta > 0$ so that if $|x - 0| < \delta$ then $||x| - 0| < \epsilon$. But $||x|| = |x|$.
So this is true if we pick $\delta = \epsilon$. (medium)

53. Use the ϵ, δ definition of a limit to prove $\lim\limits_{x \to 0} x^3 = 0$.

Answer: Given $\epsilon > 0$, we need $\delta > 0$ so that if $|x| < \delta$ then $|x^3 - 0| < \epsilon \Leftrightarrow |x|^3 < \epsilon$
$\Leftrightarrow |x| < \sqrt[3]{\epsilon}$. Take $\delta = \sqrt[3]{\epsilon}$. Then $|x - 0| < \delta \Rightarrow |x^3 - 0| < \delta^3 = \epsilon$.
Thus $\lim\limits_{x \to 0} x^3 = 0$ by the definition of a limit. (hard)

54. Use the ϵ, δ definition of a limit to prove $\lim\limits_{x \to -4} \frac{1}{(x+4)^2}$ does not exist.

Answer: Given $\epsilon > 0$, we need $\delta > 0$ so that if $|x - (-2)| < \delta$ then $|(x^2 - 1) - 3| < \epsilon$ or upon
simplifying we need $|x^2 - 4| < \epsilon$ whenever $|x + 2| < \delta$. Notice that if $|x + 2| < 1$, then
$-1 < x + 2 < 1 \Rightarrow -5 < x - 2 < -3 \Rightarrow |x - 2| < 5$. So take $\delta = \min\{\epsilon/5, 1\}$.
Then $|x - 2| < 5$ and $|x + 2| < \epsilon/5$, so $|(x^2 - 1) - 3| = |(x + 2)(x - 2)|$
$= |x + 2||x - 2| < (\epsilon/5)(5) = \epsilon$. Therefore by the definition of a limit $\lim\limits_{x \to -2} x^2 - 1 = 8$.
(hard)

55. $\boxed{\text{G}}$ Use a graph to find a number δ such that $|\sqrt{2x + 4} - 4| < 0.2$ whenever $|x - 6| < \delta$.

A) 0.6   B) 0.7   C) 0.8   D) 0.9
E) 1.0   F) 0.5   G) 0.4   H) 1.1

Answer: 0.7 (medium)

56. $\boxed{G}$ Use a graph to find the largest number δ such that $|\cos x - 1| < 0.05$ whenever $|x| < \delta$.

A) 0.32   B) 0.26   C) 0.30   D) 0.24
E) 0.34   F) 0.28   G) 0.29   H) 0.36

Answer: 0.26 (medium)

57. $\boxed{G}$ For the limit $\lim\limits_{x \to 2} \frac{4x+3}{3x-4} = 5.5$ illustrate the definition by finding a value of δ that corresponds to $\epsilon = 0.1$.

A) 0.016   B) 0.021   C) 0.026   D) 0.019
E) 0.011   F) 0.031   G) 0.036   H) 0.023

Answer: 0.016 (medium)

58.   How close to 4 do we have to take x so that $4x + 10$ is within a distance of 0.01 from 26 ?

A) 1/40   B) 1/400   C) 1/200   D) 1/2
E) 1/4   F) 1/60   G) 1/6   H) 1/20

Answer: 1/400 (medium)

Chapter 1, Section 5
Continuity

59.   At what value of x does the function $(x+1)^2/(x^2 - 1)$ have a removable discontinuity?

A) -3 B) 3   C) 2   D) -1
E) 1   F) -4 G) -2 H) 4

Answer: -1 (easy)

60.   At what value of x does the function $(x+1)^2/(x^2 - 1)$ have an infinite discontinuity?

A) 3   B) -4 C) -2 D) -3
E) -1 F) 1   G) 2   H) 4

Answer: 1 (medium)

61.   At what value of x does the function $|x - 2|/(x - 2)$ have a jump discontinuity?

A) -3 B) $-1/2$ C) 3   D) 1
E) 2   F) -2 G) 1/2   H) -1

Answer: 2 (medium)

62. At how many values of x is the function $1/(x^3 + 1)$ discontinuous?

A) 1   B) 6   C) 0   D) 7
E) 5   F) 4   G) 2   H) 3

Answer: 1 (medium)

63. Find the distance between the two values of x at which the function $1/(x^2 - 3x + 2)$ is discontinuous.

A) 3   B) 2   C) 8   D) 1
E) 5   F) 4   G) 7   H) 6

Answer: 1 (medium)

64. At how many values of x is the function $\sin \frac{1}{x}$ discontinuous?

A) 4   B) 3   C) 2   D) 1
E) 6   F) 5   G) 0   H) infinitely many

Answer: 1 (medium)

65. At how many values of x is the function $1/(\sin x)$ discontinuous?

A) 5   B) 0   C) 3   D) 4
E) 1   F) 6   G) 2   H) infinitely many

Answer: infinitely many (medium)

66. At what value or values of x is the function

$$f(x) = \begin{cases} |x+1| - 1 & \text{if } x < 0 \\ x^2 + x & \text{if } 0 \le x < 1 \\ 3 - x & \text{if } 1 \le x \end{cases}$$

discontinuous?

A) -1 B) $-1, 0, 1$ C) 1   D) 0
E) 0, 1   F) $-1, 0$ G) $-1, 1$ H) continuous everywhere

Answer: continuous everywhere (medium)

67. At what value or values of x is the function

$$f(x) = \begin{cases} x + 4 & \text{if } x \le -1 \\ x^2 & \text{if } -1 < x < 1 \\ 2 - x & \text{if } x \ge 1 \end{cases}$$

discontinuous?

A) -1 B) 0   C) 1   D) $-1, 0$
E) 0, 1   F) $-1, 1$ G) $-1, 0, 1$ H) continuous everywhere

Answer: -1 (medium)

68. For all but two choices of a, the function

$$f(x) = \begin{cases} x^3 & \text{if } x \le a \\ x^2 & \text{if } x > a \end{cases}$$

will be discontinuous at the point $x = a$. What values of a will make it continuous?

A) $-2, 2$ B) $1, 2$ C) $-2, 1$ D) $\sqrt{2}, 1$

E) $\sqrt{2}, -1$ F) $-1, 1$ G) $0, 1$ H) $-1, 0$

Answer: 0, 1 (medium)

69. At what value or values of x is the function

$$f(x) = \begin{cases} x+2 & \text{if } x \le -1 \\ x^2 & \text{if } -1 < x < 1 \\ 3-x & \text{if } x \ge 1 \end{cases}$$

discontinuous?

A) -1 B) 0 C) 1 D) $-1, 0$

E) $0, 1$ F) $-1, 1$ G) $-1, 0, 1$ H) continuous everywhere

Answer: 1 (medium)

70. For $f(x) = \frac{x-3}{x^2-9}$ an infinite discontinuity occurs at what value of x.

A) -1 B) 0 C) 1 D) -3

E) 3 F) $-3, 3$ G) $-3, 1$ H) $3, -1$

Answer: -3 (medium)

71. Find the constant(s) c that makes the function

$$f(x) = \begin{cases} c^2 - x^2 & \text{if } x < 2 \\ 2(x+c) & \text{if } x \ge 2 \end{cases}$$

continuous on $(-\infty, \infty)$.

A) $-4, -2$ B) $2, 4$ C) 2 D) 4

E) $-2, 4$ F) -2 G) -4 H) does not exist

Answer: $-2, 4$ (medium)

72. Find the constant(s) c that makes the function

$$f(x) = \begin{cases} c^2 - x^2 & \text{if } x < 2 \\ 2(c-x) & \text{if } x \ge 2 \end{cases}$$

continuous on $(-\infty, \infty)$.

A) $-4, -2$ B) $2, 0$ C) 2 D) 4

E) $-2, 4$ F) -2 G) 0 H) does not exist

Answer: 2, 0

73. Find the constant(s) c that makes the function

$$f(x) = \begin{cases} -3x & \text{if } x \leq 1 \\ (x-c)(x+c) & \text{if } x > 1 \end{cases}$$

continuous on $(-\infty, \infty)$.

A) -2 B) -1 C) 0 D) 2
E) $-2, -1$ F) $-2, 2$ G) $-1, 2$ H) does not exist

Answer: $-2, 2$ (medium)

74. Find the values of x where the function $f(x) = \frac{(x^2-1)(x^2+3x+2)}{(x^2-1)^2(x+2)(x-3)}$ has a removable discontinuity.

A) 1 B) $-1, 1$ C) $-2, 1$ D) 3
E) $2, -1, 1$ F) $-2, -1$ G) $-2, -1$ H) $-2, -1, 3$

Answer: $-2, -1$ (medium)

75. Find the values of x where the function $f(x) = \frac{(x^2-4)(x^2+8x+12)}{(x^2+5x+6)(x-2)}$ has a removable discontinuity.

A) 2 B) -2 C) $-2, 2$ D) -3
E) $-3, -2$ F) $-6, -2$ G) $-2, -1$ H) $-6, -3$

Answer: $-2, 2$ (medium)

76. Use the Intermediate Value Theorem to show that there is a root of the equation $x^5 + 2x - x + 3 = \sqrt{x^2 + 8}$ on the interval $(0, 1)$.

Answer: Let $f(x) = x^5 + 2x - x + 3 - \sqrt{x^2 + 8}$. We want to show that there is a number c between 0 and 1 such that $f(c) = 0$. Take $a = 0$, $b = 1$, and $N = 0$ in the Theorem. $f(0) = -\sqrt{8}$ and $f(1) = 2$. Thus $f(0) < 0 < f(1)$, f is continuous on $(0, 1)$ so the Intermediate Value Theorem says that there is a number c between 0 and 1 such that $f(c) = 0$. This implies that $x^5 + 2x - x + 3 = \sqrt{x^2 + 8}$ for $x = c$. (medium)

77. Use the Intermediate Value Theorem to show that there is a root of the equation $x^3 + 2x^2 - 42 = 0$ on the interval $(0, 3)$.

Answer: Let $f(x) = x^3 + 2x^2 - 42$. We want to show that there is a number c between 0 and 3 such that $f(c) = 0$. Take $a = 0$, $b = 3$, and $N = 0$ in the Theorem. $f(0) = -42$ and $f(3) = 3$. Thus $f(0) < 0 < f(3)$, f is continuous on $(0, 1)$ so the Intermediate Value Theorem says that there is a number c between 0 and 3 such that $f(c) = 0$. (medium)

78. Show that the function $f(x) = 4x^3 - 1 = 0$ has a fixed point on the interval $(\frac{1}{2}, 1)$.

Answer: $f(x)$ has a fixed point on the interval $(\frac{1}{2}, 1)$ if there exists a point c between $\frac{1}{2}$ and 1 such that $f(c) = c$. Let $g(x) = f(x) - x = 4x^3 - 1 - x$. We want to show that there is a number c between $\frac{1}{2}$ and 1 such that $g(c) = 0$. Take $a = \frac{1}{2}$, $b = 1$, and $N = 0$ in the Theorem. $g(\frac{1}{2}) = -1$ and $g(1) = 2$. Thus $g(\frac{1}{2}) < 0 < g(1)$, g is continuous on $(\frac{1}{2}, 1)$ so the Intermediate Value Theorem says that there is a number c between $\frac{1}{2}$ and 1 such that $g(c) = 0$. This implies that $f(c) = c$. (medium)

Chapter 1, Section 6
Tangents, Velocities, and Other Rates of Change

79. Suppose you drive for 60 miles at 60 miles per hour, then for 60 miles at 30 miles per hour. In miles per hour, what is your average velocity?

A) 45   B) 40   C) 36   D) 42
E) 52   F) 55   G) 50   H) 48

Answer: 40 (medium)

80. If a ball is thrown into the air with a velocity of 80 ft/s, its height in feet after t seconds is given by $y = 80t - 16t^2$. It will be at maximum height when its instantaneous velocity is zero. Find its average velocity from the time it is thrown $(t = 0)$ to the time it reaches its maximum height.

A) 50   B) 60   C) 100   D) 80
E) 40   F) 30   G) 48   H) 32

Answer: 40 (hard)

81. The curve $f(x) = -x^4 + 2x^2 + x$ has a tangent at the point $(1, 2)$. Is this line tangent to the curve at another point and, if so, where?

A) $(2, 2)$ B) $(-2, -2)$ C) $(-1, 0)$
D) $(0, 0)$ E) $(1/2, 15/16)$ F) $(-1/2, -1/16)$
G) $(1, 2)$ H) tangent at no other point

Answer: $(-1, 0)$ (hard)

82. Find an equation of the line tangent to $f(x) = x^2 - 4x$ at the point $(3, -3)$.

A) $2x - y = 9$ B) $x - 2y = 9$ C) $y - 2x = 9$
D) $2y - x = 9$ E) $x - y = 9$ F) $y - x = 9$
G) $2x - y = 4$ H) $x - 2y = 4$

Answer: $2x - y = 9$ (medium)

83. Find an equation of the line tangent to the curve $y = x + (1/x)$ at the point $(5, 26/25)$.

A) $24x - 25y = 10$ B) $24x - 25y = -10$
C) $25x - 24y = 10$ D) $25x - 24y = -10$
E) $24x - 24y = 10$ F) $24x - 24y = -10$
G) $25x - 25y = 10$ H) $25x - 25y = -10$

Answer: $24x - 25y = -10$ (medium)

84. Find the equation of the line(s) with slope $\frac{1}{2}$ tangent to the curve $y = 3x^3$.

A) $y = \frac{1}{2}x - \frac{1}{9\sqrt{2}}$

B) $y = \frac{1}{2}x + \frac{1}{9\sqrt{2}}$

C) $y = \frac{1}{2}x - \frac{1}{9\sqrt{2}}, \quad y = \frac{1}{2}x + \frac{1}{9\sqrt{2}}$

D) $y = \frac{1}{2}x - \frac{1}{\sqrt{2}}$

E) $y = \frac{1}{2}x + \frac{1}{\sqrt{2}}$

F) $y = \frac{1}{2}x - \frac{1}{\sqrt{2}}, \quad y = \frac{1}{2}x + \frac{1}{\sqrt{2}}$

G) $y = \frac{1}{2}x - \frac{1}{9\sqrt{2}}, \quad y = \frac{1}{2}x + \frac{1}{\sqrt{2}}$

H) $y = \frac{1}{2}x - \frac{1}{\sqrt{2}}, \quad y = \frac{1}{2}x + \frac{1}{9\sqrt{2}}$

Answer: $y = \frac{1}{2}x - \frac{1}{9\sqrt{2}}, \quad y = \frac{1}{2}x + \frac{1}{9\sqrt{2}}$ (hard)

85. Find the equation of the line which is tangent to the graph of the function $f(x) = 3x^2 - 3x$ and which is parallel to the x–axis .

A) $y = 3/4$ B) $y = -3/4$ C) $y = 1/2$ D) $y = -1/2$
E) $y = 1/4$ F) $y = -1/4$ G) $y = 1/3$ H) $y = -1/3$

Answer: $y = -3/4$ (hard)

Calculus, 3rd Edition
by James Stewart
Chapter 2, Section 1
Derivatives

1.   Let $f(x) = x^2 - 3$. Find $f'(x)$.

    A) $2x$ B) $2x^3 - 3x$ C) $x^3 - 3x$ D) x
    E) $2x - 3$ F) $x - 3$ G) $2x^2 - 3$ H) $x^2 - 4$

    Answer: $2x$ (easy)

2.   Let $f(x) = 3x - 2x^2$. Find $f'(x)$.

    A) $3 - 4x^2$ B) $3x^2 - 4x^3$ C) $3 - 4x$ D) $6 - 4x^2$
    E) $6 - 4x$ F) $3 - x$ G) $3x - x^2$ H) $3 - 2x$

    Answer: $3 - 4x$ (easy)

3.   Find the slope of the tangent line to the curve $y = x^2 + 2x$ at the point $(1, 3)$.

    A) 10   B) 8   C) 6   D) 4
    E) 3   F) 5   G) 1   H) 2

    Answer: 4 (easy)

4.   Find the slope of the tangent line to the curve $y = 1/(1 + x)$ at the point $(1, 1/2)$.

    A) $-1/4$ B) 2   C) -1 D) $1/4$
    E) $-1/2$ F) -2 G) 1   H) $1/2$

    Answer: $-1/4$ (medium)

5.   Find the y-intercept of the tangent line to the curve $y = x^3$ at the point $(2, 8)$.

    A) -4 B) 4   C) -16 D) 12
    E) -8 F) 8   G) -12 H) 16

    Answer: -16 (medium)

6.   Find the y-intercept of the tangent line to the curve $y = \sqrt{x+3}$ at the point $(1, 2)$.

    A) $3/4$ B) $7/4$ C) $1/4$ D) 2
    E) $1/2$ F) 1   G) $3/2$ H) $5/4$

    Answer: $7/4$ (medium)

7. At what value or values of x is the function
$$f(x) = \begin{cases} |x+1|-1 & \text{if } x < 0 \\ x^2 + x & \text{if } 0 \leq x < 1 \\ 3 - x & \text{if } 1 \leq x \end{cases}$$

not differentiable?

A) -1 B) $-1, 0, 1$ C) 1 D) 0
E) $1, 0$ F) $-1, 0$ G) $-1, 1$ H) differentiable everywhere

Answer: $-1, 1$ (hard)

8. At what value or values of x is the function
$$f(x) = \begin{cases} x+2 & \text{if } x \leq -1 \\ x^2 & \text{if } -1 < x < 1 \\ 3 - x & \text{if } 1 \leq x \end{cases}$$

not differentiable?

A) -1 B) 0 C) 1 D) $-1, 0$
E) $0, 1$ F) $-1, 1$ G) $-1, 0, 1$ H) differentiable everywhere

Answer: $-1, 1$ (hard)

9. At $x = 0$ the function
$$f(x) = \begin{cases} x^2 & \text{if } x < 0 \\ x & \text{if } x \geq 0 \end{cases}$$

is:

A) differentiable and continuous   B) continuous but not differentiable
C) differentiable but not continuous   D) neither continuous nor differentiable

Answer: continuous but not differentiable (medium)

10. Where is the greatest integer function $f(x) = [\![x]\!]$ not differentiable?

Answer: $f(x) = [\![x]\!]$ is not continuous at any integer n so f is not differentiable at n by

Theorem 2.8. If a is not an integer, then f is constant on an open interval containing a, so $f'(a) = 0$. Thus $f'(x) = 0$, x not an integer. (medium)

11. A function f is called even if $f(-x) = f(x)$ for all x in its domain and odd if $f(-x) = -f(x)$ for all such x. Prove that the derivative of an even function is an odd function.

Answer: If f is even, then $f'(-x) = \lim_{h \to 0} \frac{f(-x+h)-f(-x)}{h} = \lim_{h \to 0} \frac{-f(x-h)+f(x)}{h} =$

$-\lim_{h \to 0} \frac{f(x-h)-f(x)}{-h}$ [Let $\Delta x = -h$.] $= -\lim_{\Delta x \to 0} \frac{f(x+\Delta x)-f(x)}{\Delta x} = -f'(x)$.

Therefore f' is odd. (medium)

Chapter 2, Section 2
Differentiation Formulas

12. Let $f(x) = 1/x^2$. Find $f'(1)$.

    A) $-1/3$ B) -2 C) $1/3$ D) $-1/4$
    E) 1 F) $-1/2$ G) -1 H) $1/4$

    Answer: -2 (easy)

13. Let $f(x) = \sqrt{3x}$. Find $f'(3)$.

    A) $1/3$ B) $1/2$ C) $-1/3$ D) $-1/4$
    E) -1 F) $1/4$ G) $-1/2$ H) 1

    Answer: $1/2$ (medium)

14. Let $f(x) = (x+1)^2(x+2)$. Find $f'(0)$.

    A) 6 B) 9 C) 4 D) 12
    E) 8 F) 16 G) 5 H) 20

    Answer: 5 (medium)

15. Let $f(x) = x^3/(x+2)^2$. Find $f'(-1)$.

    A) 8 B) 5 C) 10 D) 4
    E) 20 F) 9 G) 12 H) 16

    Answer: 5 (hard)

16. The curve $y = x^3 + x^2 - x$ has two horizontal tangents. Find the difference in height of these two horizontal lines.

    A) $11/9$ B) $22/27$ C) $32/27$ D) $5/3$
    E) $14/9$ F) $4/3$ G) $13/9$ H) $7/3$

    Answer: $32/27$ (hard)

17. Let $f(x) = \sqrt[5]{x} + x^{-1.8}$. Find $f'(1)$.

    A) $1/5$ B) $2/5$ C) $-8/5$ D) $-2/5$
    E) $-1/5$ F) $4/5$ G) $8/5$ H) $-4/5$

    Answer: $-8/5$ (medium)

18.   Passing through the origin $(0, 0)$, there are two lines tangent to the curve $y = x^2 + 1$, one with negative slope, the other with positive slope. Find the value of that positive slope.

A) 1/8   B) 1/2   C) 1/4   D) 1/3
E) 4   F) 1   G) 3   H) 2

Answer: 2 (hard)

19.   If $f(x) = \frac{\sqrt{x}-1}{\sqrt{x}+1}$, find the value of $f'(4)$.

A) 1/9   B) 1/12   C) 1/15   D) 1/18
E) 1/21   F) 1/24   G) 1/27   H) 1/30

Answer: 1/18 (medium)

20.   At how many different values of x does the curve $y = x^3 + 2x$ have a tangent line parallel to the line $y = x$?

A) 0   B) 1   C) 2   D) 3
E) 4   F) 5   G) 6   H) 7

Answer: 0 (medium)

21.   Find an equation of the tangent line to the curve $y = \frac{1-x}{1+x}$ at $(-2, -3)$.
A) $x + y + 5 = 0$ B) $x + 2y + 8 = 0$ C) $x + 3y + 11 = 0$
D) $2x + y + 7 = 0$ E) $3x + y + 9 = 0$ F) $2x + 3y + 13 = 0$
G) $2x - 3y - 5 = 0$ H) $x - 3y - 7 = 0$

Answer: $2x + y + 7 = 0$ (medium)

22.   There are two lines through the point $(2, -3)$ that are tangent to the parabola $y = x^2 + x$. Find the x-coordinates of the points where these lines touch the parabola.

A) $-2, 0$ B) $1, 3$ C) $-1, 6$ D) $2, 5$
E) $0, 4$ F) $-2, 4$ G) $2, 7$ H) $-1, 5$

Answer: $-1, 5$ (hard)

23.   Given $f(3) = 5$, $f'(3) = 1.1$, $g(3) = -4$ and $g'(3) = 0.7$ find the value of $(f + g)'(3)$.

A) 1.8   B) 0.4   C) -0.9 D) -1.8
E) 0.9   F) -0.4 G) 0.77   H) -0.77

Answer: 1.8 (easy)

24.   Given $f(3) = 5$, $f'(3) = 1.1$, $g(3) = -4$ and $g'(3) = 0.7$ find the value of $(f - g)'(3)$.

A) 1.8   B) 0.4   C) -0.9 D) -1.8
E) 0.9   F) -0.4 G) 0.77   H) -0.77

Answer: 0.4 (easy)

25. Given $f(3) = 5$, $f'(3) = 1.1$, $g(3) = -4$ and $g'(3) = 0.7$ find the value of $(f \cdot g)'(3)$.

A) 1.8 B) 0.4 C) -0.9 D) -1.8
E) 0.9 F) -0.4 G) 0.77 H) -0.77

Answer: -0.9 (easy)

26. Given $f(3) = 5$, $f'(3) = 1.1$, $g(3) = -4$ and $g'(3) = 0.7$ find the value of $(f/g)'(3)$.

A) 0.025 B) 0.49375 C) -0.49375 D) -0.025
E) 1.975 F) -1.975 G) 0.5625 H) -0.5625

Answer: -0.49375 (easy)

Chapter 2, Section 3
Rates of Change in the Natural and Social Sciences

27. A stone is thrown into a pond creating a circular wave whose radius increases at the rate of 1 foot per second. In square feet per second, how fast is the area of the circular ripple increasing 3 seconds after the stone hits the water?

A) π B) 2π C) $\pi/3$ D) 6π
E) 3π F) $\pi/6$ G) $\pi/12$ H) $\pi/2$

Answer: 6π (easy)

28. The mass of a rod varies in such a fashion that the total mass at x meters from the end is x^2 kilograms. Find the density in kg/m at the point 2 meters from the end.

A) 1 B) 5 C) 3 D) 4
E) 7 F) 6 G) 2 H) 8

Answer: 4 (easy)

29. In a water pipe 2 cm in diameter, the rate of flow at a distance of 0.5 cm from the wall is 6 cm/s. If the flow obeys Poiseuille's law, find the rate of flow at the exact center of the pipe (i.e., 1 cm from the wall).

A) 6 B) 3 C) 2 D) 10
E) 8 F) 5 G) 1 H) 12

Answer: 8 (hard)

30. A spherical balloon is being inflated in such a fashion that its radius increases at a rate of 1 cm/s. In cm^3/s, how fast is the volume increasing 3 seconds after inflation starts?

A) 36 B) 12π C) 24 D) 18π
E) 36π F) 18 G) 12 H) 24π

Answer: 36π (medium)

31. A spherical balloon is being inflated in such a fashion that its radius increases at a rate 1 cm/s. In cm^2/s, how fast is the surface area increasing 3 seconds after inflation starts?

A) 18   B) 36π C) 36   D) 12
E) 24π F) 18π G) 24   H) 12π

Answer: 24π (medium)

32. Suppose the amount of a drug left in the body x hours after administration is $20/(x+1)$ mg. In mg/hr, find the rate of decrease of the drug 4 hours after administration.

A) 3   B) 2   C) 4/5   D) 1/2
E) 5/4   F) 2/5   G) 1   H) 5/2

Answer: 4/5 (easy)

33. The population of a bacteria colony after t hours is $70 + 5t + 2t^2$. Find the growth rate when $t = 3$.

A) 18   B) 9   C) 7   D) 19
E) 21   F) 13   G) 17   H) 11

Answer: 17 (easy)

34. A particle moves along a straight line with equation of motion $s = t^2 - 2t$. Find the instantaneous velocity of the particle at time $t = 1$.

A) 1   B) 4   C) 0   D) 3
E) 8   F) 6   G) 5   H) 2

Answer: 0 (easy)

35. A particle moves along a straight line with equation of motion $s = t^2 - 3t + 2$. Find the value of t at which it reverses its direction.

A) 1/2   B) 0   C) 3/2   D) 2/3
E) 1   F) 2   G) 3/4   H) 4/3

Answer: 3/2 (medium)

36. A particle moves along a straight line with equation of motion $s = t^3 + 2t$. Find the smallest value of its velocity.

A) 1/2   B) -2 C) 1/2   D) $-1/2$
E) -3 F) 2   G) 3   H) $-1/3$

Answer: 2 (hard)

37. A particle moves according to a law of motion $s = 4t^3 - 9t^2 + 6t + 2$, $t \geq 0$ where s is measured in feet and t in seconds. When is the particle at rest?

A) $t = \frac{1}{2}$ B) $t = 1$ C) $t = 0$ D) $t = \frac{1}{2}, 1$

E) $t = 1, 0$ F) $t = \frac{1}{2}, 0$ G) $t = \frac{1}{2}, 0, 1$ H) $t = \frac{3}{2}$

Answer: $t = \frac{1}{2}, 1$ (medium)

38. A particle moves according to a law of motion $s = 4t^3 - 9t^2 + 6t + 2$, $t \geq 0$ where s is measured in feet and t in seconds. When is the particle moving in a positive direction?

A) $0 \leq t < \frac{1}{2}$ B) $t > 1$ C) $t \geq \frac{3}{2}$

D) $0 \leq t < \frac{1}{2}$ or $t > 1$ E) $0 \leq t < \frac{1}{2}$ or $t > \frac{3}{2}$ F) $1 < t < \frac{3}{2}$

G) $0 \leq t < \frac{1}{2}$ or $1 < t < \frac{3}{2}$ H) $0 \leq t < \frac{3}{2}$

Answer: $0 \leq t < \frac{1}{2}$ or $t > 1$ (medium)

39. A particle moves according to a law of motion $s = \sqrt{t}\,(5 - 5t + 2t^2)$, $t \geq 0$ where s is measured in feet and t in seconds. When is the particle moving in a positive direction?

A) $0 \leq t < \frac{1}{2}$ B) $t > 1$ C) $t \geq \frac{3}{2}$

D) $0 \leq t < \frac{1}{2}$ or $t > 1$ E) $0 \leq t < \frac{1}{2}$ or $t > \frac{3}{2}$ F) $1 < t < \frac{3}{2}$

G) $0 \leq t < \frac{1}{2}$ or $1 < t < \frac{3}{2}$ H) $0 \leq t < \frac{3}{2}$

Answer: $0 \leq t < \frac{1}{2}$ or $t > 1$ (medium)

40. A particle moves according to a law of motion $s = \sqrt{t}\,(5 - 5t + 2t^2)$, $t \geq 0$ where s is measured in feet and t in seconds. When is the particle at rest?

A) $t = \frac{1}{2}$ B) $t = 1$ C) $t = 0$ D) $t = \frac{1}{2}, 1$

E) $t = 1, 0$ F) $t = \frac{1}{2}, 0$ G) $t = \frac{1}{2}, 0, 1$ H) $t = \frac{3}{2}$

Answer: $t = \frac{1}{2}, 1$ (medium)

Chapter 2, Section 4
Derivatives of Trigonometric Functions

41. Find the value of the limit $\lim_{x \to 0} \frac{\cos x - 1}{2x}$.

A) 3 B) 0 C) 1/3 D) 4
E) 1/4 F) 2 G) 1/2 H) 1

Answer: 0 (easy)

42. Find the value of the limit $\lim\limits_{x \to 0} \frac{\sin x}{2x}$.

A) 1/3   B) 3   C) 0   D) 1
E) 1/2   F) 1/4   G) 4   H) 2

Answer: 1/2 (easy)

43. Find the value of the limit $\lim\limits_{x \to 0} \frac{\tan 2x}{x}$.

A) 4   B) 1   C) 1/4   D) 2
E) 1/2   F) 0   G) 1/3   H) 3

Answer: 2 (medium)

44. Let $f(x) = x^2 \cos x$. Find $f'(0)$.

A) 1/2   B) 2   C) 0   D) 1
E) 1/3   F) 4   G) 1/4   H) 3

Answer: 0 (medium)

45. Let $f(x) = x \tan x$. Find $f'(\pi/4)$.

A) $1 + \pi/4$ B) $\pi/4$ C) $\pi/4 - 1$ D) $1 - \pi/4$
E) $\pi/2 - 1$ F) $1 - \pi/2$ G) $1 + \pi/2$ H) $\pi/2$

Answer: $1 + \pi/2$ (medium)

46. Let $f(x) = \sin^2 x$. Find $f'(\pi/4)$.

A) $\sqrt{2}$ B) $\sqrt{2}/3$ C) 2   D) 1
E) 1/2   F) 0   G) $\sqrt{3}/4$ H) $\sqrt{2}/2$

Answer: 1 (medium)

47. Let $f(x) = \frac{x}{\sin x}$. Find $f'(\pi/4)$.

A) $1 + \pi/4$ B) $1 + \pi/2$ C) $\sqrt{2}(1 + \pi/2)$
D) $1 - \pi/2$ E) $1 - \pi/4$ F) $\sqrt{2}(1 + \pi/4)$
G) $\sqrt{2}(1 - \pi/2)$ H) $\sqrt{2}(1 - \pi/4)$

Answer: $\sqrt{2}(1 - \pi/4)$ (hard)

48. Find the value of the limit $\lim\limits_{x \to 0} \frac{x^2}{\tan^2 \pi x}$.

A) π B) π^2 C) 0   D) 1
E) $1/\pi^2$ F) $1/\pi$ G) ∞ H) does not exist

Answer: $1/\pi^2$ (hard)

49. Find the value of the limit $\lim\limits_{x \to 0^+} \frac{\sin 2x \cos 4x}{\tan 3x}$.

A) 0   B) 2/3   C) 4/3   D) 2
E) 8/3   F) 10/3   G) 4   H) ∞

Answer: 2/3 (hard)

50. Find the value of the limit $\lim\limits_{t \to 0} \frac{\sin 6t}{\sin 4t}$.

A) 0   B) 0.5   C) 1   D) 1.5
E) 2   F) 2.5   G) 3   H) does not exist

Answer: 1.5 (medium)

51. Find the value of the limit $\lim\limits_{x \to 0} \frac{\sin 3x}{\tan 6x}$.

A) 0   B) 0.5   C) 1.0   D) 1.5
E) 2.0   F) 2.5   G) 3.0   H) does not exist

Answer: 0.5 (medium)

52. Prove that $\frac{d}{dx}(\sec x) = \sec x \tan x$.

Answer: $\frac{d}{dx}(\sec x) = \frac{d}{dx}\left(\frac{1}{\cos x}\right) = \frac{(\cos x)(0) - 1(-\sin x)}{\cos^2 x} = \frac{\sin x}{\cos^2 x} = \frac{1}{\cos x} \cdot \frac{\sin x}{\cos x} = \sec x \tan x$.

(medium)

53. Prove, using the definition of a derivative, that if $f(x) = \cos x$, then $f'(x) = -\sin x$.

Answer: $f(x) = \cos x \Rightarrow f'(x) = \lim\limits_{h \to 0} \frac{f(x+h) - f(x)}{h} = \lim\limits_{h \to 0} \frac{\cos(x+h) - \cos x}{h}$
$= \lim\limits_{h \to 0} \frac{\cos x \cos h - \sin x \sin h - \cos x}{h} = \lim\limits_{h \to 0} \left(\cos x \frac{\cos h - 1}{h} - \sin x \frac{\sin h}{h}\right)$
$= \cos x \lim\limits_{h \to 0} \frac{\cos h - 1}{h} - \sin x \lim\limits_{h \to 0} \frac{\sin h}{h} = (\cos x)(0) - (\sin x)(1) = -\sin x$.
(medium)

Chapter 2, Section 5
The Chain Rule

54. Let $f(x) = (x+1)^4$. Find $f'(1)$.

A) 4   B) 12   C) 8   D) 32
E) 6   F) 16   G) 24   H) 2

Answer: 32 (easy)

55. Let $f(x) = (x^2 + 1)^4$. Find $f'(0)$.

A) 0   B) 28   C) 4   D) 32
E) 16   F) 24   G) 12   H) 8

Answer: 0 (easy)

56. Let $f(x) = (x + 1)^2(x + 2)^3$. Find $f'(0)$.

A) 4   B) 24   C) 28   D) 12
E) 16   F) 8   G) 32   H) 6

Answer: 28 (medium)

57. Let $f(x) = \sin^2(2x)$. Find $f'(\pi/6)$.

A) $\sqrt{2}$ B) $\sqrt{3}/4$ C) 0   D) $\sqrt{2}/2$
E) $\sqrt{2}/4$ F) $\sqrt{3}$ G) $\sqrt{3}/2$ H) 1

Answer: $\sqrt{3}$ (medium)

58. Let $f(x) = \sqrt{\sin x + x^3 + 1}$. Find $f'(0)$.

A) 3   B) 0   C) 1   D) 4
E) 1/4   F) 2   G) 1/3   H) 1/2

Answer: 1/2 (medium)

59. Let $f(x) = \sqrt{x + \sqrt{x}}$. Find $f'(1)$.

A) $3\sqrt{2}/8$ B) $\sqrt{2}/4$ C) 1/4   D) 1/8
E) $\sqrt{2}/2$ F) 1/2   G) $\sqrt{2}$ H) 1

Answer: $3\sqrt{2}/8$ (hard)

60. Find the slope of the line tangent to the curve $y = (x^2 + 1)^3$ at the point $(1, 8)$.

A) 32   B) 4   C) 24   D) 16
E) 28   F) 6   G) 12   H) 8

Answer: 24 (medium)

61. If $f(x) = \sin\left[\frac{\pi}{\sqrt{x^2+5}}\right]$, find the value of $f'(2)$.

A) $\pi/9$ B) $\pi/5$ C) 0   D) $-\pi/27$
E) 1/2   F) $\pi\sqrt{3}/2$ G) $-\pi/9$ H) $-\sqrt{3}/2$

Answer: $-\pi/27$ (medium)

62. If $f(x) = 4\sqrt{x - \sqrt{x}}$, find the value of $f'(4)$.

A) $\frac{1}{2\sqrt{2}}$ B) $\frac{1}{4\sqrt{2}}$ C) $\frac{3}{4\sqrt{2}}$ D) $\frac{3}{2\sqrt{2}}$

E) $\frac{3}{\sqrt{2}}$ F) $\frac{5}{\sqrt{2}}$ G) $\frac{5}{2\sqrt{2}}$ H) $\frac{5}{4\sqrt{2}}$

Answer: $3/(2\sqrt{2})$ (hard)

63. Find an equation for the tangent line to the curve $y = \frac{8}{\sqrt{4+3x}}$ at the point $(4, 2)$.

A) $6x + y = 26$ B) $4x + 2y = 20$ C) $3x - 4y = 4$
D) $7x + 18y = 64$ E) $5x + 21y = 62$ F) $4x + 15y = 46$
G) $3x + 16y = 44$ H) $2x - y = 6$

Answer: $3x + 16y = 44$ (medium)

64. If $f(x) = \sqrt{2x + \sqrt{x}}$, find the value of $f'(1)$.

A) $\sqrt{2}/4$ B) $\sqrt{2}/8$ C) $3\sqrt{2}/8$ D) $3\sqrt{2}/4$

E) $3\sqrt{2}/2$ F) $5/(4\sqrt{3})$ G) $4\sqrt{2}$ H) $\sqrt{2}/4$

Answer: $5/(4\sqrt{3})$ (hard)

65. If $f(x) = \sqrt{x + \sqrt{x + \sqrt{x}}}$ find the value of $f'(1)$.

A) $\sqrt{1 + \sqrt{2}}$ B) $\frac{1}{\sqrt{1+\sqrt{2}}}$ C) $\frac{1}{2\sqrt{1+\sqrt{2}}}$

D) $\frac{1}{\sqrt{2}+\sqrt{1+\sqrt{2}}}$ E) $\frac{3}{8\sqrt{2}\sqrt{1+\sqrt{2}}}$ F) $\frac{1+\frac{1}{\sqrt{2}}}{2\sqrt{1+\sqrt{2}}}$

G) $\frac{1+\frac{3}{\sqrt{2}}}{2\sqrt{1+\sqrt{2}}}$ H) $\frac{1+\frac{3}{4\sqrt{2}}}{2\sqrt{1+\sqrt{2}}}$

Answer: $\dfrac{1+\frac{3}{4\sqrt{2}}}{2\sqrt{1+\sqrt{2}}}$ (hard)

66. Let $F(x) = \sin(g(x))$, where g is differentiable. Find $F'(x)$.

A) $g(x)\cos x$ B) $-g(x)\sin x$ C) $-g'(x)\sin x$
D) $g'(x)\cos x$ E) $g'(x)\cos(g(x))$ F) $g'(x)\sin(g(x))$
G) $\cos(g(x))$ H) $\cos(g'(x))$

Answer: $g'(x)\cos(g(x))$ (medium)

67. Suppose that $h(x) = f(g(x))$ and $g(3) = 6$, $g'(3) = 4$, $f'(3) = 2$, $f'(6) = 7$. Find the value of $h'(3)$.

A) 4   B) 8   C) 12   D) 16
E) 20   F) 24   G) 28   H) 32

Answer: 28 (medium)

68. Suppose that $F(x) = f(g(x))$ and $g(3) = 5$, $g'(3) = 3$, $f'(3) = 1$, $f'(5) = 4$. Find the value of $F'(3)$.

A) 3   B) 4   C) 7   D) 9
E) 12   F) 15   G) 17   H) 20

Answer: 12 (medium)

69. Suppose that $w = u \circ v$ and $u(0) = 1$, $v(0) = 2$, $u'(0) = 3$, $u'(2) = 4$, $v'(0) = 5$ and $v'(2) = 6$. Find $w'(0)$.

A) 5   B) 10   C) 15   D) 20
E) 25   F) 30   G) 35   H) 40

Answer: 20 (medium)

Chapter 2, Section 6
Implicit Differentiation

70. If $x^2 + y^2 = 25$, find the value of dy/dx at the point $(3, 4)$.

A) 3/5   B) $-3/5$ C) $-4/5$ D) 3/4
E) 0   F) 1   G) 4/5   H) $-3/4$

Answer: $-3/4$ (easy)

71. If $\sqrt{x+y} + \sqrt{x-y} = 4$, find the value of dy/dx at the point $(5, 4)$.

A) 4   B) 1/4   C) 2   D) -4
E) -2 F) 1/2   G) $-1/4$ H) $-1/2$

Answer: 2 (hard)

72. If $x^2 + xy + y^2 = 7$, find the value of dy/dx at the point $(1, 2)$.

A) $-3/5$ B) $-3/4$ C) 3/5   D) 4/5
E) $-4/5$ F) 3/4   G) 1   H) 0

Answer: $-4/5$ (medium)

73. If $\sqrt{x} + \sqrt{y} = 3$, find the value of dx/dy at the point $(4, 1)$.

A) -3 B) 0 C) 2 D) -1
E) 1 F) 3 G) -2 H) 4

Answer: -2 (medium)

74. If $\sin y = x$, find the value of dy/dx at the point $(1/2, \pi/6)$.

A) $2\sqrt{3}/3$ B) -2 C) $-1/2$ D) $\sqrt{2}$
E) 2 F) $1/2$ G) $-2\sqrt{3}/3$ H) $-\sqrt{2}$

Answer: $2\sqrt{3}/3$ (hard)

75. Find the y-intercept of the tangent to the ellipse $x^2 + 3y^2 = 1$ at the point $(1/2, 1/2)$.

A) 3 B) $-1/\sqrt{3}$ C) $1/3$ D) $-1/3$
E) -1 F) -3 G) $1/\sqrt{3}$ H) $2/3$

Answer: $2/3$ (medium)

76. Find the slope of the tangent to the curve $xy^2 + x^2y = 2$ at the point $(1, 1)$.

A) 5 B) -1 C) -3 D) 1
E) -5 F) 0 G) 3 H) 4

Answer: -1 (medium)

77. Find the slope of the tangent line to the curve $2x^3 + 2y^3 - 9xy = 0$ at the point $(1, 2)$.

A) 3 B) 9 C) $9/2$ D) $1/3$
E) $4/5$ F) $18/5$ G) 7 H) $-18/5$

Answer: $4/5$ (medium)

78. If $x^2 - xy + y^3 = 8$, find an expression for dy/dx.

A) $\frac{y-2x}{3y^2-x}$ B) $-\frac{2xy}{x+3y^2}$ C) $-\frac{3x^2+y}{2x-y}$ D) $\frac{x^2-y^2}{x^2+y^2}$

E) $-\frac{3xy^2}{3y^2+2x}$ F) $\frac{x+y}{x^2+2y}$ G) $-\frac{2x^2y}{x+6y^2}$ H) $\frac{xy}{x^2-y^2}$

Answer: $\frac{y-2x}{3y^2-x}$ (medium)

79. Let $y = f(x)$. If $xy^3 + xy = 6$ and $f(3) = 1$, find $f'(3)$.

A) 0 B) 1 C) 2 D) $1/3$
E) -4 F) $1/5$ G) $-1/6$ H) 8

Answer: $-1/6$ (medium)

80. If $x \cos y = y \cos x$, find the value of dy/dx when $x = 0$ and $y = 0$.

A) -2 B) -1 C) 0 D) 1
E) 2 F) $1/3$ G) $-1/2$ H) $1/4$

Answer: 1 (medium)

81. Find the slope of the tangent line to the curve $x^3 + y^3 = 6xy$ at $(3, 3)$.

A) -3 B) -2 C) -1 D) 0
E) 1 F) 2 G) 3 H) 4

Answer: -1 (medium)

82. If $x \cos y + y \cos x = 1$, find an expression for dy/dx.

A) $\dfrac{y \sin x - \cos y}{\cos x - x \sin y}$ B) $\dfrac{\cos x + \sin y}{\cos x - \sin y}$ C) $\dfrac{\cos x + x \sin y}{\sin x + y \sin y}$

D) $\dfrac{x \sin x + \sin y}{x \cos x - \cos y}$ E) $\dfrac{y - \cos x \sin y}{\sin x + \cos y}$ F) $\dfrac{x \sin x - \cos y}{y \sin x + \cos y}$

G) $\dfrac{\cos x - \sin y}{\cos x + x \sin y}$ H) $\dfrac{\sin x - \cos y}{y \cos x + x \sin y}$

Answer: $\dfrac{y \sin x - \cos y}{\cos x - x \sin y}$ (medium)

83. Find the derivative $\dfrac{dp}{dt}$ for $p = \dfrac{mv}{\sqrt{1-(v^2/c^2)}}$, where m and c are constants.

A) $\dfrac{dp}{dt} = \dfrac{m}{(1-(v^2/c^2))^{3/2}} \dfrac{dv}{dt}$ B) $\dfrac{dp}{dt} = \dfrac{m}{(1+(v^2/c^2))^{3/2}} \dfrac{dv}{dt}$

C) $\dfrac{dp}{dt} = \dfrac{m}{(1-(c^2/v^2))^{3/2}} \dfrac{dv}{dt}$ D) $\dfrac{dp}{dt} = \dfrac{m}{(1+(c^2/v^2))^{3/2}} \dfrac{dv}{dt}$

E) $\dfrac{dp}{dt} = \dfrac{m}{(1-(v^2/c^2))^{5/2}} \dfrac{dv}{dt}$ F) $\dfrac{dp}{dt} = \dfrac{mv}{(1-(v^2/c^2))^{3/2}} \dfrac{dv}{dt}$

G) $\dfrac{dp}{dt} = \dfrac{mv}{(1-(v^2/c^2))^{5/2}} \dfrac{dv}{dt}$ H) $\dfrac{dp}{dt} = \dfrac{v}{(1-(v^2/c^2))^{3/2}} \dfrac{dv}{dt}$

Answer: $\dfrac{dp}{dt} = \dfrac{m}{(1-(v^2/c^2))^{3/2}} \dfrac{dv}{dt}$ (hard)

84. Find the equation of the line normal to the curve defined by the equation $x^3 y^4 - 5 = x^3 - x^2 + y$ at the point $(2, -1)$.

A) $33x + 4y - 62 = 0$ B) $33x - 4y - 62 = 0$
C) $33x + 4y + 62 = 0$ D) $33x - 4y + 62 = 0$
E) $4x - 33y - 41 = 0$ F) $4x + 33y - 41 = 0$
G) $4x - 33y + 41 = 0$ H) $4x + 33y + 41 = 0$

Answer: $33x + 4y - 62 = 0$ (medium)

85. What is the slope of the tangent line to the curve $xy^3 + y - 1 = 0$ at the point $(0, 1)$?

A) -3 B) -2 C) -1 D) 0
E) 1 F) 2 G) 3 H) 4

Answer: -1 (medium)

86. Find the value of the derivative of $x^2 + xy^2 = 6$ when $x = 2$ and $y > 0$.

A) $-5/4$ B) $-4/5$ C) $-3/4$ D) 0
E) $5/4$ F) $4/5$ G) $3/4$ H) $1/2$

Answer: $-5/4$ (medium)

87. Find $\frac{dy}{dx}$ if $\sin(2x + 3y) = 3xy + 5y - 2$.

A) $\frac{dy}{dx} = \frac{3y - 2\cos(2x+3y)}{3\cos(2x+3y) - 3x - 5}$

B) $\frac{dy}{dx} = \frac{3y + 2\cos(2x+3y)}{3\cos(2x+3y) - 3x - 5}$

C) $\frac{dy}{dx} = \frac{3y - 2\cos(2x+3y)}{3\cos(2x+3y) + 3x - 5}$

D) $\frac{dy}{dx} = \frac{3y - 2\cos(2x+3y)}{3\cos(2x+3y) - 3x + 5}$

E) $\frac{dy}{dx} = \frac{3y + 2\cos(2x+3y)}{3\cos(2x+3y) + 3x - 5}$

F) $\frac{dy}{dx} = \frac{3y - 2\cos(2x+3y)}{3\cos(2x+3y) + 3x + 5}/5$

G) $\frac{dy}{dx} = \frac{3y + 2\cos(2x+3y)}{3\cos(2x+3y) - 3x + 5}$

H) $\frac{dy}{dx} = \frac{3y + 2\cos(2x+3y)}{3\cos(2x+3y) + 3x + 5}$

Answer: $\frac{dy}{dx} = \frac{3y - 2\cos(2x+3y)}{3\cos(2x+3y) - 3x - 5}$ (medium)

Chapter 2, Section 7
Higher Derivatives

88. Let $f(x) = \frac{1}{x^2}$. Find $f''(1)$.

A) 1 B) 4 C) 2 D) 6
E) 3 F) 0 G) 5 H) 8

Answer: 6 (medium)

89. Let $f(x) = x^3$. Find $f''(1)$.

A) 8 B) 4 C) 2 D) 3
E) 0 F) 6 G) 5 H) 1

Answer: 6 (easy)

90. Let $f(x) = x \sin x$. Find $f''(0)$.

A) $\sqrt{2}$ B) $\sqrt{2}/2$ C) 2 D) $-\sqrt{3}$
E) $-\sqrt{2}$ F) -2 G) $\sqrt{3}$ H) $-\sqrt{2}/2$

Answer: 2 (medium)

91. Let $y = \frac{x}{(x+1)}$. Find $f''(0)$.

A) -2 B) 4 C) 8 D) -6
E) -8 F) -4 G) 6 H) 2

Answer: -2 (medium)

92. Let $f(x) = x^5$. Find $f^{(5)}(3)$.

   A) 90   B) 360   C) 30   D) 60
   E) 20   F) 72   G) 120   H) 240

   Answer: 120 (easy)

93. Let $x^2 + y^2 = 25$. Find the value of d^2y/dx^2 at the point $(3, 4)$.

   A) 7/16   B) $-7/16$ C) 7/64   D) $-7/64$
   E) $-25/16$ F) 25/16   G) $-25/64$ H) 25/64

   Answer: $-25/64$ (hard)

94. A particle moves along a straight line with equation of motion $s = t^3 + t^2$. Find the value of t at which the acceleration is equal to zero.

   A) $-2/3$ B) $-1/3$ C) 2/3   D) 1/3
   E) $-1/2$ F) 1/2   G) $-3/2$ H) 3/2

   Answer: $-1/3$ (medium)

95. If $f(x) = g(g(x))$, find an expression for $f''(x)$ in terms of $g(x)$ and its derivatives.

   A) $2g''(x) \cdot g(x) + 2(g'(x))^2$ B) $g''(g'(x))$

   C) $g''(g(x)) \cdot (g'(x))^2 + g'(g(x)) \cdot g''(x)$ D) $g''(g'(x)) \cdot g'(x)$

   E) $2g'(x) \cdot g'(x) + 2g''(g(x))$ F) $g'(g(x))g''(x) + (g'(x))^2$

   G) $g'(g''(x)) \cdot g'(x) + (g''(x))^2$ H) $g'(g(x))g''(x) + (g'(x))^2$

   Answer: $g''(g(x)) \cdot (g'(x))^2 + g'(g(x)) \cdot g''(x)$ (hard)

96. If $x^2 + y^2 = 1$, find an expression for y''.

   A) $-2x/y^5$ B) x/y^3 C) $-3x/y^4$ D) $(x^3 - y^3)/y^6$
   E) $(x^3 + y^3)/y^6$ F) $-1/y^3$ G) $6x^2/y^5$ H) $-3x^3/y^4$

   Answer: $-1/y^3$ (hard)

97. If $f(x) = \cos 2x$, find the value of $f^{(8)}(0)$.

   A) 1   B) -1 C) 2   D) 0
   E) 256   F) -256 G) 128   H) -128

   Answer: 256 (medium)

98. If $g(x) = \cos 2x$, find the value of $g^{(6)}(0)$.

   A) 0   B) 2   C) -2 D) 8
   E) -8 F) 64   G) -64 H) 128

   Answer: -64 (medium)

99. If $f(x) = \tan x$, find an expression for $f'''(x)$.

A) $\sec^2 x \tan^2 x$ B) $2 \sec^4 x$
C) $2 \tan^4 x$ D) $4 \sec^4 x \tan^2 x$
E) $2 \sec^2 x \tan^2 x + 4 \tan^4 x$ F) $4 \sec^2 x \tan^2 x + \tan^4 x$
G) $2 \sec^2 x \tan^2 x + 4 \sec^4 x$ H) $4 \sec^2 x \tan^2 x + 2 \sec^4 x$

Answer: $4 \sec^2 x \tan^2 x + 2 \sec^4 x$ (hard)

100. If $x^4 + y^4 = 1$, find an expression for $\frac{d^2 y}{dx^2}$.

A) y^2/x^5 B) $-x^2/y^2$ C) $-2x^4/y^4$ D) $-2x^2/y^5$
E) $-3x^2/y^7$ F) $-5x^4/y^9$ G) $-6x^4/y^5$ H) $6x^4/y^7$

Answer: $-3x^2/y^7$ (hard)

101. If $x^3 + y^3 = 1$, find an expression for y''.

A) $-2x/y^5$ B) x/y^3 C) $-3x/y^4$ D) $(x^3 - y^3)/y^6$
E) $(x^3 + y^3)/y^6$ F) $-x^2/y^3$ G) $6x^2/y^5$ H) $-3x^3/y^4$

Answer: $-2x/y^5$ (hard)

102. Use implicit differentiation to find y'' if $2xy = y^2$.

A) $\dfrac{y^2 - 2xy}{(y-x)^3}$ B) $\dfrac{y^2 + 2xy}{(y-x)^3}$ C) $\dfrac{y^2 - 2xy}{(y+x)^3}$ D) $\dfrac{y^2 + 2xy}{(y+x)^3}$

E) $\dfrac{y^2 - xy}{(y-x)^3}$ F) $\dfrac{y^2 + xy}{(y-x)^3}$ G) $\dfrac{y^2 - xy}{(y+x)^3}$ H) $\dfrac{y^2 + xy}{(y+x)^3}$

Answer: $\dfrac{y^2 - 2xy}{(y-x)^3}$ (medium)

103. Let $f(x) = x/(x-1)$ find a formula for $f^{(n)}(x)$.

A) $f^{(n)} = (-1)^n n!(x-1)^{-(n+1)}$ B) $f^{(n)} = n!(x-1)^{-(n+1)}$
C) $f^{(n)} = (-1)^n n!(x-1)^{-n}$ D) $f^{(n)} = (-1)^n n!(x-1)^{-(n-1)}$
E) $f^{(n)} = (-1)^{n+1} n!(x-1)^{-(n+1)}$ F) $f^{(n)} = (-1)^n n!(x-1)^{n+1}$
G) $f^{(n)} = n!(x-1)^{-n+1}$ H) $f^{(n)} = (-1)^n n!(x+1)^{-(n+1)}$

Answer: $f^{(n)} = (-1)^n n!(x-1)^{-(n+1)}$ (hard)

Chapter 2, Section 8
Related Rates

104. The length of a rectangle is increasing at the rate of 2 feet per second, while the width is increasing at the rate of 1 foot per second. When the length is 5 feet and the width is 3 feet, how fast, in square feet per second, is the area increasing?

A) 5   B) 11   C) 6   D) 10
E) 15   F) 20   G) 8   H) 12

Answer: 11   (medium)

105. The length of a rectangle is decreasing at the rate of 1 foot per second, but the area remains constant. If the length is 10 feet and the width is 5 feet, in feet per second, how fast is its width increasing?

A) 1/2   B) 4   C) 1/10   D) 2
E) 5   F) 1/4   G) 10   H) 1/5

Answer: 1/2 (hard)

106. A ladder 10 feet long is leaning against a wall, with the foot of the ladder 8 feet away from the wall. If the foot of the ladder is being pulled away from the wall at 3 feet per second, how fast in feet per second is the top of the ladder sliding down the wall?

A) 6   B) 1   C) 3   D) 10
E) 5   F) 8   G) 2   H) 4

Answer: 4 (medium)

107. A cube is 4 feet on each edge, with each edge increasing 1 foot per second. In cubic feet per second, what is the rate of increase in volume?

A) 56   B) 40   C) 42   D) 72
E) 64   F) 48   G) 36   H) 96

Answer: 48 (easy)

108. Two cars are each 100 miles away from the town of Tucumcari, one directly to the north and the other directly to the east. The car to the north is heading toward the town at 60 miles per hour, while the one to the east is heading toward the town at 30 miles per hour. In miles per hour, how fast are the cars approaching each other?

A) $200\sqrt{2}$ B) 100   C) $100\sqrt{2}$ D) 200
E) $50\sqrt{2}$ F) $45\sqrt{2}$ G) 45   H) 50

Answer: $45\sqrt{2}$ (hard)

109. A kite is flying 100 feet above the ground at the end of a string 125 feet long. The girl flying the kite lets out the string at a rate of 1 foot per second. If the kite remains 100 feet above the ground, how many feet per second is its horizontal distance from the girl increasing?

A) 5/3   B) 3   C) 4/3   D) 3/5
E) 5   F) 5/4   G) 4/5   H) 4

Answer: 5/3 (hard)

110. A student 5 feet tall is 10 feet away from a lamppost 15 feet tall. She is walking away from the lamppost at 2 feet per second. How fast is the tip of her shadow moving away from the foot of the lamppost?

A) 5/2   B) 3/2   C) 3   D) 2/3
E) 1/3   F) 4   G) 6   H) 1/2

Answer: 3 (hard)

111. A plane flying horizontally at an altitude of 1 km and a speed of 500 km/h passes directly over a radar station. Find the rate (in km/h) at which the distance from the plane to the station is increasing when it is 2 km away from the station.

   A) $125\sqrt{3}$ B) $175\sqrt{3}$ C) $250\sqrt{3}$ D) $275\sqrt{3}$

   E) $125\sqrt{2}$ F) $175\sqrt{2}$ G) $250\sqrt{2}$ H) $275\sqrt{2}$

   Answer: $250\sqrt{3}$ (medium)

112. A lighthouse is on a small island 3 km away from the nearest point P on a straight shoreline, and its light makes 4 revolutions per minute. At what rate (in km/min) is the beam of light moving along the shoreline when it is 1 km away from P?

   A) 20π B) $70\pi/3$ C) $80\pi/3$ D) $100\pi/3$
   E) $110\pi/3$ F) 40π G) $130\pi/3$ H) $140\pi/3$

   Answer: $80\pi/3$ (hard)

113. A cylindrical can is undergoing a transformation in which the radius and height are varying continuously with time t. The radius is increasing at 4 in/min, while the height is decreasing at 10 in/min. Is the volume increasing or decreasing, and at what rate, when the radius is 3 inches and the height is 5 inches?

   A) increasing, 30π cubic inches per minute   B) increasing, 20π cubic inches per minute
   C) increasing, 10π cubic inches per minute   D) increasing, 40π cubic inches per minute
   E) decreasing, 30π cubic inches per minute   F) decreasing, 20π cubic inches per minute
   G) decreasing, 10π cubic inches per minute   H) decreasing, 40π cubic inches per minute

   Answer: increasing, 30π cubic inches per minute (medium)

114. A frugal young man has decided to extract one of his teeth by tying a stout rubber band from his tooth to the chain on a garage door opener which runs on a horizontal track 3 feet above his mouth. If the garage door opener moves the chain at $1/4$ ft/s, how fast is the rubber band expanding when it is stretched to a length of 5 feet?

   A) $1/5$ ft/s   B) $1/2$ ft/s   C) $1/3$ ft/s   D) $1/4$ ft/s
   E) $1/6$ ft/s   F) $2/5$ ft/s   G) $2/3$ ft/s   H) $3/5$ ft/s

   Answer: $1/5$ ft/s (medium)

115. Two straight roads intersect at right angles in Newtonville. Car A is on one road moving toward the intersection at a speed of 50 miles/h. Car B is on the other road moving away from the intersection at a speed of 30 miles/h. When car A is 2 miles from the intersection and car B is 4 miles from the intersection how fast is the distance between the cars changing.

   A) $\sqrt{20}$ miles/h.   B) $\sqrt{10}$ miles/h.   C) $\sqrt{15}$ miles/h.

   D) $\sqrt{30}$ miles/h.   E) $2\sqrt{20}$ miles/h.   F) $2\sqrt{10}$ miles/h.

   G) $2\sqrt{15}$ miles/h.   H) $2\sqrt{30}$ miles/h.

   Answer: $\sqrt{20}$ miles/h. (medium)

116. The length of a rectangle is increasing at the rate of 7 ft/s, while the width is decreasing at the rate of 3 ft/s. At one time, the length is 12 feet and the diagonal is 13 feet. At this time find the rate of change in the perimeter.

A) 2 ft/s   B) 4 ft/s   C) 6 ft/s   D) 8 ft/s
E) 10 ft/s   F) 12 ft/s   G) 14 ft/s   H) 16 ft/s

Answer: 8 ft/s (medium)

117. A particle starts at the origin and moves along the parabola $y = x^2$ such that its distance from the origin increases at 4 units per second. How fast is its x-coordinate changing as it passes through the point $(1, 1)$?

A) $4\sqrt{2}/3$ units/s   B) $\sqrt{2}/3$ units/s   C) $4\sqrt{2}$ units/s

D) $\sqrt{2}$ units/s   E) $4\sqrt{3}/3$ units/s   F) $\sqrt{3}/3$ units/s

G) $3\sqrt{3}$ units/s   H) $3\sqrt{3}/4$ units/s

Answer: $4\sqrt{2}/3$ units/s (medium)

118. When a stone is dropped in a pool, a circular wave moves out from the point of impact at a rate of six inches per second. How fast is the area enclosed by the wave increasing when the wave is two inches in radius?

A) 12 in^2/s   B) 14 in^2/s   C) 16 in^2/s   D) 18 in^2/s
E) 20 in^2/s   F) 22 in^2/s   G) 24 in^2/s   H) 26 in^2/s

Answer: 24 in^2/s (medium)

119. A particle moves along a path described by $y = x^2$. At what point along the curve are x and y changing at the same rate?

A) $(1, 1)$ B) $(1/2, 1/4)$ C) $(0, 0)$ D) $(1/3, 1/9)$
E) $(2/3, 4/9)$ F) $(1/4, 1/16)$ G) $(3/2, 9/4)$ H) $(4/3, 16/9)$

Answer: $(1/2, 1/4)$ (medium)

120. A mothball shrinks in such a way that its radius decreases by 1/6th inch per month. How fast is the volume changing when the radius is 1/4th inch? Assume the mothball is spherical.

A) $-\pi/12$ in^3/month   B) $-\pi/14$ in^3/month   C) $-\pi/16$ in^3/month
D) $-\pi/18$ in^3/month   E) $-\pi/20$ in^3/month   F) $-\pi/22$ in^3/month
G) $-\pi/24$ in^3/month   H) $-\pi/26$ in^3/month

Answer: $-\pi/24$ in^3/month (medium)

121. The electric resistance of a certain resistor as a function of temperature is given by $R = 6.000 + 0.002t^2$, where R is measured in Ohms and t in degrees Celsius. If the temperature is decreasing at the rate of 0.2°C per second, find the rate of change of resistance when $t = 38$°C.

A) -0.0304 ohms/s   B) -0.0204 ohms/s   C) -0.0104 ohms/s
D) -0.0404 ohms/s   E) 0.0104 ohms/s   F) 0.0204 ohms/s
G) 0.0304 ohms/s   H) 0.0404 ohms/s

Answer: -0.0304 ohms/s (medium)

Chapter 2, Section 9
Differentials; Linear and Quadratic Approximations

122. Let $y = x^2$, $x = 2$, and $\Delta x = 1$. Find the value of the differential dy.

A) 2   B) 1/2   C) 1/3   D) 4
E) 1/4   F) 1/8   G) 3   H) 1

Answer: 4 (easy)

123. Let $y = x^2$, $x = 3$, and $\Delta x = 1$. Find the value of the corresponding change Δy.

A) 4   B) 8   C) 7   D) 2
E) 3   F) 6   G) 1   H) 5

Answer: 7 (easy)

124. Let $y = x^2$, $x = 1$, and $\Delta x = 0.1$. Find the error $dy - \Delta y$ in approximating Δy by dy.

A) $-.2$ B) $-.1$ C) $-.03$ D) $-.07$
E) $-.05$ F) $-.01$ G) $-.02$ H) $-.3$

Answer: $-.01$ (medium)

125. Use differentials to approximate $\sqrt{26}$.

A) 5.1   B) 5.2   C) 5.15   D) 5.3
E) 5.4   F) 5.25   G) 5.35   H) 5.05

Answer: 5.1 (medium)

126. The radius of a circle is given as 10 cm, with a possible error of measurement equal to 1 mm. Use differentials to estimate the maximum error in the area, in cm^2.

A) 10π B) 2π C) 3π D) π
E) 8π F) 5π G) 6π H) 4π

Answer: 2π (medium)

127. A spherical tank has radius equal to 10 feet (120 inches). Use differentials to estimate, in cubic inches, the amount of paint needed to cover the surface with a layer 1/100 of an inch thick.

A) 288π B) 1728π C) 144π D) 480π
E) 576π F) 512π G) 960π H) 640π

Answer: 576π (medium)

128. Use differentials to approximate $\sqrt[5]{31}$.

A) 161/80   B) 77/40   C) 163/80   D) 81/40
E) 79/40   F) 159/80   G) 83/40   H) 157/80

Answer: 159/80 (medium)

129. Use differentials to obtain an approximation for $\sqrt{16.2}$.

A) 4.026   B) 4.03   C) 4.025   D) 4.05
E) 4.015   F) .02498   G) 4.0185   H) 4.0245

Answer: 4.025 (medium)

130. Let $y = x^4 + x^2 + 1$, $x = 1$, and $dx = 1$. Find the value of the differential dy.

A) 2   B) 4   C) 6   D) 8
E) 10   F) 12   G) 0   H) 1/2

Answer: 6 (easy)

131. Let $y = 2x^3 + 3x - 4$, $x = 3$, and $dx = 1$. Find the value of the differential dy.

A) 21   B) 57   C) 165   D) 18
E) 54   F) 162   G) 59   H) 53

Answer: 57 (easy)

132. Find the linearization of the function $f(x) = \sqrt{x+3}$ at $x_1 = 1$ and use it to approximate $\sqrt{3.98}$.

A) 2.005   B) 2.000   C) 1.995   D) 1.990
E) 1.985   F) 1.980   G) 1.975   H) 1.970

Answer: 1.995 (medium)

133. Find the linearization of the function $f(x) = \sqrt{x+3}$ at $x_1 = 1$ and use it to approximate $\sqrt{4.05}$.

A) 2.0125   B) 2.0120   C) 2.0115   D) 2.0110
E) 2.0105   F) 2.0100   G) 2.0130   H) 2.0135

Answer: 2.0125 (medium)

134. Find the quadratic approximation of the function $f(x) = \frac{1}{x+2}$ near 1 and use it to approximate $\frac{1}{3.1}$.

A) 0.3327   B) 0.3328   C) 0.3316   D) 0.3324
E) 0.3336   F) 0.3226   G) 0.3229   H) 0.3236

Answer: 0.3226 (medium)

135. Find the quadratic approximation of the function $f(x) = \sqrt[3]{x}$ near 1 and use it to approximate $\sqrt[3]{0.9}$.

A) 0.9656   B) 0.9650   C) 0.9660   D) 0.9666
E) 0.9655   F) 0.9651   G) 0.9665   H) 0.9566

Answer: 0.9656 (medium)

136. $\boxed{G}$ Estimate the values of x to two decimal places for which the linear approximation is accurate to within 0.1. $\sqrt{2x+2} \approx \frac{3}{2} + \frac{1}{2}x$

A) $[0, 0.46]$ B) $[0, 2.47]$ C) $[0, 2.12]$ D) $[0. 1.5]$
E) $[0.12, 2.47]$ F) $[0.12, 1.45]$ G) $[1.50, 2.73]$ H) $[0.47, 1.5]$

Answer: $[0, 2.47]$ (medium)

137. $\boxed{G}$ Estimate the values of x to two decimal places for which the linear approximation is accurate to within 0.1. $\frac{1}{\sqrt{3x^2+1}} \approx \frac{7}{8} - \frac{3}{8}x$

A) $[-0.30, -0.06]$ B) $[0.38, 1.8]$ C) $[-0.38, 1.8]$
D) $[-0.06, 1.8]$ E) $[0.06, 1.8]$ F) $[-0.30, -0.06] \cup [0.38, 1.8]$
G) $[-0.30, 1.8]$ H) $[-0.30, 0.38]$

Answer: $[-0.30, -0.06] \cup [0.38, 1.8]$ (medium)

138. $\boxed{G}$ Estimate the values of x to two decimal places for which the quadratic approximation is accurate to within 0.1. $\frac{1}{x^2+1} \approx 1 - x^2$

A) $[-0.61, 0.61]$ B) $[-0.61, 0]$ C) $[0, 0.61]$ D) $[-0.31, 0.31]$
E) $[0, 0.31]$ F) $[-0.31, 0]$ G) $[0.31, 0.61]$ H) $[-0.31, 0.61]$

Answer: $[-0.61, 0.61]$ (medium)

139. $\boxed{G}$ Estimate the values of x to two decimal places for which the quadratic approximation is accurate to within 0.1. $x \sin x \approx x^2$

A) $[0, 0.89]$ B) $[0, 0.49]$ C) $[-0.49, 0.49]$ D) $[-0.49, 0]$
E) $[-0.89, 0]$ F) $[-0.89, 0.89]$ G) $[-0.49, 0.89]$ H) $[-0.89, 0.49]$

Answer: $[-0.89, 0.89]$ (medium)

Chapter 2, Section 10
Newton's Method

140. Use Newton's method with the initial approximation $x_1 = 2$ to find x_2, the second approximation to a root of the equation $x^2 - 2 = 0$.

A) 5/7   B) 7/4   C) 4/3   D) 9/16
E) 11/16   F) 5/4   G) 13/16   H) 3/2

Answer: 3/2 (medium)

141. Use Newton's method with the initial approximation $x_1 = 1.5$ to find x_2, the second approximation to a root of the equation $x^2 - 2 = 0$.

A) 19/13   B) 20/13   C) 19/12   D) 23/15
E) 26/15   F) 17/12   G) 23/14   H) 19/14

Answer: 17/12 (medium)

142. Use Newton's method with the initial approximation $x_1 = 2$ to find x_2, the second approximation to a root of the equation $x^5 - 31 = 0$.

A) 161/80   B) 159/80   C) 83/40   D) 79/40
E) 163/80   F) 81/40   G) 157/80   H) 77/40

Answer: 159/80 (medium)

143. Use Newton's method with the initial approximation $x_1 = 2$ to find x_2, the second approximation to a root of the equation $x^5 - 34 = 0$.

A) 79/40   B) 81/40   C) 77/40   D) 161/80
E) 83/40   F) 157/80   G) 163/80   H) 159/80

Answer: 81/40 (medium)

144. If Newton's method is used to find the cube root of a number a with a first approximation x_1, find an expression for x_2.

A) $x_2 = x_1 + \dfrac{3x_1^2}{x_1^3 - a}$ B) $x_2 = \sqrt[3]{x_1} - \sqrt[3]{a}$ C) $x_2 = x_1 - \dfrac{1}{3}\, x_1^{2/3}\, (x_1^{1/3} - a)$

D) $x_2 = x_1 + \dfrac{x_1^3 + a}{3x_1^2}$ E) $x_2 = x_1 + \dfrac{3x_1^2}{x_1^3 + a}$ F) $x_2 = x_1 - \dfrac{x_1^3 - a}{3x_1^2}$

G) $x_2 = x_1^{1/3} - \dfrac{1}{3}\, x_1^{-2/3}$ H) $x_2 = \sqrt[3]{a} + \dfrac{3x_1^2}{x_1^3 - a}$

Answer: $x_2 = x_1 - \dfrac{x_1^3 - a}{3x_1^2}$ (hard)

145. If Newton's method is used to solve $2x^3 + 2x + 1 = 0$ with first approximation $x_1 = -1$, what is the second approximation, x_2 ?

A) $-.500$ B) $-.525$ C) $-.550$ D) $-.575$

E) $-.600$ F) $-.625$ G) $-.650$ H) $-.675$

Answer: $-.625$ (medium)

146. If Newton's method is used to solve $x^3 + x + 1 = 0$ with an initial approximation $x_1 = -1$, what is the second approximation, x_2 ?

A) -0.75 B) -0.80 C) -0.85 D) -0.90

E) -0.95 F) -1.05 G) -1.10 H) -1.15

Answer: -0.75 (medium)

147. If Newton's method is used to solve $x^3 + x^2 + 2 = 0$ with an initial approximation $x_1 = -2$, what is the second approximation, x_2 ?

A) -2.15 B) -2.10 C) -2.05 D) -1.95

E) -1.90 F) -1.85 G) -1.80 H) -1.75

Answer: -1.75 (medium)

148. If Newton's method is used to find the square root of a number a with a first approximation x_1, find an expression for x_2.

A) $x_2 = x_1 + \frac{2x_2}{x_1^2 - a}$ B) $x_2 = \sqrt{x_1} - \sqrt{a}$ C) $x_2 = x_1 - \frac{1}{2} x_1 (x_1^{1/2} - a)$

D) $x_2 = x_1 + \frac{x_1^2 + a}{2x_1^2}$ E) $x_2 = x_1 + \frac{2x_1^2}{x_1^2 + a}$ F) $x_2 = x_1 - \frac{x_1^2 - a}{2x_1}$

G) $x_2 = x_1^{1/2} - \frac{1}{2} x_1^{-1}$ H) $x_2 = \sqrt{a} + \frac{2x_1}{x_1^2 - a}$

Answer: $x_2 = x_1 - \frac{x_1^2 - a}{2x_1}$ (hard)

149. Use Newton's Method to find the root of $6x^3 + x^2 - 19x + 6 = 0$ that lies between 0 and 1.

A) 0.316   B) 0.333   C) 0.158   D) 0.167

E) 0.474   F) 0.500   G) 0.079   H) 0.084

Answer: 0.333 (medium)

150. Use Newton's Method to determine a root (to two decimal places) of the equation $x^3 + 8x - 23 = 0$, given an initial starting value of $x_1 = 2$.

A) 1.75   B) 1.80   C) 1.85   D) 1.90

E) 1.95   F) 2.00   G) 2.05   H) 2.10

Answer: 1.95 (medium)

151. Use Newton's Method to approximate a solution to the following equation: $x^3 + 2x = 3.1$.

A) 1.00   B) 1.01   C) 1.02   D) 1.03
E) 1.04   F) 1.05   G) 1.06   H) 1.07

Answer: 1.02 (medium)

Calculus, 3rd Edition
by James Stewart
Chapter 3, Section 1
Maximum and Minimum Values

1.   1. Find the minimum value of the function $f(x) = x^2 - 1/2$.

     A) -1 B) $3/4$ C) $1/2$ D) 1
     E) $-1/2$ F) 0 G) $-1/4$ H) $1/4$

     Answer: $-1/2$ (easy)

2.   Find the value x at which the minimum of the function $f(x) = x^2 - 1/2$ occurs.

     A) 1 B) $-1/4$ C) $-1/2$ D) $3/4$
     E) 0 F) $1/4$ G) -1 H) $1/2$

     Answer: 0 (easy)

3.   Find the minimum value of the function $f(x) = x^2 - x$.

     A) $-1/2$ B) $3/4$ C) $1/2$ D) 0
     E) $1/4$ F) 1 G) -1 H) $-1/4$

     Answer: $-1/4$ (hard) (because most answer $1/2$)

4.   Find the value x at which the minimum of the function $f(x) = x^2 - x$ occurs.

     A) $1/4$ B) 1 C) $-1/2$ D) 0
     E) $-1/4$ F) $3/4$ G) -1 H) $1/2$

     Answer: $1/2$ (medium)

5.   Find the distance between the two critical numbers of the function $f(x) = x^3 - 3x + 27$.

     A) 4 B) 1 C) 8 D) 3
     E) 2 F) 9 G) 6 H) 5

     Answer: 2 (medium)

6.   Find the difference between the local maximum and the local minimum of the function $f(x) = x^3 - 3x + 27$.

     A) 4 B) 1 C) 9 D) 2
     E) 6 F) 5 G) 8 H) 3

     Answer: 4 (medium)

7.   Find the absolute maximum of the function $f(x) = x^3 - x^2 - x$ on the interval $-10 \leq x \leq 1$.

A) $-5/27$ B) $-2/9$ C) $5/27$ D) $4/9$
E) $-7/27$ F) $7/27$ G) $-4/9$ H) $2/9$

Answer: 5/27 (medium)

8.   Find the absolute maximum of the function $f(x) = x^3 - x^2 - x$ on the interval $-10 \leq x \leq 2$.

A) 1/9   B) 1/5   C) 0   D) 1/7
E) 1   F) 1/4   G) 1/3   H) 2

Answer: 2 (medium)

9.   Find the absolute minimum and maximum values of the function $f(x) = 2x^3 - 3x^2 - 12x + 45$ on the closed interval $[-3, 3]$.

A) 41, 45   B) 0, 52   C) 25, 36   D) 0, 36
E) 0, 25   F) $-41, 52$ G) 25, 52   H) $-25, 52$

Answer: 0, 52 (medium)

10.   Find the absolute minimum and maximum values of the function $f(x) = x^3 - x^2 + 11$ on the closed interval $[-3, 0.5]$.

A) $-3, 15$ B) $-25, 11$ C) 0, 17   D) $-10, 30$
E) $-41, 20$ F) $-30, 40$ G) $-25, 87/8$ H) $-10, 20$

Answer: $-25, 11$ (medium)

11.   Find the absolute minimum and maximum values of the function $f(x) = 4x^3 - 15x^2 + 12x + 7$ on the closed interval $[0, 3]$.

A) 0, 3   B) 0, 5   C) 3, 5   D) 3, 9.75
E) 3, 16   F) 5, 7   G) 7, 16   H) 5, 10.25

Answer: 3, 16 (medium)

12.   Find the minimum and maximum values of $y = x^3 - 9x + 8$ on the interval $[-3, 1]$, if they exist.

A) $8, 8 + 6\sqrt{3}$ B) $0, 8 + 6\sqrt{3}$ C) 0, 8

D) $8, 8 + \sqrt{3}$ E) $0, 8 + \sqrt{3}$ F) $8 + \sqrt{3}, 8 + 6\sqrt{3}$

G) $\sqrt{3}, 8$ H) $\sqrt{3}, 8 + 6\sqrt{3}$

Answer: $0, 8 + 6\sqrt{3}$ (medium)

13. Let $f(x) = x^{1/2}(1 - x)$ for $x \geq 0$. Find the absolute maximum of $f(x)$ on the interval $[0, 4]$.

A) 0   B) $2/\left(3\sqrt{3}\right)$ C) -6 D) $1/3$

E) 4   F) $2/\sqrt{3}$ G) $\sqrt{3}$ H) $2\sqrt{3}$

Answer: $2/\left(3\sqrt{3}\right)$ (medium)

14. Given that $f(x) = x^3 + ax^2 + bx$ has critical numbers at $x = 1$ and $x = 3$ find a and b.

A) $-9, 6$ B) $-8, 7$ C) $-7, 8$ D) $-6, 9$

E) $-9, 3$ F) $-8, 4$ G) $-7, 5$ H) $-6, 6$

Answer: $-6, 9$ (hard)

15. For the function $f(x)$, find the maximum and minimum values on the interval $[-1, 5]$

$$f(x) = \begin{cases} x^2 - 4 & \text{if } x \leq 2 \\ x^2 - 8x + 12 & \text{if } x > 2 \end{cases}$$

A) $0, -4$ B) $4, 0$ C) $2, 0$ D) $4, -4$

E) $2, -4$ F) $4, -2$ G) $2, -2$ H) $0, -2$

Answer: $0, -4$ (medium)

16. $\boxed{G}$ Estimate to two decimal places the absolute minimum and maximum values of the function $f(x) = x^3 - 9x^2 + 21x + 10, \ 0 \leq x \leq 5$.

A) $24.65, 13.35$ B) $13.35, 10$ C) $15, 10$ D) $24.65, 10$

E) $28, 10$ F) $28, 13.35$ G) $15, 13.35$ H) $24.65, 0$

Answer: $24.65, 10$ (medium)

17. $\boxed{G}$ Estimate to two decimal places the absolute minimum and maximum values of the function $f(x) = x\sqrt{2 - x^2}$.

Answer: $1, -1$ (medium)

18. $\boxed{G}$ Estimate to two decimal places the absolute minimum and maximum values of the function $f(x) = \frac{x^2 + 2}{\sin x + 2}$ for $0 \leq x \leq \pi$.

Answer: $0.91, 5.93$ (medium)

Chapter 3, Section 2
The Mean Value Theorem

19. According to Rolle's Theorem, what is the largest number of real roots that the equation $x^7 + x = 0$ can have?

A) 4   B) 5   C) 1   D) 0   E) 2   F) 7   G) 3   H) 6

Answer: 1 (medium)

20. According to Rolle's Theorem, what is the largest number of real roots that the equation $x^7 - x = 0$ can have?

A) 2   B) 5   C) 7   D) 6
E) 4   F) 1   G) 0   H) 3

Answer: 3 (medium)

21. How many real roots does the equation $x^7 + x = 0$ have?

A) 2   B) 7   C) 5   D) 1
E) 6   F) 4   G) 0   H) 3

Answer: 1 (medium)

22. How many real roots does the equation $x^7 - x = 0$ have?

A) 4   B) 3   C) 1   D) 2
E) 6   F) 5   G) 7   H) 0

Answer: 3 (medium)

23. According to Rolle's Theorem, what is the largest number of real roots that the equation $x^7 - x + 17 = 0$ can have?

A) 2   B) 1   C) 3   D) 0
E) 7   F) 5   G) 6   H) 4

Answer: 3 (medium)

24. How many real roots does the equation $x^7 - x + 17 = 0$ have?

A) 7   B) 5   C) 1   D) 3
E) 2   F) 6   G) 0   H) 4

Answer: 1 (hard)

25. Consider the function $f(x) = x^2$ on the interval $[0, 1/2]$. According to the mean value theorem, there must be a number c in $(0, 1/2)$ such that $f'(c)$ is equal to a particular value d. What is d?

A) 3/2   B) 1   C) 1/2   D) 2
E) 2/3   F) 3/4   G) 1/4   H) 3

Answer: 1/2 (medium)

26. Tell which of the statements below are true:

    1) If $f'(c) = 0$, then $f(x)$ has a maximum or minimum value at $x = c$.

    2) If $f'(x) = g'(x)$ for all x in an interval I, then $f(x) = g(x)$ on I.

    3) If $f(x)$ is differentiable on the open interval (a,b), and c is a point of local maximum for f in (a, b), then $f'(c) = 0$.

A) none   B) 1   C) 2   D) 3
E) 1, 2   F) 1, 3   G) 2, 3   H) all

Answer: 3 (medium)

27. What value(s) of c (if any) are predicted by the Mean Value Theorem for the function $f(x) = (x - 2)^3$ on the interval $[0, 2]$?

A) 4   B) $2 + \frac{2}{\sqrt{3}}$ C) $2 - \frac{2}{\sqrt{3}}$

D) 0   E) $2 + \frac{2}{\sqrt{3}}$, $2 - \frac{2}{\sqrt{3}}$ F) 4, $2 + \frac{2}{\sqrt{3}}$, $2 - \frac{2}{\sqrt{3}}$

G) 0, $2 - \frac{2}{\sqrt{3}}$ H) no values predicted

Answer: $2 - \frac{2}{\sqrt{3}}$ (medium)

28. Find all value(s) of c (if any) that satisfy the conclusion of the Mean Value Theorem for the function $f(x) = \frac{1}{1+x}$ on the interval $[0, 1]$.

A) 1/2   B) $1/\sqrt{2}$ C) 1/4

D) 1/4   E) $\sqrt{2} - 1$ F) $2 - \sqrt{2}$
G) 0   H) no values

Answer: $\sqrt{2} - 1$ (medium)

29. $\boxed{G}$ Estimate all value(s) of c (if any) that satisfy the conclusion of the Mean Value Theorem for the function $f(x) = x + \sqrt[3]{x^2 - 1}$ on the interval $[0, 3]$.

A) 0.79   B) 1.37   C) 0.51, 1.37

D) 0.79, 1.37   E) 0.51   F) 1.84

G) 0.79, 1.84   H) no values

Answer: 0.79, 1.37 (hard)

30. Find all value(s) of c (if any) that satisfy the conclusion of the Mean Value Theorem for the function $f(x) = \frac{x+2}{x-2}$ on the interval $[0, 4]$.

A) 1   B) 2   C) 1/2   D) 3 1/2
E) 1/2, 3 1/2   F) 1, 2   G) 0, 4   H) no values

Answer: no values (medium)

Chapter 3, Section 3
Monotonic Functions and the First Derivative Test

31. At what value of x does the function $f(x) = x^2 - 2x$ change from decreasing to increasing?

    A) 1   B) -1 C) $-1/2$ D) 2
    E) 1/2   F) -2 G) 0   H) $-3/2$

    Answer: 1 (easy)

32. Find the length of the largest interval on which the function $f(x) = x - \sqrt{x}$ is decreasing.

    A) 3/2   B) $\sqrt{2}$ C) $\sqrt{3}/4$ D) $\sqrt{2}/2$
    E) $\sqrt{3}/2$ F) 1/2   G) 2/3   H) 1/4

    Answer: 1/4 (hard)

33. At what value of x does the function $f(x) = 3x - \sqrt[3]{x}$ change from decreasing to increasing?

    A) 1/8   B) 1/2   C) 1/3   D) 1/27
    E) 1/9   F) $\sqrt{3}/4$ G) $\sqrt{3}/3$ H) 1/32

    Answer: 1/27 (hard)

34. At what value of x does the function $f(x) = x^3 - 3x^2 - 9x$ change from increasing to decreasing?

    A) 4   B) 3   C) -2 D) -1
    E) 0   F) 2   G) 1   H) -3

    Answer: -1 (medium)

35. At what value of x does the function $f(x) = x^3 - 3x^2 - 9x$ change from decreasing to increasing?

    A) 3   B) 1   C) 4   D) -3
    E) 2   F) 0   G) -2 H) -1

    Answer: 3 (medium)

36. What is the length of the largest interval on which the function $f(x) = x^3 - 3x^2 - 9x$ is decreasing?

    A) $3\sqrt{2}$ B) 1   C) 4   D) $2\sqrt{2}$
    E) 3   F) $2\sqrt{3}$ G) $\sqrt{3}$ H) 2

    Answer: 4 (medium)

37. What is the length of the largest interval on which the function $\frac{x}{x^2+1}$ is increasing?

A) 3   B) $2\sqrt{3}$ C) $2\sqrt{2}$ D) 1

E) 4   F) $\sqrt{3}$ G) 2   H) $3\sqrt{2}$

Answer: 2 (hard)

38. The function $f(x) = x + \frac{1}{x}$, $x \neq 0$, is

A) increasing on $(-1, 0)$ B) decreasing on $(0, 1)$
C) increasing on $(0, 1)$ D) decreasing on $(1, \infty)$
E) increasing on $(0, \infty)$ F) decreasing on $(0, \infty)$
G) increasing on $(-\infty, 0)$ H) decreasing on $(-\infty, 0)$

Answer: decreasing on $(0, 1)$ (medium)

39. On what interval is the function $f(x) = \frac{x}{x^2+1}$ increasing?

A) $[-1, 1]$ B) $[-1, 2]$ C) $[-2, 1]$ D) $[-2, 2]$
E) $(-\infty, 1]$ F) $(-\infty, 2)$ G) $[-2, \infty)$ H) $(-\infty, \infty)$

Answer: $[-1, 1]$ (medium)

40. Find the interval on which $f(x) = x - 2\sin x$, $0 \leq x \leq 2\pi$, is increasing.

A) $[\pi/3, 5\pi/3]$ B) $[0, \pi/3]$ C) $[5\pi/3, 2\pi]$ D) $[0, \pi/2]$
E) $[\pi/2, 3\pi/2]$ F) $[3\pi/2, 2\pi]$ G) $[0, \pi]$ H) $[\pi, 2\pi]$

Answer: $[\pi/3, 5\pi/3]$ (medium)

41. Find the interval on which $f(x) = x + \cos x$, $0 \leq x \leq 2\pi$, is increasing.

A) $[\pi/3, 5\pi/3]$ B) $[0, \pi/3]$ C) $[5\pi/3, 2\pi]$ D) $[0, \pi/2]$
E) $[\pi/2, 3\pi/2]$ F) $[3\pi/2, 2\pi]$ G) $[0, \pi]$ H) $[0, 2\pi]$

Answer: $[0, 2\pi]$ (medium)

42. Find the interval on which $f(x) = x\sin x + \cos x$, $0 \leq x \leq \pi$, is increasing.

A) $[\pi/3, 5\pi/3]$ B) $[0, \pi/3]$ C) $[5\pi/3, 2\pi]$ D) $[0, \pi/2]$
E) $[\pi/2, 3\pi/2]$ F) $[3\pi/2, 2\pi]$ G) $[0, \pi]$ H) $[\pi, 2\pi]$

Answer: $[0, \pi/2]$ (medium)

43. Find the intervals on which $f(x) = 2\tan x - \tan^2 x$ is increasing.

A) $[n\pi - \pi/2, n\pi + \pi/4]$, n an integer   B) $[n\pi + \pi/2, n\pi + 3\pi/2]$, n an integer
C) $[n\pi - \pi/3, n\pi]$, n an integer   D) $[n\pi, n\pi + \pi/2]$, n an integer
E) $[n\pi - \pi/2, n\pi + \pi/2]$, n an integer   F) $[n\pi - \pi/3, n\pi + \pi/2]$, n an integer
G) $[n\pi, n\pi + \pi/3]$, n an integer   H) $[n\pi - 2\pi/3, n\pi]$, n an integer

Answer: $[n\pi - \pi/2, n\pi + \pi/4]$ (hard)

44. [G] Use the graph of $f(x) = x^5 + 2x^2 - 2$ or $f'(x)$ to estimate the intervals on which f is increasing.

A) $[2.41, \infty)$
B) $[-0.93, 0.46]$
C) $(-\infty, \infty)$
D) $(-2.41, 0.86)$
E) $(-\infty, -0.93], [0, \infty)$
F) $(-\infty, -0.93], [2.41, \infty), [-0.46, \infty)$
G) $[-0.86, \infty)$
H) $(-\infty, 0.86]$

Answer: $(-\infty, -0.93], [0, \infty)$ (medium)

45. [G] Use the graph of $f(x) = 2x - 3\sin x, 0 \leq x \leq 2\pi$ or $f'(x)$, to estimate the local maximum values.

A) 0
B) 6.28
C) 3.14
D) 3.14, 6.28
E) 0, 3.14
F) 3.14, 0.28
G) 0, 6.28
H) no values

Answer: 0, 6.28 (medium)

46. [G] Use the graph of $f(x) = \frac{2x}{1-x^2}$ or $f'(x)$, to estimate the local maximum values.

A) 0
B) 1
C) -1
D) $-1, 1$
E) $-1, 0, 1$
F) $-1.43, 1.43$
G) 20
H) no values

Answer: no values (medium)

Chapter 3, Section 4
Concavity and Points of Inflection

47. Find the x-coordinate of the point of inflection of the function $x^3 - x^2 - x + 1$.

A) $-3/4$
B) $-3/2$
C) $3/4$
D) $-1/3$
E) $3/2$
F) $1/3$
G) $-2/3$
H) $2/3$

Answer: $1/3$ (medium)

48. Find the y-coordinate of the point of inflection of the function $x^3 - x^2$.

A) $1/3$
B) $-2/27$
C) $2/27$
D) $-1/3$
E) $-2/9$
F) $2/9$
G) $-2/3$
H) $2/3$

Answer: $-2/27$ (medium)

49. Find the length of the largest interval on which the function $x^4 - 6x^3$ is concave down.

A) $\sqrt{2}/2$
B) 3
C) $2\sqrt{2}$
D) $\sqrt{2}$
E) 1
F) 4
G) $\sqrt{2}/3$
H) 2

Answer: 3 (medium)

50. Find the length of the largest interval on which the function $f(x) = x^4 - 12x^3 + 3x - 10$ is concave down.

A) $\sqrt{2}/2$ B) 6   C) $\sqrt{2}/3$ D) $2\sqrt{2}$

E) 4   F) $\sqrt{2}$ G) 3   H) 2

Answer: 6 (medium)

51. How many points of inflection does the function $f(x) = x^7 - x^2$ have?

A) 5   B) 0   C) 2   D) 7

E) 6   F) 1   G) 3   H) 4

Answer: 1 (medium)

52. How many points of inflection does the function $f(x) = x^8 - x^2$ have?

A) 1   B) 0   C) 4   D) 5

E) 6   F) 3   G) 2   H) 7

Answer: 2 (medium)

53. How many points of inflection does the function $f(x) = x^8 + x^2$ have?

A) 7   B) 3   C) 2   D) 6

E) 0   F) 1   G) 5   H) 4

Answer: 0 (medium)

54. On what interval is the graph of $f(x) = \left[1 - \frac{1}{x}\right]^2$ concave downward?

A) $(-\infty, 0)$ B) $(3/2, \infty)$ C) $(0, \infty)$ D) $(1, \infty)$

E) $(-\infty, -1)$ F) $(1, 3/2)$ G) $(-3/2, -1)$ H) $(0, 1)$

Answer: $(3/2, \infty)$ (medium)

55. Determine the largest interval on which the function $f(x) = x + \frac{1}{x}$ is concave upward.

A) $(-1, 0)$ B) $(-\infty, -1)$ C) $(-\infty, 0)$ D) $(0, \infty)$

E) $(1, \infty)$ F) $(0, 1)$ G) $(0, 1/2)$ H) $(-1/2, 0)$

Answer: $(0, \infty)$ (medium)

56. Find the largest interval on which the function $f(x) = \frac{x}{x^2+1}$ is concave upward.

A) $(0, 1)$ B) $(1, 2)$ C) $(1, \infty)$ D) $(0, \infty)$

E) $\left(1, \sqrt{3}\right)$ F) $\left(\sqrt{3}, \infty\right)$ G) $\left(\sqrt{2}, \infty\right)$ H) $(1/2, \infty)$

Answer: $\left(\sqrt{3}, \infty\right)$ (hard)

57. Determine α so that the function $f(x) = x^2 + \frac{\alpha}{x}$ has an inflection point at $x = 1$.

A) -3 B) -2 C) -1 D) 0
E) 1 F) 2 G) 3 H) 4

Answer: -1 (medium)

58. Find the values α, β, γ so the function $f(x) = x^3 + \alpha x^2 + \beta x + \gamma$ has a critical point at $(1, 5)$ and an inflection point at $(2, 3)$. All listed answers are in the form α, β, γ.

A) $-6, 9, 1$ B) $1, -6, 9$ C) $9, 1, -6$ D) $1, 9, -6$
E) $-3, 7, -1$ F) $-1, -3, 7$ G) $7, -1, -3$ H) $-1, 7, -3$

Answer: $-6, 9, 1$ (medium)

59. Find the x-coordinates of the points of inflection of $f(\theta) = \sin^2 \theta$.

A) $n\pi + \pi/4$, n an integer   B) $n\pi - \pi/4$, n an integer
C) $n\pi \pm \pi/4$, n an integer   D) $n\pi + \pi/3$, n an integer
E) $n\pi - \pi/3$, n an integer   F) $n\pi \pm \pi/3$, n an integer
G) $n\pi$, n an integer   H) $n\pi/2$, n an integer

Answer: $n\pi \pm \pi/4$, n an integer (medium)

60. Find the x-coordinates of the points of inflection of $f(\theta) = \theta + \sin \theta$.

A) $n\pi + \pi/4$, n an integer   B) $n\pi - \pi/4$, n an integer
C) $n\pi \pm \pi/4$, n an integer   D) $n\pi + \pi/3$, n an integer
E) $n\pi - \pi/3$, n an integer   F) $n\pi \pm \pi/3$, n an integer
G) $n\pi$, n an integer   H) $n\pi/2$, n an integer

Answer: $n\pi$, n an integer (medium)

61. Find the intervals on which $f(\theta) = \cos^2 \theta$ is concave up.

A) $(n\pi + \pi/4, n\pi + 3\pi/4)$, n an integer   B) $(n\pi - \pi/4, n\pi + \pi/4)$, n an integer
C) $(n\pi + \pi/4, n\pi)$, n an integer   D) $(n\pi + \pi/3, n\pi + 2\pi/3)$, n an integer
E) $(n\pi - \pi/3, n\pi + \pi/3)$, n an integer   F) $(n\pi, n\pi + \pi/3)$, n an integer
G) $(n\pi, n\pi + 2\pi/3)$, n an integer   H) $(n\pi/2, n\pi)$, n an integer

Answer: $(n\pi + \pi/4, n\pi + 3\pi/4)$, n an integer (medium)

62. Find the intervals on which $f(\theta) = \cos^2 \theta$ is concave down.

A) $(n\pi + \pi/4, n\pi + 3\pi/4)$, n an integer   B) $(n\pi - \pi/4, n\pi + \pi/4)$, n an integer
C) $(n\pi + \pi/4, n\pi)$, n an integer   D) $(n\pi + \pi/3, n\pi + 2\pi/3)$, n an integer
E) $(n\pi - \pi/3, n\pi + \pi/3)$, n an integer   F) $(n\pi, n\pi + \pi/3)$, n an integer
G) $(n\pi, n\pi + 2\pi/3)$, n an integer   H) $(n\pi/2, n\pi)$, n an integer

Answer: $(n\pi - \pi/4, n\pi + \pi/4)$, n an integer (medium)

63. Find the intervals on which $f(\theta) = \theta + \cos\theta$ is concave up.

A) $(2n\pi + \pi/4, 2n\pi + 3\pi/4)$, n an integer
B) $(2n\pi - \pi/4, 2n\pi + \pi/4)$, n an integer
C) $(2n\pi + \pi/4, 2n\pi)$, n an integer
D) $(2n\pi + \pi/3, 2n\pi + 2\pi/3)$, n an integer
E) $(2n\pi - \pi/3, 2n\pi + \pi/3)$, n an integer
F) $(2n\pi - \pi/2, 2n\pi + \pi/2)$, n an integer
G) $(2n\pi - \pi/2, 2n\pi + 3\pi/2)$, n an integer
H) $(2n\pi + \pi/2, 2n\pi + 3\pi/2)$, n an integer

Answer: $(2n\pi + \pi/2, 2n\pi + 3\pi/2)$, n an integer (medium)

64. Find the intervals on which $f(\theta) = \theta + \cos\theta$ is concave down.

A) $(2n\pi + \pi/4, 2n\pi + 3\pi/4)$, n an integer
B) $(2n\pi - \pi/4, 2n\pi + \pi/4)$, n an integer
C) $(2n\pi + \pi/4, 2n\pi)$, n an integer
D) $(2n\pi + \pi/3, 2n\pi + 2\pi/3)$, n an integer
E) $(2n\pi - \pi/3, 2n\pi + \pi/3)$, n an integer
F) $(2n\pi - \pi/2, 2n\pi + \pi/2)$, n an integer
G) $(2n\pi - \pi/2, 2n\pi + 3\pi/2)$, n an integer
H) $(2n\pi + \pi/2, 2n\pi + 3\pi/2)$, n an integer

Answer: $(2n\pi - \pi/2, 2n\pi + \pi/2)$, n an integer (medium)

Chapter 3, Section 5
Limits at Infinity; Horizontal Asymptotes

65. Find the value of the limit $\lim\limits_{x \to \infty} \frac{7+3x}{4-x}$.

A) $3/4$
B) 3
C) 7
D) $-3/4$
E) -3
F) $-7/4$
G) -7
H) $7/4$

Answer: -3 (easy)

66. Find the value of the limit $\lim\limits_{x \to \infty} 3x^{-1/2}$.

A) $1/3$
B) $-\sqrt{2}/2$
C) $\sqrt{2}$
D) $\sqrt{2}$
E) $\sqrt{2}/2$
F) 0
G) 3
H) $\sqrt{3}$

Answer: 0 (easy)

67. Find the value of the limit $\lim\limits_{x \to \infty} \frac{x^2-1}{x^2+2x+1}$.

A) $-1/2$
B) 1
C) 2
D) $1/2$
E) -1
F) $-1/3$
G) -2
H) $1/3$

Answer: 1 (medium)

68. Find the value of the limit $\lim\limits_{x \to \infty} \sqrt{\frac{x+8x^2}{2x^2-1}}$.

A) -2
B) 1
C) $-1/2$
D) 4
E) $1/2$
F) 2
G) 0
H) 1

Answer: 2 (medium)

69. Find the value of the limit $\lim\limits_{x \to \infty} \frac{\sin^3 x}{x}$.

    A) $-1/3$ B) 1 C) $1/3$ D) $-\sqrt{2}/2$

    E) -1 F) $\sqrt{2}/2$ G) 0 H) 3

    Answer: 0 (medium)

70. Find the value of the limit $\lim\limits_{x \to \infty} \left(\sqrt{x^2 + x + 1} - x \right)$.

    A) $-1/2$ B) $\sqrt{2}$ C) $-\sqrt{2}$ D) $1/4$

    E) $\sqrt{2}/2$ F) $-1/4$ G) $-\sqrt{2}/2$ H) $1/2$

    Answer: $1/2$ (hard)

71. Find the value of the limit $\lim\limits_{x \to \infty} \cos \frac{1}{x}$.

    A) $\sqrt{2}/2$ B) $-1/2$ C) $-\sqrt{3}/2$ D) 1

    E) $\sqrt{3}/2$ F) 0 G) -1 H) $-\sqrt{2}/2$

    Answer: 1 (medium)

72. Find the value of the limit $\lim\limits_{x \to \infty} \left[\sqrt{x^2 + x} - \sqrt{x^2 - x} \right]$.

    A) $-\infty$ B) -2 C) -1 D) 0
    E) $1/2$ F) 1 G) $3/2$ H) ∞

    Answer: 1 (hard)

73. Find the value of the limit $\lim\limits_{x \to \infty} \frac{6x^4 - 8x^2 + 3x - 4}{7 + 6x^3 - 2x^4}$.

    A) ∞ B) $-\infty$ C) 1 D) -1
    E) 3 F) -3 G) 0 H) does not exist

    Answer: -3 (medium)

74. Find the value of the limit $\lim\limits_{x \to \infty} \frac{3x^2 + 5x - 1}{2x^2 - 5x + 1}$.

    A) $-\infty$ B) -2 C) -1 D) 0
    E) $1/2$ F) 1 G) $3/2$ H) ∞

    Answer: $3/2$ (medium)

75. Find the value of the limit $\lim\limits_{x \to -\infty} \frac{\sqrt{x^2 + 4x}}{4x + 1}$.

    A) 0 B) 4 C) -4 D) $1/4$
    E) $-1/4$ F) ∞ G) $-\infty$ H) does not exist

    Answer: $-1/4$ (medium)

76. Find the value of the limit $\lim\limits_{x \to \infty} \left(\sqrt{x^2 + 3x} - x \right)$.

A) 3   B) 3/2   C) 0   D) 1
E) 2   F) ∞ G) $-\infty$ H) does not exist

Answer: 3/2 (hard)

77. Find the value of the limit $\lim\limits_{x \to \infty} \left(\sqrt{x^2 + 2x} - x \right)$.

A) $-\infty$ B) -2 C) -1 D) 0
E) 1   F) 2   G) ∞ H) does not exist

Answer: 1 (hard)

78. Find the value of the limit $\lim\limits_{x \to \infty} \left(\sqrt{x^2 + x} - x \right)$.

A) $-\infty$ B) -2 C) -1 D) 0
E) 1/2   F) 1   G) 3/2   H) ∞

Answer: 1/2 (hard)

79. Find the horizontal asymptote of the curve $y = \frac{3x}{x+4}$.

A) $y = 3$ B) $y = 0$ C) $y = -3$ D) $y = 2$
E) $y = -1$ F) $y = 1$ G) $y = -2$ H) $y = -4$

Answer: $y = 3$ (medium)

80. Find the value of the limit $\lim\limits_{x \to \infty} \frac{4x^2+x}{x^2-2}$ if possible.

A) -2 B) 1   C) 2   D) 4
E) -1 F) -3 G) -4 H) 3

Answer: 4 (medium)

81. Find the limit of $x - \sqrt{x^2 - 4}$ as x approaches infinity.

A) -2 B) 1   C) 2   D) 4
E) -1 F) -3 G) 0   H) 3

Answer: 0 (medium)

82. Find the value of the limit $\lim\limits_{x \to \infty} \frac{3x^2+4x+2}{5-x+x^3}$.

A) $-1/2$ B) 1   C) 2   D) 1/2
E) -1 F) $-1/3$ G) -2 H) 0

Answer: 0 (medium)

83. Find the value of the limit $\displaystyle\lim_{x \to \infty} \frac{1}{\sqrt{x+1}-\sqrt{x}}$.

A) 1   B) 1/2   C) 2   D) -2
E) ∞ F) $-\infty$ G) $-1/2$ H) 0

Answer: ∞ (hard)

84. Find the value of x at which the curve $y = \frac{3x}{x+4}$ has a vertical asymptote.

A) -1 B) 3   C) 2   D) -4
E) 1   F) 0   G) -2 H) -3

Answer: -4 (medium)

85. Find the value(s) of x at which the curve $y = \frac{x^2-4}{9-x^2}$ has a vertical asymptote(s).

A) -3 B) 3   C) 2   D) -2
E) 3, 2   F) $-3, -2$ G) $-3, -3, 2$ H) $-3, 3$

Answer: $-3, 3$ (medium)

86. Find the value of x at which the curve $y = \frac{x^2-16}{x^2-5x+4}$ has a vertical asymptote.

A) -1 B) 3   C) 2   D) -4
E) 1   F) 0   G) -2 H) -3

Answer: 1 (medium)

87. Find the value(s) of x at which the curve $y = \frac{3x^2+100}{4x^2-100}$ has a vertical asymptote(s).

A) -5 B) 5   C) $-5, 5$ D) -4
E) 4   F) $-4, 4$ G) $-4, 4, 5$ H) $-5, \div4, 4$

Answer: $-5, 5$ (medium)

88. Find the value of x at which the curve $y = \frac{x^3-2x+3}{x^2+4x+4}$ has a vertical asymptote.

A) -1 B) 3   C) 2   D) -4
E) 1   F) 0   G) -2 H) -3

Answer: -2 (medium)

Chapter 3, Section 6
Curve Sketching

89. Find the smallest number in the domain of the function $f(x) = \sqrt{1 - x - x^2}$.

   A) $(-1 - \sqrt{5})/2$ B) $(1 + \sqrt{5})/2$ C) $(-1 + \sqrt{5})/2$

   D) $-\sqrt{3}/2$ E) $\sqrt{3}/2$ F) $-\sqrt{3}$.

   G) $(1 - \sqrt{5})/2$ H) $\sqrt{3}$

   Answer: $(-1 - \sqrt{5})/2$ (medium)

90. Find the period of the function $f(x) = \tan 2x$.

   A) $3\pi/2$ B) $3\pi/4$ C) 3π D) $\pi/2$

   E) 4π F) 2π G) $\pi/3$ H) π

   Answer: $\pi/2$ (medium)

91. Find the slope of the slant asymptote of the curve $y = \frac{3x^2}{2x-1}$.

   A) $3/2$ B) $-2/3$ C) $-1/3$ D) $1/2$

   E) $1/3$ F) $-1/2$ G) $2/3$ H) $-3/2$

   Answer: $3/2$ (medium)

92. Find the critical number c for $f(x) = x^4 - 3x^3 + 3x^2 - x$ at which $f(c)$ is not a local maximum and not a local minimum.

   A) $-1/2$ B) -3 C) -1 D) 0

   E) $-1/3$ F) 3 G) $1/3$ H) 1

   Answer: 1 (hard)

93. Find the distance along the x-axis between the point of local minimum and the point of local maximum of the function $f(x) = x^3 - 3x + 7$.

   A) $1/3$ B) 3 C) $3/7$ D) $49/3$

   E) 2 F) 1 G) $7/3$ H) $1/2$

   Answer: 2 (medium)

94. Find the value of x at which the direction of concavity of the function $f(x) = \frac{7x^2}{2x-3}$ changes.

   A) $7/2$ B) $3/2$ C) $2/3$ D) $-7/2$

   E) $-3/2$ F) $-2/3$ G) $2/7$ H) $-2/7$

   Answer: $3/2$ (medium)

95. Find the maximum value of the function $f(x) = \frac{x^2+2x-4}{x^2}$.

A) -5 B) -1 C) $-1/2$ D) $1/4$
E) $11/9$ F) $5/4$ G) $7/4$ H) $9/4$

Answer: 5/4 (medium)

96. Determine the largest interval on which the function $f(x) = \frac{x^2+2x-4}{x^2}$ is concave upward.

A) $(-\infty, -4)$ B) $(-\infty, -2)$ C) $(-\infty, 0)$ D) $(-4, 0)$
E) $(0, 2)$ F) $(0, 4)$ G) $(4, \infty)$ H) $(6, \infty)$

Answer: $(6, \infty)$ (medium)

97. On what interval is the function $f(x) = \frac{x^2+2x-4}{x^2}$ increasing?

A) $(-\infty, -4]$ B) $(-\infty, -2]$ C) $(-\infty, 0)$ D) $[-4, -2]$
E) $[-4, 0)$ F) $(0, 4]$ G) $(0, \infty)$ H) $[4, \infty)$

Answer: $(0, 4]$ (hard)

98. Sketch the curve $y = x^4 - 6x^2$.

A)
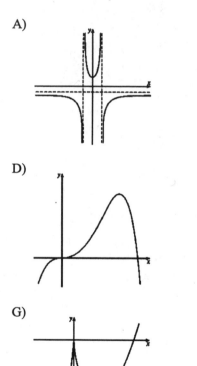

B)
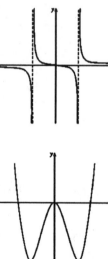

C)
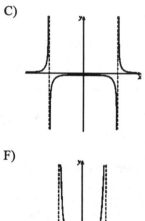

D)

E)

F)

G)

H)
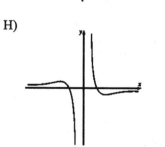

Answer: (medium)

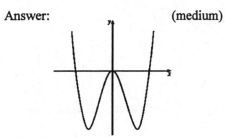

99.   Sketch the curve $y = 4x^3 - x^4$.

A)

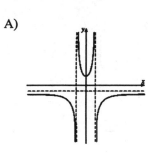

B)

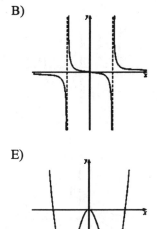

C)

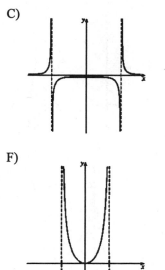

D)

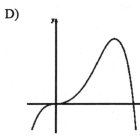

E)

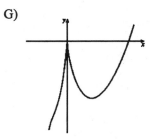

F)

G)

H)

Answer: (medium)

100. Sketch the curve $y = \frac{1}{x^2 - 9}$.

A)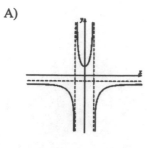

B)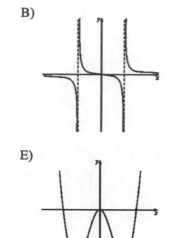

C)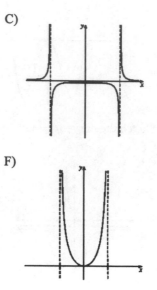

D)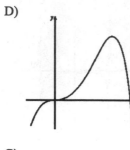

E)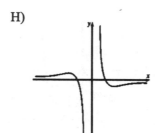

F)

G)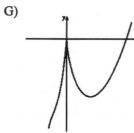

H)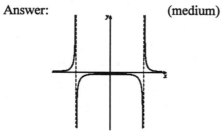

Answer: 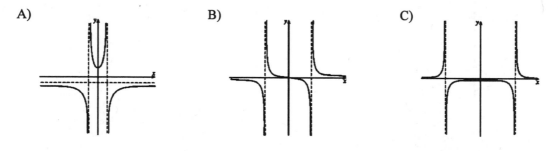 (medium)

101. Sketch the curve $y = \frac{x}{x^2 - 9}$.

A)

B)

C)

D)

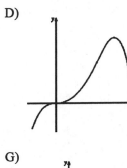

E)

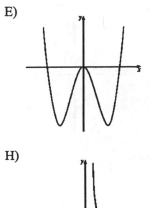

F)

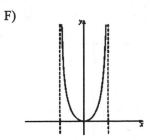

G)

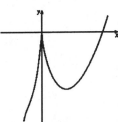

H)

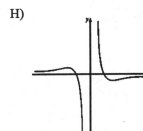

Answer: 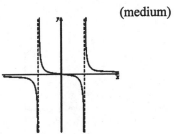 (medium)

102. Sketch the curve $y = \frac{1+x^2}{1-x^2}$.

A)

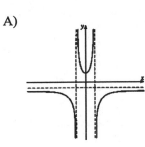

B)

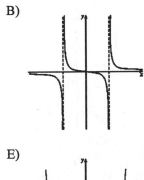

C)

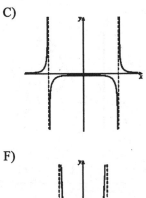

D)

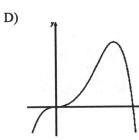

E)

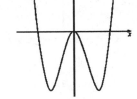

F)

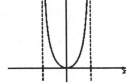

G)

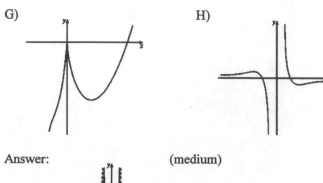

H)

Answer: (medium)

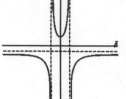

103.   Sketch the curve $y = \frac{1-x^2}{x^3}$.

A)

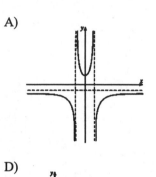

B)

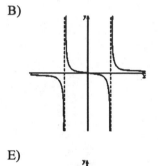

C)

D)

E)

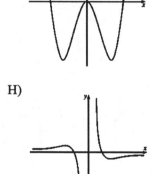

F)

G)

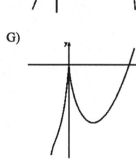

H)

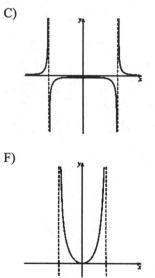

Answer: (medium)

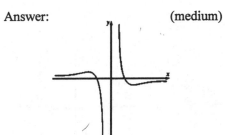

104. Sketch the curve $y = x^{5/3} - 5x^{2/3}$.

A)

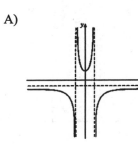

B)

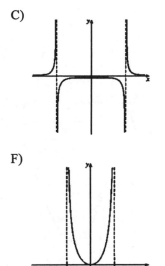

C)

D)

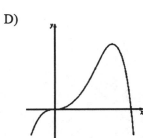

E)

F)

G)

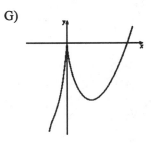

H)

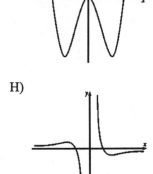

Answer: (medium)

105. Sketch the curve $y = 2x + \cot x$, $0 < x < \pi$.

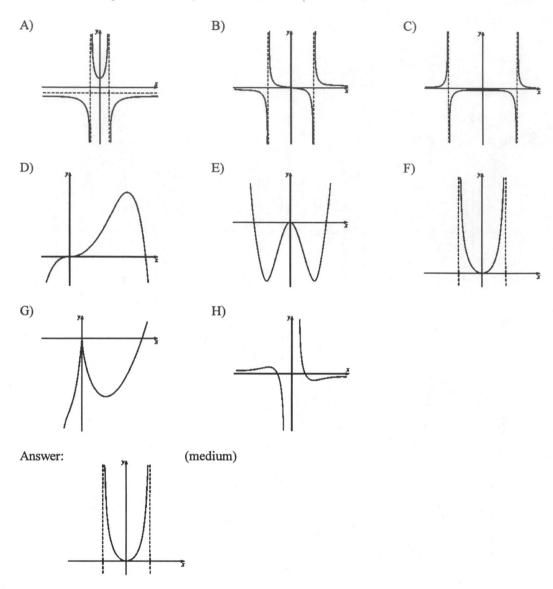

A)

B)

C)

D)

E)

F)

G)

H)

Answer: (medium)

Chapter 3, Section 7
Graphing with Calculators and Calculus

106. **G** Let $f(x) = \frac{x^3+x^2-2x}{x^2+2x-8}$. Use the graph of f' to estimate the intervals to two decimal places on which f is increasing.

Answer: $(-\infty, -6.60)$, $(-1.24, 0.61)$, $(3.24, \infty)$ (medium)

107. **G** Let $f(x) = 9x^5 + x^4 + 8x^3 + 3x^2 + x + 19$. Use the graph of f'' to estimate the intervals to two decimal places on which f is concave down.

Answer: $(-\infty, -0.12)$ (medium)

108. $\boxed{\text{G}}$ Let $f(x) = 5x^5 + 3x^4 + 8x^3 - 12x + 11$. Use the graph of f' to estimate the intervals to two decimal places on which f is decreasing.

Answer: $(-0.67, 0.56)$ (medium)

109. $\boxed{\text{G}}$ Let $f'(x) = \frac{(x-3)^4(x-2)^2(x+7)}{x^4+1}$. Use the graph of f' to find the local maximum values.

Answer: none (medium)

110. $\boxed{\text{G}}$ Let $f'(x) = \frac{x^2(x^2-10)+25}{x^2+2x-8}$. Use the graph of f' to estimate the critical points of f to two decimal places.

Answer: $-2.24, 2.24$ (easy)

111. $\boxed{\text{G}}$ Let $f''(x) = 5(x-5)^{16}(x-1)^{31}(x+8)^{25}$. Use the graph of f'' to estimate the interval on which f is concave down.

Answer: $(-8, 1)$ (medium)

112. $\boxed{\text{G}}$ Let $f'(x) = \frac{(2-\sin x)^3(2+\cos x)^2(2+x-\sin x)}{x^6+x^4+x^2+1}$. Use the graph of f' to estimate to two decimal places the critical points of f.

Answer: -2.55 (medium)

113. $\boxed{\text{G}}$ Let $f(x)\,g'(x) = \frac{x^4+3x^2-11x+9}{x^2+6}$ and $f'(x)\,g(x) = \frac{-17x^2+11x+40}{x^2+6}$. Use the appropriate graph to estimate to two decimal places the critical points of $f(x)g(x)$.

Answer: $-2.65, 2.65$ (medium)

114. $\boxed{\text{G}}$ Let $g(x)$ be a bounded, strictly negative function and let $f(x)g'(x) = \frac{x^2-1}{x^2+3}$ and let $f'(x)g(x) = \frac{2(x^2-3)}{x^2+1}$. Use a graph to estimate to two decimal places the critical points of $\frac{f(x)}{g(x)}$.

Answer: $-2.03, 2.03$ (medium)

115. $\boxed{\text{G}}$ Let $f''(x) = 3(x^2+2)(x-3)^{11}(x+5)^9$. Use the graph of f'' to estimate the interval on which f is concave down.

Answer: $(-5, 3)$ (medium)

Chapter 3, Section 8
Applied Maximum and Minimum Problems

116. We are given two numbers that sum to 100, and we wish to make their product as large as possible. How large is that product?

A) 2100 B) 2000 C) 3000 D) 2700
E) 2250 F) 3200 G) 2500 H) 1850

Answer: 2500 (easy)

117.   Two numbers a and b sum to 60. We wish to make ab^2 as large as possible. Find the value of a.

A) 30   B) 20   C) 18   D) 21
E) 32   F) 16   G) 28   H) 24

Answer: 20 (medium)

118.   A farmer has 20 feet of fence, and he wishes to make from it a rectangular pen for his pig Wilbur, using a barn as one of the sides. In square feet, what is the maximum area possible for this pen?

A) 64   B) 75   C) 60   D) 32
E) 56   F) 25   G) 40   H) 50

Answer: 50 (easy)

119.   It is desired to make a rectangular pen with perimeter equal to 40 feet. It is not necessary, however, to achieve maximum area. In fact, any area that is greater than or equal to 75% of the maximum area will be satisfactory. Under these conditions, find the maximum number of feet the longer side can be.

A) 15   B) 14   C) 12.5   D) 12
E) 11   F) 13   G) 13.5   H) 10.5

Answer: 15 (medium)

120.   A lakefront runs east-west. A man in a rowboat is 5 miles due north of a point A on the shore. He wishes to get to B, 5 miles due east of A, in the least time. He rows 3 miles per hour and walks 5 miles per hour. What is the minimum time, in minutes?

A) 180   B) 160   C) 140   D) 120
E) 90   F) 150   G) 170   H) 130

Answer: 140 (hard)

121.   A drinking cup is made in the shape of a right circular cylinder. For a fixed volume, we wish to make the total material used, the circular bottom and the cylindrical side, as small as possible. Under this condition, what is the ratio of the height to the diameter?

A) 4   B) $\pi/4$ C) 2   D) 1
E) $\pi/8$ F) $4/\pi$ G) $8/\pi$ H) 1/2

Answer: 1/2 (hard)

122.   A right circular cylindrical container is made by cutting the circular top and bottom out of two squares whose sides are equal to the diameter of the top and bottom. The remnants of the squares are wasted. Therefore, subject to fixed volume, it is required to minimize the total area of the two squares plus that of the side of the container. What is the ratio of the height to the diameter?

A) $4/\pi$ B) 2   C) $\pi/4$ D) $\pi/8$
E) $8/\pi$ F) 1   G) 1/2   H) 4

Answer: $4/\pi$ (hard)

123. Find the point on the line $y = 2x - 3$ that is nearest to the origin.

A) $(.5, -2)$ B) $(7.5, -1.5)$ C) $(.875, -1.25)$
D) $(1, -.5)$ E) $(1.1, -.8)$ F) $(1.2, -.6)$
G) $(1.25, -.5)$ H) $(1.5, 0)$

Answer: $(1.2, -.6)$ (medium)

124. Find the shortest distance from the point $(1, 4)$ to a point on the parabola $y^2 = 2x$.

A) 1 B) $\sqrt{2}$ C) $\sqrt{3}$ D) 2

E) $\sqrt{5}$ F) $\sqrt{6}$ G) $\sqrt{7}$ H) $2\sqrt{2}$

Answer: $\sqrt{5}$ (hard)

125. Find the area of the largest rectangle that can be inscribed in the ellipse $\frac{x^2}{a^2} + \frac{y^2}{b^2} = 1$.

A) $ab/2$ B) ab C) $3ab/2$ D) $2ab$
E) $5ab/2$ F) $3ab$ G) $7ab/2$ H) $4ab$

Answer: $2ab$ (hard)

126. Acme Company's daily profit is given by the following equation: $P(x) = -0.03x^3 + 36x + 500$, $x \geq 0$, where x is the number of units sold each day and $P(x)$ is the daily profit in dollars. How many units would have to be sold to maximize Acme's daily profit?

A) 23 B) 22 C) 21 D) 20
E) 19 F) 18 G) 17 H) 16

Answer: 20 (medium)

127. A cardboard box of 32 in^3 volume with a square base and open top is to be constructed. Find the minimum area of cardboard needed neglecting waste.

A) 54 in^2 B) 48 in^2 C) 46 in^2 D) 42 in^2
E) 40 in^2 F) 36 in^2 G) 32 in^2 H) 28 in^2

Answer: 48 in^2 (medium)

128. Farmer Brown wants to fence in a rectangular plot in a large field, using a rock wall which is already there as the north boundary. The fencing for the east and west sides of the plot will cost $\$ 3$ a yard, but she needs to use special fencing which will cost $\$ 5$ a yard on the south side of the plot. If the area of the plot is to be 600 square yards, find the dimensions for the plot which will minimize the cost of the fencing. Dimensions below are listed east by south.

A) $10\sqrt{5}$ by $12\sqrt{5}$ yards   B) $12\sqrt{5}$ by $10\sqrt{5}$ yards
C) 10 by 60 yards   D) 60 by 10 yards
E) $8\sqrt{5}$ by $15\sqrt{5}$ yards   F) $15\sqrt{5}$ by $8\sqrt{5}$ yards
G) 15 by 40 yards   H) 40 by 15 yards

Answer: $10\sqrt{5}$ by $12\sqrt{5}$ yards (hard)

129. A closed top container is to be constructed in the shape of a right cylinder. If the surface area is fixed find the ratio of the height to the radius which will maximize the volume.

A) 2:1   B) 3:1   C) 3:2   D) 5:3
E) 1:2   F) 1:3   G) 2:3   H) 3:5

Answer: 2:1 (medium)

130. A gas pipeline is to be constructed from a storage tank, which is right on a road, to a house which is 600 feet down the road and 300 feet back from the road. Pipe laid along the road costs $8.00 per foot, while pipe laid off the road costs $10.00 per foot. What is the minimum cost for which this pipeline can be built? (Assume the pipeline path is piecewise linear, with at most two pieces.)

A) $5000   B) $5500   C) $5900   D) $6100
E) $6600   F) $7000   G) $7100   H) $7500

Answer: $6600 (hard)

131. A plastic right cylinder with closed ends is to hold V cubic feet. If there is no waste in construction, find the ratio between the height and diameter that results in the minimum use of materials.

A) $1:\pi$ B) $1:\pi/2$ C) $1:2\pi$ D) $1:2$
E) $2:\pi$ F) $2:\pi/3$ G) $1:\pi/3$ H) $1:3$

Answer: $1:\pi$ (medium)

132. A right circular cone is inscribed in a hemisphere of radius 2 with the apex of the cone and the center of the base of the hemisphere being the same point. Find the dimensions of one such cone with maximum volume. [NOTE: The volume of a cone is given by $V = \frac{1}{3}\pi r^2 h$.] Dimensions are listed as height by radius.

A) $\frac{2\sqrt{3}}{3}$ by $\frac{2\sqrt{6}}{3}$ B) $\frac{2\sqrt{6}}{3}$ by $\frac{2\sqrt{3}}{3}$ C) $\sqrt{3}$ by $\sqrt{6}$

D) $\frac{\sqrt{3}}{3}$ by $\frac{\sqrt{6}}{3}$ E) $\frac{\sqrt{6}}{3}$ by $\frac{\sqrt{3}}{3}$ F) $\sqrt{6}$ by $\sqrt{3}$

G) $\frac{\sqrt{3}}{2}$ by $\frac{\sqrt{6}}{2}$ H) $\frac{\sqrt{6}}{2}$ by $\frac{\sqrt{3}}{2}$

Answer: $\frac{2\sqrt{3}}{3}$ by $\frac{2\sqrt{6}}{3}$ (hard)

133. A square is to be cut from each corner of a piece of paper which is 8 cm by 10 cm and the sides are to be folded up to create an open box. What should the side of the square be for maximum volume? (State your answer correct to two decimal places.)

A) 1.35 cm   B) 1.39 cm   C) 1.41 cm   D) 1.47 cm
E) 1.52 cm   F) 1.55 cm   G) 1.60 cm   H) 1.62 cm

Answer: 1.47 cm (medium)

Chapter 3, Section 9
Applications to Economics

134. A company has cost function $C(x) = 1000 + 10x + x^2$. Find the average cost of producing 100 units.

    A) 150   B) 200   C) 210   D) 120
    E) 250   F) 90   G) 180   H) 100

Answer: 120 (easy)

135. A company has cost function $C(x) = 1000 + 10x + x^2$. Find the marginal cost of producing 100 units.

    A) 210   B) 120   C) 90   D) 150
    E) 250   F) 200   G) 100   H) 180

Answer: 210 (medium)

136. A company has cost function $C(x) = 2000 + 50x + x^2$ and demand function $p(x) = 100$. How many units should it make to maximize its profit?

    A) 15   B) 25   C) 8   D) 5
    E) 30   F) 10   G) 20   H) 35

Answer: 25 (medium)

137. A company has cost function $C(x) = 2000 + 50x + x^2$ and demand function $p(x) = 200$. Find the maximum profit the company can make.

    A) 3625   B) 3875   C) 4025   D) 4275
    E) 4500   F) 3945   G) 4225   H) 3600

Answer: 3625 (hard)

138. A school band decides to raise money by means of a car wash. Labor and material are donated, so pure profit is realized from sale of the tickets. They know that if they charge $ 5 per ticket, they will sell 1000, while if they charge $ 4 per ticket they will sell 1500. Assuming the demand function is linear, what should they charge per ticket to maximize their profit?

    A) $ 3.75   B) $ 2.25   C) $ 2.75   D) $ 2.50
    E) $ 3.00   F) $ 4.00   G) $ 3.50   H) $ 3.25

Answer: $ 3.50 (hard)

139. The cost of operating a bus from Azusa to Yreka is $200 + 8x$, where x is the number of passengers. If a ticket is $ 40, there will be 10 passengers, while if a ticket is $ 35, there will be 15 passengers. Assuming the demand function is linear, what should the price of a ticket be to maximize profit?

    A) $ 37   B) $ 27   C) $ 29   D) $ 31
    E) $ 33   F) $ 39   G) $ 35   H) $ 41

Answer: $ 29 (hard)

140. The cost of operating a bus between Moose Jaw and Saskatoon is $100 + 5x$, where x is the number of passengers. If a ticket is $\$20$, there will be 10 passengers, while if a ticket is $\$15$, there will be 20 passengers. Assuming the demand function is linear, what is the maximum profit possible?

A) 50   B) 120   C) 100   D) 90
E) 60   F) 80   G) 110   H) 70

Answer: 100 (hard)

141. Suppose that the cost function for an article is given by $C(x) = 0.004x^3 - 0.02x^2 + 6x + 1000$. Assume the cost unit is dollars and find the minimum marginal cost.

A) $\$5.87$ B) $\$5.93$ C) $\$5.97$ D) $\$6.01$
E) $\$6.09$ F) $\$6.14$ G) $\$6.19$ H) $\$6.25$

Answer: $\$5.97$ (medium)

142. If total cost, c, is related to sales, x, by $c = 0.6x^2 - 179x + 100$, find the amount of sales which will lead to maximum profit.

A) 210   B) 120   C) 90   D) 150
E) 250   F) 200   G) 100   H) 180

Answer: 150 (medium)

143. If the cost of manufacturing x units per day of a certain commodity is $c = 600 + 0.04x + 0.002x^2$ and if each unit sells for $\$10.00$, what daily production will maximize the profit?

A) 2420 units   B) 2430 units   C) 2440 units
D) 2450 units   E) 2460 units   F) 2470 units
G) 2480 units   H) 2490 units

Answer: 2490 units (medium)

144. Suppose that $C(x)$ is the number of dollars in the total cost of producing x tables $(x > 6)$ and $C(x) = 25 + 4x + 18x^{-1}$. Find the marginal cost when $x = 10$.

A) $\$3.72$ B) $\$3.75$ C) $\$3.79$ D) $\$3.82$
E) $\$3.89$ F) $\$3.93$ G) $\$3.97$ H) $\$4.00$

Answer: $\$3.82$ (medium)

Chapter 3, Section 10
Antiderivatives

145. Find the most general antiderivative of the function $f(x) = x^2$.

A) $3x^3 + C$ B) $2x + C$ C) $x/2 + C$ D) $2x^2 + C$
E) $x^3/3 + C$ F) $3x + C$ G) $x/3 + C$ H) $3x^2 + C$

Answer: $x^3/3 + C$ (easy)

146. Find the most general antiderivative of $\sec^2 x + \cos x$.

A) $\frac{1}{3}\sec^3 x + \sin x + C$ B) $\tan^2 x - \sin x + C$ C) $\tan x + \sin x + C$

D) $\tan x - \sin x + C$ E) $\tan^2 x + \sin x + C$ F) $\frac{1}{3}\sec^3 x + \frac{1}{2}\cos^2 x + C$

G) $\frac{1}{3}\sec^3 x - \sin x + C$ H) $\frac{1}{3}\sec^3 x - \frac{1}{2}\cos^2 x + C$

Answer: $\tan x + \sin x + C$ (medium)

147. Given $f'(x) = \sqrt{x}$ and $f(0) = 0$, find $f(1)$.

A) 1/3   B) 2   C) 3/2   D) -2

E) 2/3   F) 1/2   G) $-1/2$ H) 3

Answer: 2/3 (medium)

148. Given $f''(x) = 1$, $f'(0) = 7$, and $f(0) = 3$, find $f(1)$.

A) 10/3   B) 17/3   C) 7/2   D) 3/10

E) 17/2   F) 13/3   G) 23/3   H) 21/2

Answer: 21/2 (medium)

149. A cyclist traveling at 40 ft/s decelerates at a constant 4 ft/s^2. How many feet does she travel before coming to a complete stop?

A) 180   B) 200   C) 240   D) 160

E) 480   F) 400   G) 360   H) 250

Answer: 200 (medium)

150. A custard pie is thrown vertically up from the ground with velocity 48 ft/s. Find the greatest distance above the ground that it rises.

A) 64   B) 72   C) 36   D) 128

E) 96   F) 48   G) 112   H) 32

Answer: 36 (medium)

151. A chocolate cream pie is thrown vertically up from the ground with velocity 72 ft/s. Find the amount of time in seconds until it hits the ground.

A) 6.5   B) 4.5   C) 6   D) 7.5

E) 5.5   F) 7   G) 5   H) 4

Answer: 4.5 (medium)

152. If $f''(x) = -4\sin 2x$, $f(0) = 0$, $f'(0) = 2$, find the value of $f(\pi/4)$.

A) $1/\sqrt{2}$ B) $\sqrt{2}$ C) $-1/\sqrt{2}$ D) 0

E) 1   F) -1 G) $-\sqrt{3}/2$ H) $-\sqrt{2}$

Answer: 1 (medium)

153. If $f'(x) = 3x^2 + 2$ and $f(0) = 1$, find the value of $f(1)$.

A) 1   B) 2   C) 3   D) 4
E) 5   F) 6   G) 7   H) 8

Answer: 4 (medium)

154. If $f''(x) = 12x^2 - 2$, $f(0) = 2$, and $f'(0) = 3$, find $f(1)$.

A) 1   B) 2   C) 3   D) 4
E) 5   F) 6   G) 7   H) 8

Answer: 5 (medium)

155. Find $f(x)$ if $f'(x) = 3x - x^2$ and $f(1) = 4$.

A) $f(x) = \frac{3}{2}x^2 - \frac{1}{3}x^3 + \frac{17}{6}$ B) $f(x) = \frac{3}{2}x^2 - \frac{1}{3}x^3 + \frac{13}{6}$

C) $f(x) = \frac{3}{2}x^2 - \frac{1}{3}x^3 + \frac{17}{8}$ D) $f(x) = \frac{3}{2}x^2 - \frac{1}{3}x^3 + \frac{13}{8}$

E) $f(x) = 3x^2 - x^3 + \frac{17}{6}$ F) $f(x) = 3x^2 - x^3 + \frac{13}{6}$

G) $f(x) = 3x^2 - x^3 + \frac{17}{8}$ H) $f(x) = 3x^2 - x^3 + \frac{13}{8}$

Answer: $f(x) = \frac{3}{2}x^2 - \frac{1}{3}x^3 + \frac{17}{6}$ (medium)

156. An astronaut stands on a platform 3 meters above the moon's surface and throws a rock directly upward with an initial velocity of 32 m/s. Given that the acceleration due to gravity on the moon's surface is $1.6\,\text{m/s}^2$ how high, above the surface of the moon, will the rock travel?

A) 317 m   B) 320 m   C) 323 m   D) 326 m
E) 329 m   F) 331 m   G) 334 m   H) 337 m

Answer: 323 m (hard)

157. Find the position function $s(t)$ given acceleration $a(t) = 3t$ if $v(2) = 0$ and $s(2) = 1$.

A) $s(t) = (t^3/2) - 6t + 9$ B) $s(t) = (t^3/3) - 6t + 9$
C) $s(t) = (t^3/2) - 3t + 9$ D) $s(t) = (t^3/3) - 3t + 9$
E) $s(t) = (t^3/2) - 6t + 1$ F) $s(t) = (t^3/3) - 6t + 1$
G) $s(t) = (t^3/2) - 3t + 1$ H) $s(t) = (t^3/3) - 3t + 1$

Answer: $s(t) = (t^3/2) - 6t + 9$ (medium)

1. Find the value of the sum $\sum_{i=0}^{4} i$.

A) 9	B) 12	C) 6	D) 5
E) 7	F) 11	G) 8	H) 10

   Answer: 10 (easy)

2. If we write $1 + \frac{1}{2} + \frac{1}{3} + \frac{1}{4}$ in the sigma notation $\sum_{i=1}^{4}$?, what do we put in place of the question mark?

A) $i/2$	B) i^{-1}	C) $i - 1$	D) $2i$
E) $i + 1$	F) i^2	G) i^{-2}	H) $1/(1 + i)$

   Answer: i^{-1} (easy)

3. Find the value of the summation $\sum_{i=1}^{5} i^2$.

A) 55	B) 85	C) 65	D) 25
E) 95	F) 45	G) 35	H) 75

   Answer: 55 (medium)

4. Find the value of the summation $\sum_{i=1}^{20} \left(\frac{1}{i} - \frac{1}{1+i} \right)$.

A) 21/19	B) 20/19	C) 18/19	D) 20/21
E) 19/18	F) 19/21	G) 21/20	H) 19/20

   Answer: 20/21 (medium)

5. Find a formula for the sum $\sum_{i=1}^{n} (2i - 1)$.

A) $n^2/2$	B) n^2	C) $2/n^3$	D) $2n^2$
E) n^3	F) $n^3/2$	G) $2n^3$	H) $2/n^2$

   Answer: n^2 (medium)

6. Find the value of the sum $\sum\limits_{i=1}^{6} 2^i$.

A) 64 B) 127 C) 128 D) 63
E) 255 F) 191 G) 256 H) 192

Answer: 127 (medium)

7. Find the value of $\sum\limits_{i=1}^{10} (i+1)^2 - \sum\limits_{i=1}^{10} i^2$.

A) 111 B) 144 C) 133 D) 132
E) 145 F) 120 G) 121 H) 110

Answer: 120 (medium)

8. Find the value of the summation $\sum\limits_{k=0}^{8} \cos k\pi$.

A) 0 B) 1/2 C) 1 D) 3/2
E) $\pi/2$ F) $3\pi/2$ G) π H) $2\pi/3$

Answer: 1 (medium)

9. Find the value of the limit $\lim\limits_{n \to \infty} \sum\limits_{i=1}^{n} \frac{1}{n} \left[\left(\frac{i}{n}\right)^3 + 1 \right]$.

A) 0 B) 1/4 C) 1/2 D) 1/3
E) 3/4 F) 2/3 G) 1 H) 5/4

Answer: 5/4 (medium)

10. Find the value of the limit $\lim\limits_{n \to \infty} \sum\limits_{i=1}^{n} \frac{3}{n} \left[\left(1 + \frac{3i}{n}\right)^3 - 2\left(1 + \frac{3i}{n}\right) \right]$.

A) 95/2 B) 191/4 C) 48 D) 193/4
E) 97/2 F) 195/4 G) 49 H) 197/4

Answer: 195/4 (hard)

Chapter 4, Section 2
Area

11. Suppose we wish to approximate the area under the curve $y = x^2$ between $x = 1$ and $x = 3$ using a partition P consisting of 10 equal length subintervals. What is the norm $\|P\|$ of the partition?

A) 1/2 B) 1/10 C) 1/5 D) 5
E) 1/20 F) 10 G) 2 H) 1

Answer: 1/5 (easy)

12. Suppose we wish to approximate the area under the curve $y = x^2$ between $x = 1$ and $x = 3$ using the partition $P = \{1, 1.5, 1.75, 2, 3\}$. What is the norm $\|P\|$ of the partition?

A) 3/4   B) 4   C) 3   D) 1/4
E) 1/8   F) 1   G) 1/2   H) 2

Answer: 1 (medium)

13. Suppose we wish to approximate the area under the curve $y = x$ between $x = 1$ and $x = 2$ using a partition consisting of 2 equal-length subintervals. What is the smallest value the approximation could be?

A) 5/16   B) 0   C) 1/4   D) 3/8
E) 5/4   F) 7/16   G) 1/2   H) 3/16

Answer: 5/4 (medium)

14. Suppose we wish to approximate the area under the curve $y = 2x$ between $x = 3$ and $x = 5$ using a partition consisting of 2 equal-length subintervals. What is the largest value the approximation could be?

A) 18   B) 10   C) 16   D) 20
E) 8   F) 14   G) 12   H) 22

Answer: 18 (medium)

15. Finding the area under the parabola $y = x^2$ from 0 to 2 can be done by using the limit of a sum of the form $\lim_{n \to \infty} \frac{c}{n^3} \sum_{i=1}^{n} i^2$. What is the value of the number c?

A) 2   B) 1   C) 4   D) 8
E) 1/6   F) 1/4   G) 1/3   H) 1/2

Answer: 8 (hard)

16. Finding the area under the parabola $y = x^2$ from 0 to 1 can be done by using the limit of a sum of the form $\lim_{x \to \infty} \frac{c}{n^3} \sum_{i=1}^{n} i^2$. What is the value of the number c?

A) 8   B) 1/6   C) 1   D) 1/2
E) 4   F) 1/3   G) 2   H) 1/4

Answer: 1 (hard)

Chapter 4, Section 3
The Definite Integral

17. Let $f(x) = x$ on the interval $[1, 2]$. Let the interval be partitioned as follows: $P = \{1, 1.5, 2\}$. Find the value of the Riemann sum $\sum_{i=1}^{n} f(x_i^*)\Delta x_i$ if each x_i^* is the left endpoint of its subinterval.

    A) 7/4   B) 5/4   C) 5/2   D) 7/3
    E) 7/6   F) 7/2   G) 5/6   H) 5/3

    Answer: 5/4 (easy)

18. Let $f(x) = x$ on the interval $[0, 2]$. Let the interval be partitioned as follows: $P = \{0, 1, 2\}$. Find the value of the Riemann sum $\sum_{i=1}^{n} f(x_i^*)\Delta x_i$ if each x_i^* is the right endpoint of its interval.

    A) 1/2   B) 5/2   C) 2   D) 7/2
    E) 9/2   F) 4   G) 3/2   H) 3

    Answer: 3 (easy)

19. Let $f(x) = x$ on the interval $[0, 1]$. Let the interval be partitioned as follows: $P = \{0, 0.5, 1\}$. Find the value of the Riemann sum $\sum_{i=1}^{n} f(x_i^*)\Delta x_i$ if each x_i^* is the midpoint of its subinterval.

    A) 3/4   B) 5/8   C) 1   D) 1/2
    E) 1/4   F) 7/8   G) 3/8   H) 1/8

    Answer: 1/2 (easy)

20. Let $f(x) = x^2$ on the interval $[0, 2]$. Let the interval be partitioned as follows: $P = \{0, 1.5, 2\}$. Find the value of the Riemann sum $\sum_{i=1}^{n} f(x_i^*)\Delta x_i$ if each x_i^* is the left endpoint of its subinterval.

    A) 1/2   B) 5/16   C) 7/16   D) 5/8
    E) 3/8   F) 11/16   G) 7/8   H) 9/8

    Answer: 9/8 (medium)

21. Let $f(x) = x^2$ on the interval $[0, 2]$. Let the interval be partitioned as follows: $P = \{0, 1, 2\}$. Find the value of the Riemann sum $\sum_{i=1}^{n} f(x_i^*)\Delta x_i$ if each x_i^* is the midpoint of its subinterval.

    A) 5/6   B) 7/6   C) 7/3   D) 7/4
    E) 5/2   F) 5/3   G) 5/4   H) 7/2

    Answer: 5/2 (medium)

22. Find the Riemann sum for $f(x) = 16 - x^2$ on the interval $[0, 4]$ if the partition points are $\{0, 1, 2, 3, 4\}$ and right end points are used.

   A) 20   B) 22   C) 24   D) 26
   E) 28   F) 30   G) 32   H) 34

   Answer: 34 (medium)

23. Use the Midpoint Rule with $n = 5$ to approximate $\int_1^2 \frac{1}{x}\, dx$.

   A) 0.6909   B) 0.6913   C) 0.6919   D) 0.6925
   E) 0.6928   F) 0.6932   G) 0.6937   H) 0.6945

   Answer: 0.6919 (medium)

24. Use the Midpoint Rule with $n = 4$ to approximate $\int_0^{\pi/4} \tan x\, dx$.

   A) 0.2914   B) 0.3160   C) 0.3289   D) 0.3317
   E) 0.3450   F) 0.3601   G) 0.3764   H) 0.3844

   Answer: 0.3450 (medium)

25. If $\int_0^1 f(x)\, dx = 2$ and $\int_1^2 f(x)\, dx = 1$, find the value of $\int_0^2 f(x)\, dx$.

   A) 3   B) 5   C) 1   D) 6
   E) 2   F) 0   G) 4   H) cannot be determined

   Answer: 3 (easy)

26. If $\int_0^1 f(x)\, dx = 7$ and $\int_0^3 f(x)\, dx = 6$, find the value of $\int_1^3 f(x)\, dx$.

   A) 1   B) 3   C) 0   D) -3
   E) -1 F) -2 G) 2   H) cannot be determined

   Answer: -1 (easy)

27. If $\int_0^1 f(x)\, dx = 2$ and $\int_0^3 f(x)\, dx = 3$, find the value of $\int_0^2 f(x)\, dx$.

   A) -2 B) 0   C) 1   D) -1
   E) -3 F) 2   G) 3   H) cannot be determined

   Answer: cannot be determined (medium)

28. If $\int_0^4 f(x)\, dx = 3$ and $\int_0^4 g(x)\, dx = 1$, find the value of $\int_0^4 (f(x) + g(x))\, dx$.

   A) 3   B) 10   C) 6   D) 4
   E) 2   F) 8   G) 1   H) cannot be determined

   Answer: 4 (easy)

29. If $\int_0^4 f(x)\,dx = 5$ and $\int_0^4 g(x)\,dx = 2$, find the value of $\int_0^4 f(x)g(x)\,dx$.

A) 10 B) 6 C) 1 D) 8
E) 4 F) 3 G) 2 H) cannot be determined

Answer: cannot be determined (medium)

30. If $\int_0^3 f(x)\,dx = 4$, $\int_3^6 f(x)\,dx = 4$, and $\int_2^6 f(x)\,dx = 5$, find the value of $\int_0^2 f(x)\,dx$.

A) -3 B) 3 C) 2 D) -1
E) 0 F) 1 G) -2 H) cannot be determined

Answer: 3 (medium)

31. If $\int_0^3 f(x)\,dx = 12$ and $\int_0^6 f(x)\,dx = 42$ find the value of $\int_3^6 (2f(x) - 3)\,dx$.

A) 50 B) 51 C) 52 D) 56
E) 53 F) 54 G) 55 H) cannot be determined

Answer: 51 (medium)

Chapter 4, Section 4
The Fundamental Theorem of Calculus

32. Let $f(x) = \int_0^x t^3\,dt$. Find the value of $f'(2)$.

A) -24 B) -12 C) 8 D) 24
E) 4 F) -4 G) 12 H) -8

Answer: 8 (easy)

33. Let $f(x) = \int_x^{10} t^3\,dt$. Find the value of $f'(2)$.

A) 8 B) 4 C) -24 D) 12
E) -4 F) -8 G) 24 H) -12

Answer: -8 (easy)

34. Let $f(x) = \int_0^{x^2} t^2\,dt$. Find the value of $f'(1)$.

A) 4 B) 6 C) 8 D) 0
E) 2 F) 1 G) 3 H) 5

Answer: 2 (medium)

35. Let $f(x) = \int_x^{x^2} t^2\,dt$. Find the value of $f'(1)$.

A) 3 B) 8 C) 4 D) 0
E) 5 F) 2 G) 6 H) 1

Answer: 1 (medium)

36. Let $f(x) = \int_{x^3}^{10} (t^2 + 1)^{60}\, dt$. Find the value of $f'(0)$.

A) 5   B) 1   C) 2   D) 0
E) 3   F) 6   G) 7   H) 4

Answer: 0 (hard)

37. Using the fundamental theorem of calculus, find the value of $\displaystyle\lim_{\|P\| \to 0} \sum_{i=1}^{n} \sqrt{x_i^*}\, \Delta x_i$ on the interval $[1, 4]$.

A) 7/3   B) 10/3   C) 3   D) 13/3
E) 14/3   F) 8/3   G) 4   H) 11/3

Answer: 14/3 (medium)

38. Find the value of the integral $\int_4^6 x\, dx$.

A) 16   B) 18   C) 15   D) 20
E) 4   F) 8   G) 10   H) 12

Answer: 10 (easy)

39. Find the value of the integral $\int_0^1 (x+1)^2\, dx$.

A) 7/3   B) 0   C) 1   D) 5/3
E) 2   F) 1/3   G) 4/3   H) 2/3

Answer: 7/3 (medium)

40. Find the value of the integral $\int_1^2 \frac{1}{x^2}\, dx$.

A) 2/3   B) 1/2   C) $-1/2$ D) $-1/3$
E) $-2/3$ F) 1   G) 1/3   H) -1

Answer: 1/2 (medium)

41. Find the value of the integral $\int_{-1}^8 \sqrt[3]{x}\, dx$.

A) 49/4   B) 41/4   C) 45/4   D) 35/4
E) 39/4   F) 37/4   G) 47/4   H) 43/4

Answer: 45/4 (medium)

42. Find the value of the integral $\int_{-3}^3 (|x| + |x+1|)\, dx$.

A) 19   B) 16   C) 11   D) 0
E) 9   F) 17   G) 13   H) 12

Answer: 19 (hard)

43. If $F(x) = \int_0^{\sqrt{x}} \sin(t^2)\, dt$, find $F'(\pi/4)$.

A) $1/\sqrt{2}$ B) π C) $\sqrt{\pi/2}$ D) $\sqrt{2\pi}$
E) $1/\sqrt{2\pi}$ F) $\pi/2$ G) $\pi^2/16$ H) $\sin(\pi^2/16)$

Answer: $1/\sqrt{2\pi}$ (medium)

44. Find the value of the integral $\int_{-1}^{1} (1+x)^2\, dx$.

A) $1/3$ B) $-8/3$ C) $3/8$ D) 0
E) $2/3$ F) $8/3$ G) $4/3$ H) 3

Answer: $8/3$ (medium)

45. If $F(x) = \int_x^{x^2} \ln \sqrt{t}\, dt$, find the value of $F'(1/4)$.

A) 0 B) 1 C) $3/2$ D) 2
E) $5/2$ F) 3 G) $7/2$ H) 4

Answer: 0 (hard); requires Chapter 6

46. Find the value of the integral $\int_{-2}^{0} |x+1|\, dx$.

A) $1/2$ B) $1/4$ C) $3/4$ D) $3/2$
E) $5/4$ F) $5/2$ G) 1 H) 0

Answer: 1 (medium)

47. If $F(x) = \int_0^{x^2} \sqrt{1+8t^3}\, dt$, find the value of $F'(1)$.

A) 1 B) 2 C) 3 D) 4
E) 5 F) 6 G) 7 H) 8

Answer: 6 (medium)

48. If $\int_3^b 3x^2\, dx = 37$, find the value of b.

A) 4 B) 5 C) 6 D) 7
E) 8 F) 9 G) 10 H) 11

Answer: 4 (medium)

49. If $F(x) = \int_2^{1/x} \sin^4 t\, dt$, find $F'(2/\pi)$.

A) $-\pi^2/4$ B) $\pi^2/4$ C) $2 - \pi^2/4$ D) 1
E) 0 F) $\sin^4 2$ G) $1/2$ H) does not exist

Answer: $-\pi^2/4$ (hard)

50. If $F(x) = \int_2^{3x} e^{t^4}\, dt$, find the value of $F'(0)$.

A) 1 B) 2 C) 3 D) 4
E) 6 F) 8 G) e^8 H) e^{16}

Answer: 3 (medium); requires Chapter 6

51. Find the value of the integral $\int_0^1 (1 + \sqrt{x})^2\, dx$.

A) 17/6 B) 3 C) 19/6 D) 10/3
E) 7/2 F) 11/3 G) 23/6 H) 4

Answer: 17/6 (medium)

52. If $F(x) = \int_0^{\sqrt{x}} \frac{1}{\sqrt{1+t^4}}\, dt$, find the value of $F'(1)$.

A) 1/2 B) $\sqrt{2}/2$ C) $\sqrt{2}/4$ D) 1/4
E) $\sqrt{2}/8$ F) 1/8 G) $\sqrt{2}/16$ H) 1/16

Answer: $\sqrt{2}/4$ (medium)

53. If $F(x) = \int_1^{\sqrt{x}} \frac{e^t}{t}\, dt$, find the value of $F'(1)$.

A) 0 B) 1/3 C) 1/2 D) 1
E) $e/3$ F) $e/2$ G) e H) e^2

Answer: $e/2$ (medium); requires Chapter 6

54. If $F(x) = \int_0^{\sqrt{x}} \sqrt{t^4 + 20}\, dt$, find the value of $F'(4)$.

A) 1/2 B) 1 C) 3/2 D) 2
E) 5/2 F) 3 G) 7/2 H) 4

Answer: 3/2 (medium)

55. Find the value of the integral $\int_1^2 \frac{x^2-1}{x}\, dx$.

A) 1/2 B) 1 C) 3/2
D) 2 E) $(1/2) \ln 2$ F) $1 + \ln 2$
G) $(3/2) - \ln 2$ H) $2 + \ln 2$

Answer: $(3/2) - \ln 2$ ((medium); requires Chapter 6)

56. The velocity of a particle moving along a line is $2t$ meters per second. Find the distance traveled in meters during the time interval $1 \le t \le 3$.

A) 9 B) 5 C) 2 D) 8
E) 4 F) 3 G) 6 H) 7

Answer: 8 (easy)

57. The velocity of a particle moving along a line is $t^3 - t$ meters per second. Find the distance traveled in meters during the time interval $0 \leq t \leq 2$.

A) 7/4   B) 4/3   C) 2/3   D) 3/4
E) 3/2   F) 2/5   G) 5/2   H) 9/4

Answer: 5/2 (medium)

58. The acceleration of a particle moving along a line is $\sqrt{t}$ meters per second. It starts from a resting position at $t = 0$. Find the distance traveled in meters during the time interval $0 \leq t \leq 1$.

A) 3/4   B) 7/4   C) 3/2   D) 4/3
E) 2/5   F) 5/2   G) 2/3   H) 4/15

Answer: 4/15 (medium)

59. Let $y = \int_1^{3x} \frac{dt}{t^2+t+1}$. Find $\frac{d^2y}{dx^2}$.

A) $\frac{(18x+3)}{(9x^2+3x+1)^2}$ B) $\frac{3(18x+3)}{(9x^2+3x+1)^2}$ C) $\frac{-3(18x+3)}{(9x^2+3x+1)^2}$

D) $\frac{3(18x+3)}{(9x^2+3x+1)^3}$ E) $\frac{-3(18x+3)}{(9x^2+3x+1)^3}$ F) $\frac{(18x+3)}{(9x^2+3x+1)^3}$

G) $\frac{(18x+3)^2}{(9x^2+3x+1)^3}$ H) $\frac{-3(18x+3)^2}{(9x^2+3x+1)^2}$

Answer: $\frac{-3(18x+3)}{(9x^2+3x+1)^2}$ (medium)

60. Let $f(x) = \int_0^x \frac{t^2-4}{1+\cos^2 t} \, dt$. At what value of x does the local maximum of $f(x)$ occur?

A) -4 B) -3 C) -2 D) -1
E) 0   F) 1   G) 2   H) 3

Answer: -2 (hard)

61. Evaluate $\frac{d}{dt} \int_{t^2}^2 \sqrt{x+1} \, dx$.

A) $\sqrt{t^2+1}$ B) $-\sqrt{t^2+1}$ C) $2t$

D) $\sqrt{t+1}$ E) $2t\left(\sqrt{t^2+1}\right)$ F) $2t\left(-\sqrt{t^2+1}\right)$

G) $2t\left(\sqrt{t+1}\right)$ H) $2t\left(-\sqrt{t+1}\right)$

Answer: $2t\left(-\sqrt{t^2+1}\right)$ (medium)

62. Evaluate $\int_{-3}^4 ||x| - 4| \, dx$.

A) 29/2   B) 15   C) 31/2   D) 16
E) 35/2   F) 33/2   G) 17   H) cannot be determined

Answer: 31/2 (medium)

63. Solve for x when $\int_0^1 t^x \, dt = 5$.

A) $-4/5$ B) $-3/5$ C) $-2/5$ D) $-1/5$
E) 0   F) 1/5   G) 2/5   H) 3/5

Answer: $-4/5$ (medium)

64. If $\int_0^5 kx \, dx = 30$, find k.

A) 12/5   B) 11/5   C) 2   D) 9/5
E) 8/5   F) 7/5   G) 6/5   H) 1

Answer: 12/5 (medium)

Chapter 4, Section 5
The Substitution Rule

65. Find the value of the integral $\int_0^3 \sqrt{x+1} \, dx$.

A) 13/3   B) 5   C) 6   D) 16/3
E) 20/3   F) 14/3   G) 19/3   H) 17/3

Answer: 14/3 (easy)

66. Find the value of the integral $\int_0^{\pi/4} \cos 2x \, dx$.

A) $\pi/14$ B) π C) $\sqrt{3}/2$ D) $\pi/2$
E) $\sqrt{2}/4$ F) 2π G) $\sqrt{2}/2$ H) $1/2$

Answer: 1/2 (easy)

67. Find the value of the integral $\int_0^1 (2x)^7 \, dx$.

A) 64   B) 32   C) 2   D) 128
E) 256   F) 8   G) 4   H) 16

Answer: 16 (easy)

68. Find the value of the integral $\int_0^1 (x^2+1)^5 x \, dx$.

A) 13/2   B) 17/2   C) 17/3   D) 29/4
E) 27/5   F) 21/4   G) 25/17   H) 28/3

Answer: 21/4 (medium)

69. Find the value of the integral $\int_0^1 \frac{x^2}{(x^3+1)^2} \, dx$.

A) 3/4   B) 2   C) 3/7   D) 7/3
E) 1/6   F) 3/2   G) 2/3   H) 1

Answer: 1/6 (medium)

70. Find the value of the integral $\int_0^{\pi/4} \sin^2 x \cos x \, dx$.

A) $\sqrt{2}/18$ B) $\pi/4$ C) $3\pi/2$ D) $\sqrt{2}/12$
E) $\sqrt{2}/6$ F) $\sqrt{2}/9$ G) $2\pi/3$ H) $\pi/2$

Answer: $\sqrt{2}/12$ (medium)

71. Find the value of the integral $\int_0^{\pi/4} \sin 2x \sin x \, dx$.

A) $\sqrt{2}/9$ B) $\sqrt{2}/6$ C) $2\pi/3$ D) $\sqrt{2}/12$
E) $\pi/4$ F) $3\pi/2$ G) $\sqrt{2}/18$ H) $\pi/2$

Answer: $\sqrt{2}/6$ (hard)

72. Find the value of the integral $\int_0^{\pi/3} \sec x \tan x \, (1 + \sec x) \, dx$.

A) 4 B) 5/2 C) 3 D) 11/2
E) 9/2 F) 2 G) 7/2 H) 5

Answer: 5/2 (medium)

73. Find the value of the integral $\int_1^4 \frac{1}{(1+\sqrt{x})^2} \, \frac{1}{\sqrt{x}} \, dx$.

A) 6/5 B) 1/3 C) 2/3 D) 5/2
E) 4/9 F) 3/2 G) 5/6 H) 1/6

Answer: 1/3 (hard)

74. Find the value of the integral $\int_0^1 \frac{x}{x+1} \, dx$.

A) $1 - \ln 2$ B) $\ln 4$ C) e^2 D) $e - 1$
E) $e^2 - 1$ F) $1/e$ G) $\ln 4 - 1$ H) $\ln 6$

Answer: $1 - \ln 2$ ((hard); requires Chapter 6)

75. Find the value of the integral $\int_0^{\pi/2} \cos x \sin(\sin x) \, dx$.

A) $\pi/2$ B) $1 - (\pi/4)$ C) $\sin 1$
D) $1 - \cos 1$ E) $(\pi/2) - \sin 1$ F) $(\pi/4) + \cos 1$
G) $1 + (3\pi/4)$ H) $1 + \tan 1$

Answer: $1 - \cos 1$ (medium)

76. Find the value of the integral $\int_{-1}^1 \frac{\tan x}{1+x^2} \, dx$.

A) 0 B) $\pi/2$ C) π D) 2
E) -2 F) $\ln 2$ G) $1 + \ln 2$ H) does not exist

Answer: 0 (medium)

77. Find the value of the integral $\int_{-1}^{1} \frac{x}{\sqrt{x^2+1}} \, dx$.

A) $2\left(\sqrt{2}-1\right)$ B) $\sqrt{2}-1$ C) 0 D) 1
E) 3 F) $1/\sqrt{2}$ G) $\sqrt{2}$ H) does not exist

Answer: 0 (medium)

78. Find the value of the integral $\int_{0}^{1} \frac{x}{\sqrt{x^2+1}} \, dx$.

A) $2\left(\sqrt{2}-1\right)$ B) $\sqrt{2}-1$ C) 0 D) 1
E) 3 F) $1/\sqrt{2}$ G) $\sqrt{2}$ H) does not exist

Answer: $\sqrt{2}-1$ (medium)

79. Find the value of the integral $\int_{0}^{\pi/2} \frac{\cos x}{1+\sin^2 x} \, dx$.

A) 0 B) $\pi/4$ C) $\pi/2$ D) $3\pi/4$
E) π F) $3\pi/2$ G) 2π H) $5\pi/2$

Answer: $\pi/4$ (hard); requires Chapter 6

80. Find the value of the integral $\int_{0}^{\pi/4} \sec^2 x \sin(\tan x) \, dx$.

A) $\pi/2$ B) $1-\pi/4$ C) $\sin 1$
D) $1-\cos 1$ E) $(\pi/2)-\sin 1$ F) $(\pi/4)+\cos 1$
G) $1+(3\pi/4)$ H) $1+\tan 1$

Answer: $1-\cos 1$ (medium)

81. Find the value of the integral $\int_{-\pi/2}^{\pi/2} \frac{x^2 \sin x}{1+x^6} \, dx$.

A) 0 B) $1/2$ C) 1 D) 2
E) $\pi/6$ F) $\pi^2/4$ G) $(\pi^3/3)-1$ H) $\pi/2$

Answer: 0 (medium)

82. Find the value of the integral $\int_{1}^{3} \frac{x}{\sqrt{1+3x^2}} \, dx$.

A) $(2/3)(\sqrt{7}-1)$ B) $\sqrt{7}-1$ C) 0
D) $1/3$ E) $2/3$ F) $1/\sqrt{7}$
G) $\sqrt{7}$ H) does not exist

Answer: $(2/3)(\sqrt{7}-1)$ (medium)

83. Find the value of the integral $\int_{1}^{9} \frac{3x}{\sqrt{10-x}} \, dx$.

A) 68 B) 126 C) 0 D) 34
E) 58 F) 27 G) 26 H) does not exist

Answer: 68 (hard)

84. Find the value of the integral $\int_1^8 \frac{4\left(x^{2/3}+14\right)^3}{\sqrt[3]{x}} \, dx$.

A) 163001/2
B) 163053/2
C) 81500
D) 81527
E) 3976
F) 7952
G) 15905/2
H) 16783/2

Answer: 163053/2 (hard)

85. Evaluate the integral $\int \frac{r}{\left(r^2+b^2\right)^{3/2}} \, dr$ where b is a constant.

A) $r^2 + b^2 + C$
B) $\left(r^2 + b^2\right)^{1/2} + C$
C) $-\left(r^2 + b^2\right) + C$
D) $-\left(r^2 + b^2\right)^{1/2} + C$
E) $\left(r^2 + b^2\right)^{-1/2} + C$
F) $-\left(r^2 + b^2\right)^{-1/2} + C$
G) $\left(r^2 + b^2\right)^{3/2} + C$
H) $-\left(r^2 + b^2\right)^{3/2} + C$

Answer: $-\left(r^2 + b^2\right)^{-1/2} + C$ (medium)

Calculus, 3rd Edition
by James Stewart
Chapter 5, Section 1
Areas between Curves

1. Find the area of the region bounded by the curves $y = x^2$ and $y = 1$.

    A) 4/3   B) 2/3   C) 11/9   D) 5/3
    E) 8/9   F) 1   G) 14/9   H) 2

    Answer: 4/3 (easy)

2. Find the area of the region bounded by the curves $y = x^2$ and $y = x$.

    A) 1/8   B) 2/3   C) 1/12   D) 1/2
    E) 1/3   F) 1/9   G) 1/6   H) 5/6

    Answer: 1/6 (easy)

3. Find the area of the region bounded by the curves $y = x^2$ and $y = 1 - x^2$.

    A) $\sqrt{2}/2$ B) $\sqrt{3}/6$ C) $\sqrt{3}/2$ D) $2\sqrt{2}/3$
    E) $\sqrt{3}/3$ F) $\sqrt{3}/4$ G) $\sqrt{2}/4$ H) $\sqrt{2}/6$

    Answer: $2\sqrt{2}/3$ (medium)

4. Find the area of the region bounded by the curves $y = x^2$ and $y = x^3$.

    A) 1/4   B) 1/9   C) 1/18   D) 1/15
    E) 1/12   F) 1/6   G) 1/24   H) 1/3

    Answer: 1/12 (medium)

5. Find the area of the region bounded by the curves $y = x^2$ and $x = y^2$.

    A) 1/6   B) 1/4   C) 1/15   D) 1/18
    E) 1/9   F) 1/3   G) 1/12   H) 1/24

    Answer: 1/3 (medium)

6. Find the area of the region bounded by the curves $y = x$ and $y = x^3$.

    A) 5/3   B) 2/3   C) 3/2   D) 4/3
    E) 1/3   F) 1/2   G) 1   H) 3/4

    Answer: 1/2 (hard)

7. Find the area beneath a single arc of the function $y = \sin x$ (for example, over the interval $[0, \pi]$).

A) π B) $1/4$ C) 1 D) 2π
E) $\pi/2$ F) $\pi/4$ G) $1/2$ H) 2

Answer: 2 (medium)

8. Find the area of the region bounded by the curves $x = 1 - y^4$ and $x = y^3 - y$.

A) 1 B) $6/5$ C) $7/5$ D) $8/5$
E) $9/5$ F) 2 G) $11/5$ H) $12/5$

Answer: 8/5 (hard)

9. Find the area of the region bounded by the parabolas $y = 2x - x^2$ and $y = x^2$.

A) $1/2$ B) $2/3$ C) $3/4$ D) $2/5$
E) $1/3$ F) $1/4$ G) $1/5$ H) $3/5$

Answer: 1/3 (medium)

10. Find the area of the region bounded by the parabolas $y = 4x^2$ and $y = x^2 + 3$.

A) $1/2$ B) 1 C) $3/2$ D) 2
E) $5/2$ F) 3 G) $7/2$ H) 4

Answer: 4 (medium)

11. Find the area of the region bounded by the parabola $x = y^2$ and the line $x - 2y = 3$.

A) $29/3$ B) $32/3$ C) $35/3$ D) $38/3$
E) $41/3$ F) $44/3$ G) $47/3$ H) $50/3$

Answer: 32/3 (medium)

12. Find an expression as a limit of Riemann sums for the area between the curves $y = -x$ and $y = x - x^2$, using equal subintervals and right end points.

A) $\displaystyle \lim_{n \to \infty} \frac{2}{n} \sum_{i=1}^{n} \left[2\left(\frac{2i}{n}\right) - \left(\frac{2i}{n}\right)^2 \right]$
B) $\displaystyle \lim_{n \to \infty} \frac{1}{n} \sum_{i=1}^{n} \left(\frac{i}{n}\right)^2$

C) $\displaystyle \lim_{n \to \infty} \frac{1}{n} \sum_{i=1}^{n} \left[\left(\frac{i}{n}\right)^2 - \left(\frac{i}{n}\right) \right]$
D) $\displaystyle \lim_{n \to \infty} \frac{2}{n} \sum_{i=1}^{n} \left[-1 + \left(\frac{2i}{n}\right)^2 \right]$

E) $\displaystyle \lim_{n \to \infty} \frac{2}{n} \sum_{i=1}^{n} \left[2\left(\frac{2i}{n}\right)^2 - \left(\frac{2i}{n}\right) \right]$
F) $\displaystyle \lim_{n \to \infty} \frac{1}{n} \sum_{i=1}^{n} \left[2\left(\frac{2i}{n}\right) - \left(\frac{2i}{n}\right)^2 \right]$

G) $\displaystyle \lim_{n \to \infty} \frac{1}{n} \sum_{i=1}^{n} \left[\left(-1 + \left(\frac{i}{n}\right)^2\right) - 1 \right]$
H) $\displaystyle \lim_{n \to \infty} \sum_{i=1}^{n} \left[\left(-1 + \left(\frac{2i}{n}\right)^2\right) + 3\left(-1 + \left(\frac{2i}{n}\right)\right) \right]$

Answer: $\displaystyle \lim_{n \to \infty} \frac{2}{n} \sum_{i=1}^{n} \left[2\left(\frac{2i}{n}\right) - \left(\frac{2i}{n}\right)^2 \right]$ (hard)

13. Find the area of the region bounded by the curves $f(y) = x^3 + x^2$ and $g(y) = 2x^2 + 2x$.

Answer: $\frac{37}{12}$ (medium)

14. Find the area of the region bounded by the curves $f(y) = x^2 - 4x + 5$ and $g(y) = 5 - x$.

Answer: $\frac{9}{2}$ (easy)

15. Find the area of the region bounded by the curves $f(y) = x^2 - 1$ and $g(y) = -x^2 + x + 2$.

Answer: $\frac{125}{24}$ (medium)

16. Find the area of the region bounded by the curves $f(y) = 4 - x^2$ and $g(y) = x^2 + 2$.

Answer: $\frac{8}{3}$ (easy)

17. Find the area of the region bounded by the curves $f(y) = \sqrt{x}$, $g(y) = \frac{5-x}{4}$, and $h(y) = \frac{3x-8}{2}$.

Answer: $\frac{23}{12}$ (medium)

18. Find the area of the region bounded by the curves $f(y) = x^3 - x^2 - 2x$ and $g(y) = 0$.

Answer: $\frac{37}{12}$ (medium)

19. Find the area of the region bounded by the curves $f(y) = x^2 + 2x - 1$ and $g(y) = x^3 - 1$.

Answer: $\frac{37}{12}$ (medium)

20. Find the area of the region bounded by the x-axis and the graph of $y = 6x(x - 2)^2$.

Answer: 8 (easy)

21. Find the area of the region bounded by the curves $x = y^2 - 7$ and $x = y - 1$.

Answer: $\frac{125}{6}$ (medium)

22. Let R be the region bounded by: $y = x^3$, the tangent to $y = x^3$ at $(1, 1)$, and the x-axis. Find the area of R integrating a) with respect to x, b) with respect to y.

Answer: a) and b) each $\frac{1}{12}$ (medium)

23. Find the area of the region bounded by the curves $f(y) = x^2 - 2x$ and $g(y) = -2x^2 + 3x + 2$.

Answer: $5\frac{35}{54}$ (medium)

24. Find the area of the region bounded by the curves $f(y) = x^2$ and $g(y) = x + 1$.

Answer: $\frac{5\sqrt{5}}{6}$ (medium)

Chapter 5, Section 2
Volumes

25. Find the volume of the solid obtained when the region bounded by the x-axis, the y-axis, and the line $y - x = 3$ is rotated about the x-axis.

    A) 3π B) 2π C) 8π D) 10π
    E) 9π F) 12π G) 4π H) 6π

    Answer: 9π (easy)

26. Find the volume of the solid obtained when the region bounded by the line $y = x$, the line $x = 3$, and the x-axis is rotated about the y-axis.

    A) 36π B) 42π C) 16π D) 18π
    E) 24π F) 30π G) 48π H) 27π

    Answer: 18π (medium)

27. Suppose the disk method is used to find the volume of the solid obtained when the region bounded by the curve $x = y^2$ and the line $x = 4$ is rotated about the x-axis. What is the area of the largest cross-section?

    A) 6π B) 3π C) 12π D) 10π
    E) 9π F) 8π G) 2π H) 4π

    Answer: 4π (easy)

28. Find the volume of the solid obtained when the region bounded by the curve $x = y^2$ and the line $x = 4$ is rotated about the x-axis.

    A) 10π B) 4π C) 9π D) 12π
    E) 6π F) 8π G) 3π H) 2π

    Answer: 8π (medium)

29. Find the volume of the solid obtained when the region bounded by the curves $y = x^2/4$ and $x = y^2/4$ is rotated about the x-axis.

    A) 15.6π B) 16.8π C) 18.2π D) 17.8π
    E) 15.8π F) 19.2π G) 17.3π H) 18.4π

    Answer: 19.2π (medium)

30. Find the volume of the solid obtained when the region bounded by the curve $y = \sin x$, $0 \le x \le \pi$, and the x-axis is rotated about the x-axis.

    A) $\pi^2/2$ B) $\pi^2/3$ C) π D) $\pi/2$
    E) $\pi/4$ F) π^2 G) $\pi/3$ H) $\pi^2/4$

    Answer: $\pi^2/2$ (medium)

31. Find the volume of the solid obtained when the region bounded by the curve $y = x^2$ and the line $y = 4$ is rotated about the line $y = 4$.

A) $32\pi/15$ B) $32\pi/5$ C) $128\pi/15$ D) $64\pi/5$
E) $64\pi/15$ F) $512\pi/15$ G) $256\pi/5$ H) $128\pi/5$

Answer: $512\pi/15$ (hard)

32. The base of a solid S is the parabolic region $\{(x, y) \mid y^2 \le x \le 1\}$. Cross-sections perpendicular to the x-axis are squares. Find the volume of S.

A) 1.5   B) 1.6   C) 1.7   D) 1.8
E) 1.9   F) 2.0   G) 2.1   H) 2.2

Answer: 2.0 (medium)

33. Find the volume of the solid obtained by rotating the region bounded by the curves $y = \sqrt{x}$ and $y = x^2$ about the line $y = 3$.

A) 1.5π B) 1.6π C) 1.7π D) 1.8π
E) 1.9π F) 2π G) 2.1π H) 2.2π

Answer: 1.7π (medium)

34. A hole of radius 4 is bored through the center of a sphere of radius 5. Find the volume of the remaining portion of the sphere.

A) 16π B) 20π C) 24π D) 28π
E) 32π F) 36π G) 40π H) 44π

Answer: 36π (hard)

35. Find the volume of the solid obtained by rotating the region bounded by the curves $y = x$ and $y = x^2$ about the line $y = 2$.

A) $\pi/5$ B) $4\pi/15$ C) $\pi/3$ D) $2\pi/5$
E) $7\pi/15$ F) $8\pi/15$ G) $3\pi/5$ H) $2\pi/3$

Answer: $8\pi/15$ (medium)

36. The base of S is a circular disc with radius 3. Parallel cross-sections perpendicular to the base are isosceles triangles with height 2 and unequal side in the base. Find the volume of S.

A) 3π B) 4π C) 5π D) 6π
E) 7π F) 8π G) 9π H) 10π

Answer: 9π (hard)

37. Find the volume of the solid obtained by rotating about the line $y = 1$ the region bounded by $y = \cos x$, $y = 0$, $x = 0$, and $x = \pi/2$.

A) π

B) π^2

C) $\pi^2 - (\pi/2)$

D) $\pi^2 - \pi$

E) $\pi^2 - 2\pi$

F) $2\pi - (\pi^2/4)$

G) $2\pi - (\pi^2/2)$

H) $\pi - (\pi^2/4)$

Answer: $2\pi - (\pi^2/4)$ (hard)

38. The region bounded by the curves $y = x - x^2$ and $y = 0$ is rotated about the x-axis. Find the volume of the resulting solid.

A) $\pi/3$

B) $\pi/4$

C) $\pi/5$

D) $\pi/6$

E) $\pi/12$

F) $\pi/24$

G) $\pi/30$

H) $\pi/36$

Answer: $\pi/30$ (medium)

39. Find the volume of the solid obtained by rotating the region bounded by the curves $y = 2 - x^2$ and $y = 1$ about the x-axis.

A) $\pi/15$

B) $2 - \pi^2$

C) 15π

D) $7/15$

E) $3 - \pi^2$

F) 4π

G) $56\pi/15$

H) $128\pi/15$

Answer: $56\pi/15$ (medium)

40. Find the volume of the solid obtained by rotating about the x-axis the region bounded by $y = x^2$, $y = 0$, and $x = 1$.

A) π

B) $\pi/2$

C) $\pi/3$

D) $\pi/4$

E) $\pi/5$

F) $\pi/6$

G) $\pi/7$

H) $\pi/8$

Answer: $\pi/5$ (medium)

41. A solid has a circular base of radius 1. Parallel cross-sections perpendicular to the base are equilateral triangles. Find the volume of the solid.

A) $\pi/2$

B) $\sqrt{3}/2$

C) $3\pi/2$

D) $3\sqrt{3}/2$

E) $2\pi/3$

F) $4\sqrt{3}/3$

G) $3\pi/4$

H) $2\sqrt{2}/3$

Answer: $4\sqrt{3}/3$ (medium)

42. Find the volume of the solid obtained by rotating about the x-axis the region bounded by the curves $y = x$ and $y = x^2$.

A) $\pi/30$

B) $2\pi/15$

C) $7\pi/30$

D) $\pi/3$

E) $13\pi/30$

F) $8\pi/15$

G) $19\pi/30$

H) $11\pi/15$

Answer: $2\pi/15$ (medium)

43. The base of a solid S is a semi-circular disc $\{(x, y) \mid x^2 + y^2 \leq 1, \ x \geq 0\}$. Cross-sections of S perpendicular to the x-axis are squares. Find the volume of S.

   A) $2\pi/3$ B) π^2 C) $\pi^2/4$ D) $8/3$
   E) $1/3$ F) 1 G) π H) 2

   Answer: 8/3 (medium)

44. The volume of a sphere of radius r is $\frac{4\pi r^3}{3}$. Verify this formula by revolving the circle $x^2 + y^2 = r^2$ about the x-axis.

   Answer: Volume $= 2 \int_0^r \pi y^2 \, dx = 2\pi \int_0^r \left(r^2 - x^2\right) dx$
   $$= 2\pi \left(r^3 x - \tfrac{1}{3} x^3\right)\Big|_0^r$$
   $$= 2\pi \left(r^3 - \tfrac{1}{3} r^3\right) = 2\pi \left(\tfrac{2}{3} r^3\right) = \tfrac{4}{3}\pi r^3 \quad \text{(medium)}$$

45. Find the volume of the solid generated by revolving about the line $y = 4$ the smaller region bounded by the curve $x^2 = 4y$ and the lines $x = 2$ and $y = 4$.

   Answer: $\frac{106}{15}\pi$ (easy)

46. Consider the region in the xy-plane between $x = 0$ and $x = \pi/2$, bounded by $y = 0$ and $y = \sin x$. Find the volume of the solid generated by revolving this region about the x-axis.

   Answer: $\frac{\pi^2}{4}$ (medium)

47. Find the volume of the solid formed when the region bounded by the curves $y = x^3 + 1$, $x = 1$ and $y = 0$ is rotated about the x-axis.

   Answer: $\frac{23}{14}\pi$ (easy)

48. Find the volume of the solid obtained when the region enclosed by $y = x^2$ and $y = 2 - x^2$ is revolved about the x-axis.

   Answer: $\frac{16\pi}{3}$ (medium)

49. Find the volume of the solid generated by revolving about the line $y = -1$ the region bounded by the graphs of the equations $y = x^2 - 4x + 5$ and $y = 5 - x$.

   Answer: $\frac{162\pi}{5}$ (medium)

50. A curve described by the equation $(x - 1)^2 = 32 - 3y$ is rotated about the line $x = 1$ to generate a solid of revolution. Find the volume of this solid for the region bounded by $x = 1$, $y = 1$, and $y = 4$ and to the right of $x = 1$.

   Answer: $\frac{141\pi}{2}$ (medium)

51. Find the volume of the solid of revolution obtained by revolving the region bounded by $y = x^2$, the x-axis, and $x = 2$ around the line $y = -1$.

   Answer: $\frac{176\pi}{15}$ (medium)

52. Consider the plane region bounded by the curves given by $y = x^2 + 1$ and $y = x + 3$. Find the volume of the solid of revolution generated by revolving the region around the x-axis.

Answer: $\frac{117\pi}{5}$ (easy)

53. Find the volume of one octant of the region common to two right circular cylinders of radius 1 whose axes intersect at right angles as shown below:

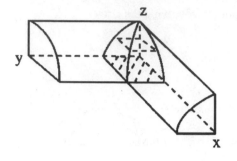

Answer: $\frac{2}{3}$ (hard)

54. Find the volume of the solid generated when the region in the first quadrant bounded by the curve $y = 4x - x^3$ and the x-axis is rotated about the x-axis.

Answer: $\frac{1024\pi}{105}$ (easy)

Chapter 5, Section 3
Volumes by Cylindrical Shells

55. Find the volume of the solid obtained when the region bounded by the curve $y = 2x - x^2$ and the x-axis is rotated about the y-axis.

A) $10\pi/3$ B) $20\pi/3$ C) $8\pi/3$ D) $4\pi/3$
E) $16\pi/3$ F) $32\pi/3$ G) $5\pi/3$ H) $40\pi/3$

Answer: $8\pi/3$ (medium)

56. Find the volume of the solid obtained when the region bounded by the curve $y = \sin x$, $0 \le x \le \pi$, and the x-axis is rotated about the y-axis.

A) $\pi^3/2$ B) π^2 C) π^3 D) $4\pi^2$
E) $2\pi^2$ F) $2\pi^3$ G) $\pi^2/2$ H) $4\pi^3$

Answer: $2\pi^2$ (hard)

57. Find the volume of the solid obtained when the region above the x-axis bounded by the x-axis and the curve $y = x - x^3$ is rotated about the y-axis.

A) $2\pi/7$ B) $8\pi/35$ C) $4\pi/15$ D) $8\pi/15$
E) $4\pi/35$ F) $2\pi/5$ G) $4\pi/5$ H) $4\pi/7$

Answer: $4\pi/15$ (medium)

58. Find the volume of the solid obtained when the region bounded by the curves $y = 2x - x^2$ and $y = x^2 - 2x$ is rotated about the y-axis.

   A) $40\pi/3$ B) $8\pi/3$ C) $20\pi/3$ D) $16\pi/3$
   E) $4\pi/3$ F) $10\pi/3$ G) $5\pi/3$ H) $32\pi/3$

   Answer: $16\pi/3$ (medium)

59. Find the volume of the solid obtained when the region bounded by the lines $y = x$, $x = 1$, $x = 2$, and the x-axis is rotated about the y-axis.

   A) $16\pi/3$ B) 8π C) $20\pi/3$ D) $22\pi/3$
   E) 6π F) $14\pi/3$ G) 4π H) $10\pi/3$

   Answer: $14\pi/3$ (medium)

60. Find the volume of the solid obtained when the region bounded by the curve $y = 5x^3$, $x = 1$, $x = 2$, and the x-axis is rotated about the y-axis.

   A) $127\pi/3$ B) $62\pi/3$ C) 31π D) 15π
   E) 5π F) 127π G) 62π H) $31\pi/3$

   Answer: 62π (medium)

61. Suppose the method of cylindrical shells is used to find the volume the volume of the solid obtained when the region bounded by the lines $y = x$, $y = 2x$, $x = 1$, and $x = 2$ is rotated about the y-axis. What is the largest circumference of a cylindrical shell?

   A) 2π B) 6π C) π D) 3π
   E) 5π F) 4π G) 9π H) 8π

   Answer: 4π (easy)

62. The region bounded by the curves $y = x - x^2$ and $y = 0$ is rotated about the y-axis. Find the volume of the resulting solid.

   A) $\pi/3$ B) $\pi/4$ C) $\pi/5$ D) $\pi/6$
   E) $\pi/12$ F) $\pi/24$ G) $\pi/30$ H) $\pi/36$

   Answer: $\pi/6$ (medium)

63. Find the volume of the solid obtained by rotating about the y-axis the region bounded by $y = \sqrt{1 + x^2}$, $y = 0$, $x = 0$, and $x = 1$.

   A) $\frac{\pi}{3}\left(\sqrt{3} - 1\right)$ B) $\frac{2\pi}{3}\left(2\sqrt{2} - 1\right)$ C) $\frac{4\pi}{3}\left(3\sqrt{3} - 1\right)$

   D) $\frac{\pi}{4}\left(5\sqrt{5} - 1\right)$ E) $\frac{3\pi}{4}\left(5\sqrt{2} - 1\right)$ F) $\frac{5\pi}{4}\left(3\sqrt{2} - 1\right)$

   G) $\frac{\pi}{5}\left(7\sqrt{7} - 1\right)$ H) $\frac{4\pi}{5}\left(7\sqrt{5} - 1\right)$

   Answer: $\frac{2\pi}{3}\left(2\sqrt{2} - 1\right)$ (medium)

64. Write the integral that gives the volume of the solid obtained by rotating the region
$R = \{(x, y) \mid 0 \le y \le f(x), a \le x \le b\}$ about the y-axis.

A) $\int_a^b f(x)\, dx$ B) $\int_a^b \pi f(x)\, dx$ C) $\int_a^b 2\pi x\, f(x)\, dx$

D) $\int_a^b 2\pi y\, f(x)\, dx$ E) $\int_a^b [f(x)]^2\, dx$ F) $\int_a^b \pi [f(x)]^2\, dx$

G) $\int_a^b \pi x [f(x)]^2\, dx$ H) $\int_a^b x^2\, f(x)\, dx$

Answer: $\int_a^b 2\pi x\, f(x)\, dx$ (easy)

65. Find the volume of the solid obtained by rotating about the y-axis the region bounded by
$y = \cos x$, $y = 0$, $x = 0$, and $x = \pi/2$.

A) π B) π^2 C) $\pi^2 - (\pi/2)$

D) $\pi^2 - \pi$ E) $\pi^2 - 2\pi$ F) $2\pi - (\pi^2/4)$

G) $2\pi - (\pi^2/2)$ H) $\pi - (\pi^2/4)$

Answer: $\pi^2 - 2\pi$ (hard)

66. Find the volume of the region obtained by rotating about the y-axis the region bounded by
$y = \sin x$ and $y = 0$ from $x = 0$ to $x = \pi$.

A) $\pi/4$ B) $\pi/2$ C) π D) 2π

E) $\pi^2/4$ F) $\pi^2/2$ G) π^2 H) $2\pi^2$

Answer: $2\pi^2$ (hard)

67. The region in the xy-plane bounded by $y = x^2$, $y = 0$ and $x = 1$ is revolved around the
y-axis. Find the volume of the solid generated.

Answer: $\frac{\pi}{2}$ (medium)

68. Given the curves A: $y^2 = 2(x - 1)$ and B: $y^2 = 4x(x - 2)$. Sketch the curves labeling all points of
intersection. Find the volume of the solid of revolution generated by revolving the bounded region about the
x-axis. Find the volume of the solid of revolution generated by revolving the bounded region about the y-axis.

Answer:

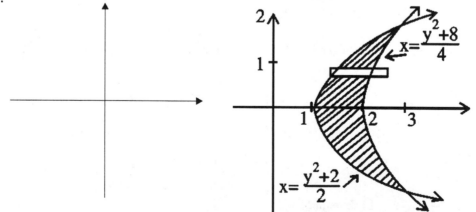

Around x-axis: 2π; around y-axis: $\frac{48\pi}{5}$; (medium)

69.　Use cylindrical shells to find the volume of the solid obtained by revolving around the y-axis the region bounded by the curves $y^2 = 8x$ and $x = 2$.

　　Answer: $\frac{128\pi}{5}$　(medium)

70.　A cylindrical hole has been drilled straight through the center of a sphere of radius R. Use the method of cylindrical shells to find the volume of the remaining solid if it is 6 cm high.

　　Answer: 36π　(medium)

71.　Let R be the region bounded by the curves: $y = \frac{1}{x}$, $y = x^2$, $x = 0$, $y = 2$. Suppose R is revolved around the x-axis. Set up (but do NOT evaluate) the integral for the volume of rotation using the method of cylindrical shells.

　　Answer: $2\pi \int_0^1 y^{\frac{3}{2}} \, dy + 2\pi \int_1^2 dy$　(medium)

72.　Find the volume of the solid generated by revolving about the line $x = -1$, the region bounded by the curves $y = -x^2 + 4x - 3$ and $y = 0$.

　　Answer: 8π　(medium)

73.　Find the volume of the solid formed when the region R bounded by $y = x^3 + 1$, $x = 1$ and $y = 1$ is rotated about the line $x = -1$.

　　Answer: $\frac{9\pi}{10}$　(medium)

Chapter 5, Section 4
Work

74.　An anchor weighing 60 pounds is lifted 10 feet. How much work in foot-pounds is done?

　　A)　900　　　　　B)　600　　　　　C)　200　　　　　D)　1200
　　E)　800　　　　　F)　100　　　　　G)　60　　　　　H)　300

　　Answer: 600　(easy)

75.　A spring stretches 1 foot beyond its natural position under a force of 100 pounds. How much work in foot-pounds is done in stretching it 3 feet beyond its natural position?

　　A)　600　　　　　B)　30　　　　　C)　1500　　　　　D)　450
　　E)　100　　　　　F)　900　　　　　G)　150　　　　　H)　300

　　Answer: 450　(medium)

76.　A rope 100 feet long weighing 2 pounds per foot hangs over the edge of a building 100 feet tall. How much work in foot-pounds is done in pulling the rope to the top of the building?

　　A)　7500　　　　　B)　5000　　　　　C)　1000　　　　　D)　500
　　E)　10000　　　　F)　750　　　　　G)　1250　　　　　H)　12500

　　Answer: 10000　(medium)

77. A rope 100 feet long weighing 2 pounds per foot hangs over the edge of a building 100 feet tall. How much work in foot-pounds is required to pull 20 feet of the rope to the top of the building?

   A) 4000   B) 3500   C) 3800   D) 4200
   E) 4100   F) 3700   G) 3900   H) 3600

   Answer: 3600 (medium)

78. A right circular cylinder tank of height 1 foot and radius 1 foot is full of water. Taking the density of water to be a nice round 60 pounds per cubic foot, how much work in foot-pounds is required to pump all of the water up and over the top of the tank?

   A) 8π B) 24π C) 16π D) 6π
   E) 5π F) 4π G) 30π H) 18π

   Answer: 30π (medium)

79. A right circular conical tank of height 1 foot and radius 1 foot at the top is full of water. Taking the density of water to be a nice round 60 pounds per cubic foot, how much work in foot-pounds is required to pump all the water up and over the top of the tank?

   A) 24π B) 16π C) 5π D) 8π
   E) 6π F) 30π G) 4π H) 18π

   Answer: 5π (hard)

80. Assuming adiabatic expansion $(PV^{1.4} = k)$, how much work in foot-pounds is done by a steam engine cylinder starting at a pressure of 200 lb/in^2 and a volume of 25 in^3 and expanding to a volume of 800 in^3 ?

   A) 9175   B) 9225   C) 9275   D) 9125
   E) 9375   F) 9325   G) 9075   H) 9425

   Answer: 9375 (hard)

81. Find the work done in stretching a spring 6 inches beyond its natural length, if the spring constant $k = 20$ lb/ft.

   Answer: 2.5 ft-lbs. (easy)

82. A hemispherical tank with radius 8 feet is filled with water to a depth of 6 feet. Find the work required to empty the tank by pumping the water to the top of the tank.

   Answer: 900 πw ft-lbs where w is the number of pounds in the weight of 1 ft^3 of water.
       (medium)

83. Suppose a hemispherical tank of radius 10 feet is filled with a liquid whose density is 62 pounds per cubic foot. Find the work required to pump all of the liquid out through the top of the tank.

   Answer: $155,000 \pi$ ft-lbs (medium)

84. An atom is moving radially outward from the origin opposite the pull of the force
$F = \frac{a}{(r-b)^3} - \frac{c}{r^6}$ where a, b, c are constants and r is the radial distance from the origin.
How much work must be done to move the atom from R_1 to R_2?

Answer: $W = \text{Work} = \frac{a}{2}\left(\frac{1}{(R_1-b)^2} - \frac{1}{(R_2-b)^2}\right) + \frac{c}{5}\left(\frac{1}{R_2^5} - \frac{1}{R_1^5}\right)$ (medium)

Chapter 5, Section 5
Average Value of a Function

85. Find the average value of the function $f(x) = 2 + 3x$ on the interval $[0, 4]$.

A) 2	B) 4	C) 16	D) 10
E) 14	F) 8	G) 6	H) 12

Answer: 8 (medium)

86. Find the average value of the function $f(x) = x^3$ on the interval $[1, 3]$.

A) 8	B) 2	C) 14	D) 10
E) 6	F) 4	G) 16	H) 12

Answer: 10 (medium)

87. Find the average value of the function $f(x) = \sin x$ on the interval $[0, \pi]$.

A) 2π	B) 3π	C) π	D) 4π
E) $3/\pi$	F) $4/\pi$	G) $1/\pi$	H) $2/\pi$

Answer: $2/\pi$ (medium)

88. The density of a rod 4 meters long is $2 + x$ kg/m at a distance of x meters from one end of the rod. Find the average density of the rod.

A) 3	B) 5/2	C) 3/2	D) 17/4
E) 7/2	F) 15/4	G) 4	H) 1/2

Answer: 4 (easy)

89. The density of a rod 4 meters long is $\sqrt{x}$ kg/m at a distance of x meters from one end of the rod. Find the average density of the rod.

A) 6	B) 4/3	C) 3	D) 1
E) 2	F) 16/3	G) 4	H) 8/3

Answer: 4/3 (medium)

90.   Find the average value of the function $f(x) = \sin 3x$ on the interval $[0, \pi]$.

A) 1   B) 3/2   C) 2   D) 5/2
E) $1/\pi$ F) $3/2\pi$ G) $2/3\pi$ H) $5/2\pi$

Answer: $2/3\pi$ (medium)

91.   Find the average value of $f(x) = x^2 - 2x$ on the interval $[0, 3]$.

Answer: 0 (easy)

92.   Find the average value of $f(x) = x^3 - x$ on the interval $[1, 3]$.

Answer: 8 (easy)

93.   Find the average value of $f(x) = \sqrt{x}$ on the interval $[4, 9]$.

Answer: $\frac{38}{15}$ (easy)

94.   The temperature (in °F) in a certain city t hours after 9 a.m. was approximated by the function
$$T(t) = 50 + 14 \sin \frac{\pi t}{12}$$
Find the average temperature during the period from 9 a.m. to 9 p.m..

Answer: 59°F (medium)

95.   The temperature of a metal rod, 5 m long, is $4x$ (in °C) at a distance x meters from one end of the rod. What is the average temperature of the rod?

Answer: 10°C (medium)

Calculus, 3rd Edition
by James Stewart
Chapter 6, Section 1
Inverse Functions

1   Find the inverse function for $f(x) = 2x + 5$.

A) $x + (5/2)$ B) $x - (5/2)$ C) $(x/2) + 5$ D) $(x + 5)/2$
E) $2x - 5$ F) $(x - 5)/2$ G) $2x + 5$ H) $(x/2) - 5$

Answer: $(x - 5)/2$ (easy)

2.   Find the inverse function for $f(x) = \frac{x-1}{x+1}$.

A) $(x + 1)/(x - 1)$ B) $x/(x + 1)$ C) $(x + 1)/x$
D) $(1 + x)/(1 - x)$ E) $(x + 1)/(x - 1)$ F) $x/(x - 1)$
G) $(x - 1)/(x + 1)$ H) $(x - 1)/x$

Answer: $(1 + x)/(1 - x)$ (medium)

3.   Find the domain of the inverse function for $f(x) = \sqrt{3 + 7x}$.

A) $[0, \infty)$ B) $[7/3, \infty)$ C) $(-\infty, 0]$ D) $[-3/7, \infty)$
E) $[-7/3, \infty)$ F) $(-\infty, 7/3]$ G) $(-\infty, 3/7]$ H) $(-\infty, -7/3]$

Answer: $[0, \infty)$ (medium)

4.   Find the range of the inverse function for $f(x) = \sqrt{3 + 7x}$.

A) $(-\infty, 0]$ B) $(-\infty, 3/7]$ C) $[0, \infty)$
D) $[7/3, \infty)$ E) $(-\infty, -7/3]$ F) $(-\infty, 7/3]$
G) $[-3/7, \infty)$ H) $[-7/3, \infty)$

Answer: $[-3/7, \infty)$ (medium)

5.   If the function $f(x) = 3x + 4$ has domain $[2, \infty)$, what is the range of its inverse?

A) $[0, \infty)$ B) $[-2/3, \infty)$ C) $[-3/2, \infty)$
D) $[-3/4, \infty)$ E) $[-4/3, \infty)$ F) $[10, \infty)$
G) $[2, \infty)$ H) $[4, \infty)$

Answer: $[2, \infty)$ (easy)

6.   If the function $f(x) = 3x + 4$ has domain $[2, \infty)$, what is the domain of its inverse?

A) $[-3/2, \infty)$ B) $[2, \infty)$ C) $[-3/4, \infty)$
D) $[10, \infty)$ E) $[-2/3, \infty)$ F) $[-4/3, \infty)$
G) $[4, \infty)$ H) $[0, \infty)$

Answer: $[10, \infty)$ (medium)

7.   Given the function $\sin x$ with domain $[-\pi/2, \pi/2]$, find the domain of its inverse.

A) $[-\sqrt{3}/2, \sqrt{3}/2]$ B) $[0, \infty)$ C) $[-\pi, \pi]$
D) $[-1, 1]$ E) $[-\pi/2, \pi/2]$ F) $[-1/2, 1/2]$
G) $(-\infty, \infty)$ H) $[-1/\sqrt{2}, 1/\sqrt{2}]$

Answer: $[-1, 1]$ (easy)

8.   Let $f(x) = x + \cos x$ and let g be the inverse function of f. Find the value of $g'(1)$.

A) 0   B) 1/2   C) 1   D) 3/2
E) 2   F) 5/2   G) 3   H) 7/2

Answer: 1 (hard)

9.   Suppose g is the inverse function of f and $f(4) = 5$ and $f'(4) = 2/3$. Find the value of $g'(5)$.

A) 1/2   B) 1   C) 3/2   D) 2
E) 5/2   F) 3   G) 7/2   H) 4

Answer: 3/2 (easy)

10.   Suppose g is the inverse function of a $1-1$ differentiable function f and let $G(x) = 1/g(x)$. If $f(3) = 2$ and $f'(3) = 1/9$, find the value of $G'(2)$.

A) 9   B) -1 C) 1/9   D) -9
E) 1   F) 0   G) 6   H) $-1/9$

Answer: -1 (hard)

11.   Find the inverse of $f(x) = x^2 - 2x + 3 (x \geq 1)$.

Answer: $f^{-1}(x) = 1 + \sqrt{x - 2}$, $y \geq 1$ (medium)

12.   Find the inverse of the function $f(x) = \sqrt{x - 5}$. State the domain of the inverse.

Answer: $f^{-1}(x) = x^2 + 5$, the domain is $[0, \infty)$. (easy)

13.   Suppose $G(x) = \int_1^x \sqrt{t^2 + 3}\, dt$. Does the function G have an inverse function? Justify your answer.

Answer: By the Fundamental Theorem, $G'(x) = \sqrt{x^2 + 3}$. So, $G'(x) > 0$ for all x. Therefore, G is an increasing function and G must have an inverse function. (medium)

14.   If $f(x) = x^2 - x - 6$, $x \geq 1$, find $(f^{-1})'(6)$.

Answer: $\frac{1}{7}$ (medium)

15. Sketch the graph of f for $f(x) = \sqrt[3]{x}$ and determine if f^{-1} exists. If so, find a formula for $y = f^{-1}(x)$ and also sketch the graph of f^{-1}.

Answer:

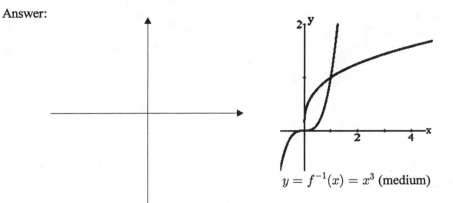

$y = f^{-1}(x) = x^3$ (medium)

16. Determine whether or not the given function is one-to-one: $f(x) = x^2 - 2x + 5$.

Answer: not one-to-one (easy)

17. Determine whether or not the given function is one-to-one: $g(x) = |x|$.

Answer: not one-to-one (easy)

18. Determine whether or not the given function is one-to-one: $h(x) = x^4 + 5$, $0 \le x \le 2$.

Answer: one-to-one (easy)

19. Find the inverse of $f(x) = \frac{x-2}{x+2}$.

Answer: $f^{-1}(x) = \frac{2(1+x)}{1-x}$ (easy)

Chapter 6, Section 2
Exponential Functions and Their Derivatives

20. For what value of x is $2^x = (1/2)^x$?

A) $\sqrt{2}$ B) 2   C) $-\sqrt{2}$ D) -2
E) 1   F) 0   G) 1/2   H) -1

Answer: 0 (easy)

21. Find the minimum value of $2^{|x|}$.

A) $-\sqrt{2}$ B) 1/2   C) 2   D) -2
E) 0   F) 1   G) -1 H) $\sqrt{2}$

Answer: 1 (easy)

22.   How can $7^{\sqrt{2}}$ be calculated?

A) by taking a derivative   B) by taking a square root once
C) by taking an integral   D) by solving a cubic equation
E) by taking a square root twice   F) by trigonometry
G) by solving a quadratic equation   H) as a limit of other powers of 7

Answer: as a limit of other powers of 7 (medium)

23.   Find the value of the limit $\lim\limits_{x \to \infty} (\pi/4)^x$.

A) π B) ∞ C) 0   D) -1
E) 1   F) $\pi/4$ G) $-\pi$ H) $-\infty$

Answer: 0 (medium)

24.   Find the value of the limit $\lim\limits_{x \to \infty} 4^{(x+1)/x}$.

A) ∞ B) $-1/4$ C) $1/4$ D) 0
E) -4 F) 4   G) 2   H) -2

Answer: 4 (medium)

25.   Find the value of the limit $\lim\limits_{x \to 0^+} 4^{(x+1)/x}$.

A) 0   B) -4 C) $1/4$ D) -2
E) 4   F) 2   G) ∞ H) $-1/4$

Answer: ∞ (medium)

26.   Find the value of the limit $\lim\limits_{x \to 0^-} 4^{(x+1)/x}$.

A) 4   B) -2 C) ∞ D) $-1/4$
E) $1/4$ F) -4 G) 2   H) 0

Answer: 0 (medium)

27.   Find the value of the limit $\lim\limits_{x \to 3^-} 2^{1/(x-3)}$.

A) $-\infty$ B) -2 C) -1 D) 0
E) $1/2$ F) 1   G) $3/2$ H) ∞

Answer: 0 (medium)

28.   If $0 < a < 1$, find the value of the limit $\lim\limits_{x \to \infty} a^x$.

A) ∞ B) 1   C) a D) $1/a$
E) $\sqrt{a}$ F) a^2 G) 0   H) $-\infty$

Answer: 0 (easy)

29. Find the value of the limit $\lim\limits_{x \to 2^+} 3^{1/(2-x)}$.

A) $-\infty$ B) -2 C) -1 D) 0
E) 1/2 F) 1 G) 3/2 H) ∞

Answer: 0 (medium)

30. Make a rough sketch of the graph of $y = (1.1)^x$. Do not use a calculator. Use the basic graphs from Section 6.1 and any needed transformations.

Answer: (easy)

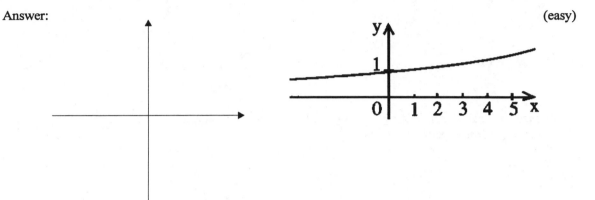

31. Make a rough sketch of the graph of $y = 2^{x+1}$. Do not use a calculator. Use the basic graphs from Section 6.1 and any needed transformations.

Answer: (easy)

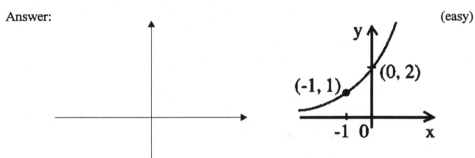

32. Make a rough sketch of the graph of $y = -3^x$. Do not use a calculator. Use the basic graphs from Section 6.1 and any needed transformations.

   Answer: (medium)

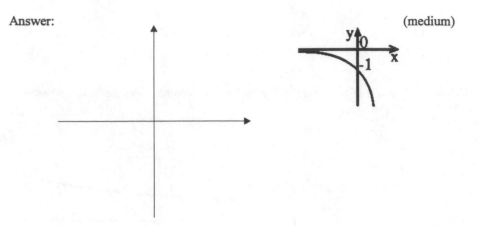

33. Make a rough sketch of the graph of $y = 2^{|x|}$. Do not use a calculator. Use the basic graphs from Section 6.1 and any needed transformations.

   Answer: (medium)

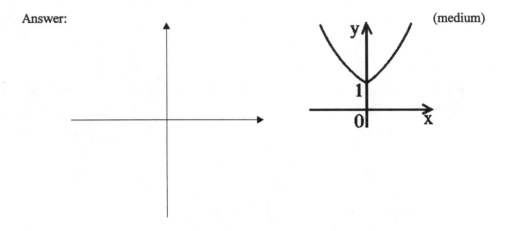

34. Make a rough sketch of the graph of $y = 2 + 5\left(1 - 10^{-x}\right)$. Do not use a calculator. Use the basic graphs from Section 6.1 and any needed transformations.

   Answer: (medium)

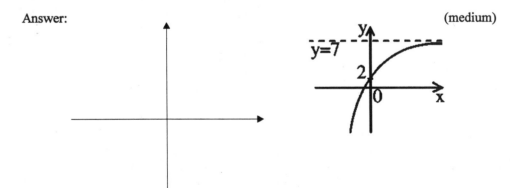

35. Find the limit: $\lim\limits_{x \to -\infty} (1.1)^x$.

Answer: 0 (easy)

36. Find the limit: $\lim\limits_{x \to -\infty} \pi^{-x}$.

Answer: ∞ (medium)

37. Find the limit: $\lim\limits_{x \to -(\pi/2)^+} 2^{\tan x}$.

Answer: 0 (medium)

38. Find the limit: $\lim\limits_{x \to -\infty} 3^{\frac{1}{x}}$.

Answer: 1 (medium)

39. Find the limit: $\lim\limits_{x \to 0^-} 3^{\frac{1}{x}}$.

Answer: 0 (medium)

40. Let $f(x) = e^{-x}$. Find the value of $f'(1)$.

A) $2e$ B) e C) $2e^{-1}$ D) $-2e$
E) e^{-1} F) $-e$ G) $-2e^{-1}$ H) $-e^{-1}$

Answer: $-e^{-1}$ (easy)

41. Let $f(x) = e^{-x^2}$. Find the value of $f'(1)$.

A) $2e^{-1}$ B) $2e$ C) $-2e$ D) $-e$
E) e F) $-2e^{-1}$ G) e^{-1} H) $-e^{-1}$

Answer: $-2e^{-1}$ (medium)

42. Let $f(x) = e^{x^2}$. Find the value of $f''(0)$.

A) e B) 1 C) -1 D) e^{-1}
E) -2 F) $2e^{-1}$ G) $2e$ H) 2

Answer: 2 (medium)

43. Let $f(x) = e^{\ln 2x}$. Find the value of $f'(\pi)$.

A) 1 B) 2 C) 2π D) -1
E) -2π F) 0 G) -2 H) π

Answer: 2 (medium)

44. Let $f(x) = e^{e^x}$. Find the value of $f'(1)$.

A) e^{e+2} B) e^e C) e^{e-1} D) e^{e-2}
E) e F) e^{e+1} G) e^2 H) $2e^2$

Answer: e^{e+1} (hard)

45. Find the value of the integral $\int_0^1 2^x \, dx$.

A) $e - 1$ B) $e^2 - 1$ C) $e^2 - e$ D) 2
E) $1/\ln 2$ F) 4   G) 1   H) $\ln 2$

Answer: $1/\ln 2$ (medium)

46. Find the value of the integral $\int_0^1 xe^{-x^2} \, dx$.

A) $-e/2$ B) $e/2$ C) $(1 - e^{-1})/2$ D) e
E) $-e$ F) $-e^{-1}$ G) $e^{-1}/2$ H) e^{-1}

Answer: $(1 - e^{-1})/2$ (medium)

47. How many points of inflection does $f(x) = x^3 e^{-x}$ have?

A) 0   B) 1   C) 2   D) 3
E) 4   F) 5   G) 6   H) infinitely many

Answer: 3 (hard)

48. Find the absolute maximum of the function $f(x) = \frac{e^{-x}}{1+x^2}$.

A) 4/3   B) 1   C) e^{-1} D) $e^{-1}/2$
E) 2   F) 1/2   G) 3/2   H) no absolute maximum

Answer: no absolute maximum (medium)

49. Find the interval on which $f(x) = xe^{-x}$ is increasing.

A) $(-\infty, 1]$ B) $(-\infty, 2]$ C) $(-\infty, 3]$ D) $[1, 2]$
E) $[1, e]$ F) $(-\infty, e]$ G) $(-\infty, \infty)$ H) $(-\infty, 1/e)$

Answer: $(-\infty, 1]$ (medium)

50. Find the interval on which $f(x) = xe^{-x}$ is concave upward.

A) $(-\infty, 0)$ B) $(-\infty, 1)$ C) $(-\infty, 2)$ D) $(0, 1)$
E) $(1, 2)$ F) $(1, \infty)$ G) $(2, \infty)$ H) $(-\infty, \infty)$

Answer: $(2, \infty)$ (medium)

51. Find the interval on which the function $f(x) = e^x/x$ is increasing.

A) $(-\infty, -1]$ B) $(-\infty, 0)$ C) $[-1, 1]$ D) $(0, 1/e]$
E) $[1/e, 1]$ F) $(0, e]$ G) $[1/e, \infty)$ H) $[1, \infty)$

Answer: $[1, \infty)$ (medium)

52. On the domain $(0, \infty)$ find the minimum value of $f(x) = e^x/x$.

A) 0 B) $1/e^2$ C) $1/e$ D) 1
E) $e - 1$ F) e G) $e^2 - 1$ H) e^2

Answer: e (medium)

53. Let $f(x) = e^x/x$. Find $f''(x)$.

A) $e^x(x+4)/x^4$ B) $e^x(x^2-1)/x^4$
C) $e^x(x^2+x)/x^4$ D) $e^x(x^2+3)/x^4$
E) $e^x(x-2)/x^3$ F) $e^x(x^2+5x)/x^3$
G) $e^x(x^2-2x+2)/x^3$ H) $e^x(x^3-4x^2+3)/x^3$

Answer: $e^x(x^2-2x+2)/x^3$ (medium)

54. Find y' if $y = e^{\sqrt{x^3+1}}$.

Answer: $\dfrac{3x^2 e^{\sqrt{x^3+1}}}{2\sqrt{x^3+1}}$ (medium)

55. Find $\dfrac{dy}{dx}$ if $y = e^{xy} + e^{99}$

Answer: $\dfrac{dy}{dx} = \dfrac{ye^{xy}}{1 - xe^{xy}}$ (medium)

56. Find y' if $y = xe^{(x^2+7)}$.

Answer: $2x^2 e^{x^2+7} + e^{x^2+7}$ (medium)

57. Evaluate the integral: $\int xe^{x^2}\, dx$.

Answer: $\frac{1}{2}e^{x^2} + C$ (easy)

58. Evaluate the integral: $\int e^{\frac{1}{x}} x^{-2}\, dx$

Answer: $-e^{\frac{1}{x}} + C$ (medium)

59. Evaluate the integral: $\int e^x \sin(e^x)\, dx$

Answer: $-\cos(e^x) + C$ (easy)

60. Find $f(x)$ if $f''(x) = 3e^x + 5\sin x$, $f(0) = 1$, and $f'(0) = 2$.

Answer: $f(x) = 3e^x - 5\sin x + 4x - 2$ (medium)

61. Find the value of the limit $\lim\limits_{x \to 0^-} e^{\cot x}$.

A) $-\infty$ B) $-e$ C) -1 D) 0
E) 1   F) e G) ∞ H) does not exist

Answer: 0 (medium)

62. From the choices below, pick the limit whose value is e.

A) $\lim\limits_{x \to 0}(1+x)^x$ B) $\lim\limits_{x \to 0}(1+x)^{1/x}$ C) $\lim\limits_{x \to 0}\left(1+\frac{1}{x}\right)^x$

D) $\lim\limits_{x \to 0}\left(1+\frac{1}{x}\right)^{1/x}$ E) $\lim\limits_{x \to 0} x^{1+(1/x)}$ F) $\lim\limits_{x \to 0} x^{1/x}$

G) $\lim\limits_{x \to 0} x^x$ H) $\lim\limits_{x \to \infty} x^{\ln x}$

Answer: $\lim\limits_{x \to 0}(1+x)^{1/x}$ (medium)

63. Find the value of the limit $\lim\limits_{x \to -\infty} \frac{e^x}{x}$.

A) $-\infty$ B) $-e$ C) -1 D) 0
E) e^{-1} F) 1   G) e H) ∞

Answer: 0 (medium)

64. Find the value of the limit $\lim\limits_{x \to 0^+} \frac{e^x}{x}$.

A) $-\infty$ B) $-e$ C) -1 D) 0
E) e^{-1} F) 1   G) e H) ∞

Answer: ∞ (medium)

65. Find the value of the limit $\lim\limits_{x \to 0^-} \frac{e^x}{x}$.

A) $-\infty$ B) $-e$ C) -1 D) 0
E) e^{-1} F) 1   G) e H) ∞

Answer: $-\infty$ (medium)

66. Find the value of the limit $\lim\limits_{x \to 0}(1+x)^{1/x}$.

A) 1   B) $1/e$ C) $e-1$ D) e^2-1
E) $e+1$ F) e G) $1/(e-1)$ H) $1/(e+1)$

Answer: e (easy)

Chapter 6, Section 3
Logarithmic Functions

67. Find the value of $\log_2 1$.

   A) -1 B) $-1/2$ C) 0 D) 10^2
   E) 1 F) $1/2$ G) 2 H) -2

   Answer: 0 (easy)

68. Find the value of $\log_2 16$.

   A) $1/8$ B) 3 C) 2 D) 0
   E) $1/4$ F) 4 G) 1 H) $1/2$

   Answer: 4 (easy)

69. Find the value of $\log_{16} 2$.

   A) $1/2$ B) 2 C) 4 D) 1
   E) 3 F) 0 G) $1/8$ H) $1/4$

   Answer: 1/4 (medium)

70. Find the value of $\ln e$.

   A) -1 B) $1/\sqrt{e}$ C) e D) 0
   E) $\sqrt{e}$ F) $1/e$ G) 1 H) $-e$

   Answer: 1 (easy)

71. Find the value of $\ln \sqrt{e^3}$.

   A) $2/3$ B) $\sqrt{e}$ C) $e^3/2$ D) $3/2$
   E) e^3 F) $e^3 - 2$ G) $2e/3$ H) $2/e^3$

   Answer: 3/2 (medium)

72. Find the value of $e^{\ln 8}$.

   A) 3 B) 8 C) 1 D) 2
   E) $1/8$ F) $1/3$ G) e^3 H) 4

   Answer: 8 (easy)

73. Find the value of $\log_2 e - \log_2 (e/16)$.

   A) -2 B) e^{-2} C) 4 D) e^{16}
   E) -4 F) e^2 G) 2 H) e^{-16}

   Answer: 4 (medium)

74. Find the value of the limit $\lim\limits_{x \to \infty} \frac{e^x}{e^x+10}$.

A) 1
B) ln 10
C) 1/ln 10
D) 10
E) 1/10
F) 0
G) ln (1/10)
H) -1

Answer: 1 (medium)

75. Find the value of the limit $\lim\limits_{x \to \infty} \frac{\ln x}{\ln \sqrt{x}+10}$.

A) 1/2
B) ∞
C) 1/11
D) 0
E) 1/10
F) ln 2
G) 2
H) 1

Answer: 2 (medium)

76. Solve the equation $\log_2(\ln x) = 1$.

A) 2^e
B) $2e$
C) $e/2$
D) 1
E) $\sqrt{e}$
F) $1/e$
G) $2/e$
H) e^2

Answer: e^2 (medium)

77. Solve the equation $e^{2x-2} = 4$.

A) ln 2
B) $1 - \ln 2$
C) $1 + \ln 2$
D) $1 - 2\ln 2$
E) $1 + 2\ln 2$
F) $2 + \ln 2$
G) $2 - \ln 2$
H) $2 - 2\ln 2$

Answer: $1 + \ln 2$ (medium)

78. Find the value of the limit $\lim\limits_{x \to 0^+} \frac{\ln x}{x}$.

A) $-\infty$
B) -1
C) 0
D) $1/e$
E) 1
F) e
G) $e^{1/e}$
H) ∞

Answer: $-\infty$ (medium)

79. Solve the equation $e^{2x-4} = 16$.

A) ln 2
B) $-\ln 2$
C) $1 + \ln 2$
D) $1 - \ln 2$
E) $1 + 2\ln 2$
F) $1 - 2\ln 2$
G) $2 + 2\ln 2$
H) $2 - 2\ln 2$

Answer: $2 + 2\ln 2$ (medium)

80. Find the value of the limit $\lim\limits_{x \to 1^+} e^{1/(x-1)}$.

A) $-\infty$
B) -2
C) -1
D) 0
E) 1/2
F) 1
G) 3/2
H) ∞

Answer: ∞ (medium)

81. Find the value of the limit $\lim\limits_{x \to 0^-} \frac{1}{1+e^{1/x}}$.

A) 1   B) 1/2   C) 0   D) ∞
E) $-\infty$ F) -1 G) $-1/2$ H) 2

Answer: 1 (medium)

82. Solve the equation $e^{x-2} = 4$.

A) $\ln 2$ B) $-\ln 2$ C) $1 + \ln 2$ D) $1 - \ln 2$
E) $1 + 2\ln 2$ F) $1 - 2\ln 2$ G) $2 + 2\ln 2$ H) $2 - 2\ln 2$

Answer: $2 + 2\ln 2$ (medium)

83. Find the domain of the function $f(x) = \ln(\ln(\ln x))$.

A) $(0, \infty)$ B) $[1, \infty)$ C) $(1, \infty)$ D) $[e, \infty)$
E) (e, ∞) F) $(-\infty, 0)$ G) $(-\infty, 1)$ H) $(-\infty, e)$

Answer: (e, ∞) (medium)

84. Solve the equation $e^{x-1} = 4$.

A) $\ln 2$ B) $-\ln 2$ C) $1 + \ln 2$ D) $1 - \ln 2$
E) $1 + 2\ln 2$ F) $1 - 2\ln 2$ G) $2 + 2\ln 2$ H) $2 - 2\ln 2$

Answer: $1 + 2\ln 2$ (medium)

85. Find the value of $\log_{32} 8$.

Answer: $\frac{3}{5}$ (easy)

86. Find the value of $25^{\log_5 10}$.

Answer: 100 (easy)

87. Suppose pH $= -\log [\text{H}^+]$. Suppose further that for vinegar, the hydrogen ion concentration in moles per liter, is given by $[\text{H}^+] = 5.2 \left(10^{-4}\right)$. Find the pH of the vinegar.

Answer: pH $= 3.28$ (medium)

88. Express $\log_2 x + 5 \log_2(x + 1) + \frac{1}{2} \log_2(x - 1)$ as a single logarithm.

Answer: $\log_2[x(x+1)^5 \sqrt{x-1}]$ (easy)

89. Express $\ln x + a \ln y - b \ln z$ as a single logarithm.

Answer: $\ln\left(\frac{xy^a}{z^b}\right)$ (easy)

90. Make a rough sketch of the graph of $y = 1 + \log_5(x-1)$. Do not use a calculator. Just use the graphs given in your text and any needed transformations.

Answer: (easy)

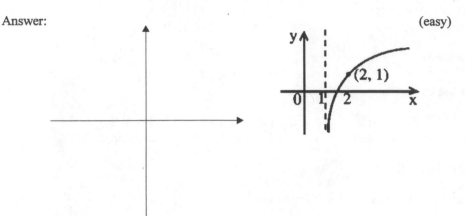

91. Make a rough sketch of the graph of $y = \ln\left(\frac{1}{x}\right)$. Do not use a calculator. Just use the graphs given in your text and any needed transformations.

Answer: (easy)

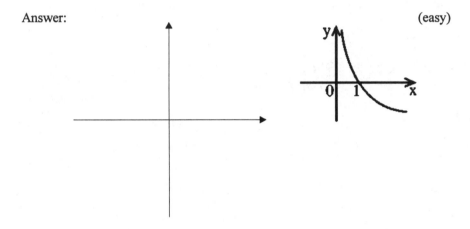

92. Solve for x: $5^{\log_5(2x)} = 6$.

Answer: $x = 3$ (easy)

93. Solve for x: $\ln x^2 = 2\ln 4 - 4\ln 2$.

Answer: $x = \pm 1$ (easy)

94. A sound so faint that it can just be heard has intensity $I_0 = 10^{-12}$ watt/m² at a frequency of 1000 hertz (Hz). The loudness, in decibels (dB), of a sound with intensity I is then defined to be $L = 10\log_{10}(I/I_0)$. Rock music with amplifiers is measured at 120 dB. The noise from a power mower is measured at 106 dB. Find the ratio of the intensity of the rock music to that of the power mower.

Answer: $10^{1.4} \doteq 25$ (medium)

95. Find $f^{-1}(x)$ for $f(x) = \sqrt{e^x + 2}$.

Answer: $f^{-1}(x) = \ln\left(x^2 - 2\right)$ (medium)

Chapter 6, Section 4
Derivatives of Logarithmic Functions

96. Let $f(x) = \log_2 x$. Find the value of $f'(1)$.

A) 2   B) e^2 C) $\ln(1/2)$ D) $e^{-1/2}$
E) 2^e F) $1/2$ G) $1/\ln 2$ H) $e^{1/2}$

Answer: $1/\ln 2$ (medium)

97. Let $f(x) = \ln(x^2)$. Find the value of $f'(1)$.

A) 2^e B) e^2 C) $\ln(1/2)$ D) 2
E) $e^{-1/2}$ F) $1/\ln 2$ G) $1/2$ H) $e^{1/2}$

Answer: 2 (medium)

98. Let $f(x) = \ln(\ln(x))$. Find the value of $f'(e)$.

A) $1/e^2$ B) e^2 C) $1+e$ D) $1/e$
E) $\ln 2$ F) 1   G) e H) 0

Answer: $1/e$ (medium)

99. Let $f(x) = \log_2(3x)$. Find the value of $f'(1)$.

A) $\ln(1/2)$ B) $e^{-1/3}$ C) e^3 D) 3
E) $e^{1/3}$ F) 3^e G) $1/3$ H) $1/\ln 2$

Answer: $1/\ln 2$ (hard)

100. Let $f(x) = \ln(\ln(x))$. Find the value of $f''(e)$.

A) $2e^{-1}$ B) e^{-1} C) $-e^{-1}$ D) $-e^{-2}$
E) $-2e^{-2}$ F) e^{-2} G) $-2e^{-1}$ H) $2e^{-2}$

Answer: $-2e^{-2}$ (hard)

101. Find the value of the integral $\int_1^e \frac{1}{x}\, dx$.

A) 1   B) e C) $1/2$ D) -1
E) -2 F) $-1/2$ G) $\sqrt{e}$ H) 2

Answer: 1 (easy)

102. Find the value of the integral $\int_1^{\sqrt{e}} \frac{1}{x}\, dx$.

A) 2   B) -2 C) $-1/2$ D) e
E) $\sqrt{e}$ F) 1   G) $1/2$ H) $\sqrt{e}/2$

Answer: $1/2$ (medium)

103. Find the value of the integral $\int_0^1 \frac{1}{1+x} \, dx$.

A) $(1/2) \ln 2$ B) $1/\ln 2$ C) 2   D) $\ln 2$
E) $1/2$ F) 1   G) $2 \ln 2$ H) 0

Answer: $\ln 2$ (medium)

104. Find the value of the integral $\int_0^1 \frac{x}{1+x^2} \, dx$.

A) 1   B) $\frac{1}{2} \ln 2$ C) $2 \ln 2$ D) $1/\ln 2$
E) $\ln 2$ F) $1/2$ G) 2   H) 0

Answer: $\frac{1}{2} \ln 2$ (medium)

105. Find the value of $\int_e^{e^2} \frac{\ln x}{x} \, dx$.

A) $\ln 2$ B) $\frac{1}{2} \ln 2$ C) $1/2$ D) $3/2$
E) 1   F) $1/\ln 2$ G) 0   H) $2 \ln 2$

Answer: $3/2$ (medium)

106. Let $f(x) = \frac{\ln x}{x}$. Find the interval on which f is decreasing.

A) $(0, 1/e]$ B) $(0, 1]$ C) $(0, 2]$ D) $(1/e, 1]$
E) $[1/e, 2]$ F) $[1/e, e]$ G) $[1/e, \infty)$ H) $[e, \infty)$

Answer: $[e, \infty)$ (medium)

107. Let $f(x) = \frac{\ln x}{x}$. Find the maximum value of f.

A) 0   B) $1/e$ C) 1   D) e
E) $e^{1/e}$ F) e^e G) e^{-e} H) e^2

Answer: $1/e$ (medium)

108. Let $f(x) = \frac{\ln x}{x}$. Find the interval on which f is concave upward.

A) $(0, 1/e]$ B) $(0, 1)$ C) $(0, e)$ D) $(1/e, e)$
E) $(1, e)$ F) $(\sqrt{e}, \infty)$ G) (e, ∞) H) $(e^{3/2}, \infty)$

Answer: $(e^{3/2}, \infty)$ (hard)

109. Find the value of the integral $\int_{-e^2}^{-e} \frac{3}{x} \, dx$.

A) -3 B) $-e$ C) e^3 D) $1/3$
E) $\ln 2$ F) $-\ln 3$ G) $e - \ln 3$ H) $e^2 - \ln 3$

Answer: -3 (medium)

110. Let $f(x) = x \ln(x^2 - 3)$. Find the value of $f'(2)$.

A) 0   B) 2   C) 4   D) 6
E) 8   F) 10   G) 12   H) 14

Answer: 8 (medium)

111. Find the value of the integral $\int_e^{e^4} \frac{dx}{x\sqrt{\ln x}}$.

A) 0   B) 1   C) 2   D) 3
E) 4   F) 5   G) 6   H) 7

Answer: 2 (medium)

112. Let $f(x) = 2x + \ln x$ and let g be the inverse function of f. Find the value of $g'(2)$.

A) 1   B) 1/2   C) 1/3   D) 1/4
E) $1/\ln 2$ F) $1/(2 \ln 2)$ G) $1/e$ H) $1/e^2$

Answer: 1/3 (hard)

113. Let $f(x) = \sqrt{x} \ln x$. Find the interval on which f is increasing.

A) $(0, \infty)$ B) $(0, 1]$ C) $[1, \infty)$ D) $(0, e^{-1}]$
E) $[e^{-1}, \infty)$ F) $(0, e^{-2}]$ G) $[e^{-2}, \infty)$ H) $(0, \sqrt{e})$

Answer: $[e^{-2}, \infty)$ (medium)

114. Let $f(x) = \sqrt{x} \ln x$. Find the interval on which f is concave upward.

A) $(0, \infty)$ B) $(0, 1)$ C) $(1, \infty)$ D) $(0, e^{-1})$
E) (e^{-1}, ∞) F) $(0, e^{-2})$ G) (e^{-2}, ∞) H) (e, ∞)

Answer: (0, 1) (hard)

115. Find the minimum value of the function $f(x) = x \ln x$.

A) $-e$ B) -1 C) $-1/e$ D) 0
E) e F) $e^{1/e}$ G) e^e H) e^{-e}

Answer: $-1/e$ (medium)

116. Let $f(x) = \ln(\ln(\ln x))$. Find the value of $f'(e^2)$.

A) $1/\ln 2$ B) $1/\ln 4$ C) $1/\ln 8$ D) $1/e$
E) $1/e^2$ F) $1/(e^2 \ln 2)$ G) $1/(e^2 \ln 4)$ H) $1/(e^2 \ln 8)$

Answer: $1/(e^2 \ln 4)$ (medium)

117. Find the interval on which the graph of $f(x) = \ln(x^2 + 1)$ is concave upward.

A) $(-1, 1)$ B) $(-1, 2)$ C) $(-2, 1)$ D) $(-2, 2)$
E) $(-1, 3)$ F) $(-3, 2)$ G) $(-3, 3)$ H) $(-\infty, \infty)$

Answer: $(-1, 1)$ (medium)

118. Find the range of the function $e^{\sin x}$.

A) $[-1, 1]$ B) $[e^{-\pi/2}, e^{\pi/2}]$ C) $[0, e]$
D) $[0, 1]$ E) $[-e, e]$ F) $[e^{-\pi}, e^{\pi}]$
G) $[e^{-1}, e]$ H) $[0, e^{\pi/2}]$

Answer: $[e^{-1}, e]$ (easy)

119. Use logarithmic differentiation to find $\frac{dy}{dx}$ if $y = x^{e^x}$.

Answer: $x^{e^x} (e^x) \left(\frac{1}{x} + \ln x\right)$ (medium)

120. Find y' if $y = \ln\sqrt{\frac{4x-7}{x^2+2x}}$.

Answer: $\frac{2}{4x-7} - \frac{x+1}{x^2+2x}$ (medium)

121. If $y = \frac{(x+3)\,(x^2+1)^3(x+1)^2}{(x^2+10)^{1/2}}$, find y' by logarithmic differentiation.

Answer: $\left(\frac{1}{x+3} + \frac{6x}{x^2+1} + \frac{2}{x+1} - \frac{x}{x^2+10}\right) \cdot \frac{(x+3)\,(x^2+1)^3(x+1)^2}{(x^2+10)^{1/2}}$ (hard)

122. Find $\frac{dy}{dx}$ if $y = \ln\left(\frac{\tan x}{x^2+1}\right)$.

Answer: $\frac{\sec^2 x}{\tan x} - \frac{2x}{x^2+1}$ (medium)

123. Find y' if $y = (\sqrt{x})^x$, $x > 0$.

Answer: $\frac{(\sqrt{x})^x}{2} (1 + \ln x)$ (medium)

124. Find $\frac{dy}{dx}$ for $y = 3^{x^2} + e^\pi + (1+x^2)^{\sqrt{2}}$

Answer: $3^{x^2} + \sqrt{2}\left(1+x^2\right)^{\left(\sqrt{2}-1\right)}(2x)$ (medium)

125. Find $\frac{dy}{dx}$ for $y = (1+x^2)^{x^3} + \sin x$.

Answer: $(1+x^2)^{x^3} \left[3x^2 \ln(1+x^2) + \frac{2x^4}{1+x^2}\right] + \cos x$ (hard)

126. Find the derivative y' for $y = 3^x$.

Answer: $(\ln 3) \cdot 3^x$ (easy)

127. Find the derivative y' for $y = x^x$.

Answer: $(1 + \ln x) \cdot x^x$ (medium)

128. Find y' if $y = (\ln x)^{\tan x}$.

Answer: $(\ln x)^{\tan x} \left[\frac{\tan x}{x \ln x} + \ln(\ln x) \sec^2 x \right]$ (hard)

129. Find the derivative of $(\ln \sec x)^4$.

Answer: $4 \tan x (\ln \sec x)^3$ (medium)

130. Differentiate and simplify: $y = \ln(x^3 - 2x)$.

Answer: $y' = \frac{3x^2 - 2}{x^3 - 2x}$ (medium)

131. Differentiate and simplify: $f(x) = x^{\sin x}$.

Answer: $f'(x) = x^{\sin x} \left(\frac{1}{x} \sin x + \ln x \cos x \right)$ (medium)

132. Find the area under the curve $y = \frac{1}{x}$ from $x = 1$ to $x = e^2$.

Answer: 2 (medium)

133. Let $f(x) = x^{2x}$. Find the value of $f'(1)$.

A) 2 B) $e - 1$ C) $e^e - 1$ D) $e + 1$
E) e F) e^{e+1} G) e^{e-1} H) e^2

Answer: 2 (hard)

134. Find the value of the integral $\int_0^1 \frac{e^x}{e^x + 1} \, dx$.

A) $e + 1$ B) $\ln(e - 1)$ C) $(e - 1)/2$ D) $\ln[(e + 1)/2]$
E) $\frac{1}{2} \ln(e - 1)$ F) $(e + 1)/2$ G) $\frac{1}{2} \ln(e + 1)$ H) $e - 1$

Answer: $\ln[(e + 1)/2]$ (medium)

135. Let $f(x) = x^{\ln x}$. Find $f'(x)$.

A) $x \ln x$ B) $(\ln x)/x$
C) $2x^{\ln x}(\ln x)/x$ D) $x^{\ln x}(1 + x \ln x)$
E) $x^{\ln x}(1 + (\ln x)/x)$ F) $x^{\ln x}(\ln x + \ln(\ln x))$
G) $x^{\ln x}(x + \ln x)$ H) $x^{\ln x}/\ln x$

Answer: $2x^{\ln x}(\ln x)/x$ (hard)

136. Let $f(x) = (\sin x)^x$. Find the value of $f'(\pi/2)$.

A) 0 B) 1 C) 2 D) $e^{\pi/2}$
E) e^π F) $\pi/2$ G) π H) 2π

Answer: $e^{\pi/2}$ (hard)

137. Let $f(x) = \int_2^{ex} \frac{dt}{\sqrt{\ln t}}$. Find the value of $f'(2)$.

A) e^2 B) $e^2/\sqrt{2}$ C) $1/\left(4e^2\sqrt{2}\right)$ D) $1/\left(4\sqrt{2}\right)$
E) $1/\ln 2$ F) $e/\ln 2$ G) $\sqrt{2}/e$ H) does not exist

Answer: $e^2/\sqrt{2}$ (medium)

138. Find the value of $\int_0^{\ln 2} 3e^{4x}\, dx$.

A) $45/4$ B) 11 C) $43/4$ D) $21/2$
E) $41/4$ F) 10 G) $39/4$ H) $19/2$

Answer: $45/4$ (medium)

139. Let $f(x) = \ln\left(3x^2 + 1 + e^{-x}\right)$. Find the value of $f'(0)$.

A) -1 B) 0 C) $1/2$ D) $-1/2$
E) e^{-1} F) $\sqrt{e}$ G) $1 + \ln 2$ H) $3\ln 2$

Answer: $-1/2$ (medium)

140. Let $f(x) = 2^{3^x}$. Find the value of $f'(1)$.

A) $3\ln 2$ B) $8\ln 2$ C) $24\ln 2$ D) $3\ln 3$
E) $8\ln 3$ F) $24\ln 3$ G) $8\ln 2\ln 3$ H) $24\ln 2\ln 3$

Answer: $24\ln 2\ln 3$ (hard)

141. Let $f(x) = x^{1/x}$. Find the value of $f'(e)$.

A) 0 B) 1 C) 2 D) 3
E) 4 F) 5 G) 6 H) 7

Answer: 0 (medium)

142. Let $f(x) = x^x$. Find the value of $f'(2)$.

A) 1 B) 2 C) 4 D) $\ln 2$
E) $1 + \ln 2$ F) $2(1 + \ln 2)$ G) $4(1 + \ln 2)$ H) $4(1 + \ln 4)$

Answer: $4(1 + \ln 2)$ (medium)

143. Find the absolute minimum of $f(x) = x^x$, $x > 0$.

A) 0 B) 1 C) 4 D) e
E) e^e F) $e^{1/e}$ G) $e^{-1/e}$ H) e^{-e}

Answer: $e^{-1/e}$ (medium)

144. Let $f(x) = 5^{\tan x}$. Find the value of $f'(\pi/4)$.

A) 1 B) 2 C) 5 D) 10
E) $\ln 5$ F) $2 \ln 5$ G) $5 \ln 5$ H) $10 \ln 5$

Answer: $10 \ln 5$ (medium)

145. Find an equation of the tangent line to the curve $y = e^{-x}$ which is perpendicular to the line $2x - y = 8$.

A) $x + y = 1$ B) $x + y = 2$ C) $x + y = \ln 2$
D) $x + 2y = 1$ E) $x + 2y = 2$ F) $x + 2y = \ln 2$
G) $x + 2y = 1 + \ln 2$ H) $x + 2y = 2 + \ln 2$

Answer: $x + 2y = 1 + \ln 2$ (hard)

146. Let $f(x) = x^{\tan x}$. Find the value of $f'(x)$.

A) $x^{\tan x} \ln x$ B) $x^{\tan x} \sec^2 x$
C) $x^{\tan x} \sec^2 x \ln x$ D) $x^{\tan x} \tan x$
E) $x^{\tan x} \left(\sec^2 x \ln x + \tan x \right)$ F) $x^{\tan x} \left(\sec^2 x \ln x + (\tan x/x) \right)$
G) $x^{\tan x} \left(\sec^2 x + \ln x \right)$ H) $x^{\tan x} \left(\sec^2 x + \ln x \tan x \right)$

Answer: $x^{\tan x} \left(\sec^2 x \ln x + (\tan x/x) \right)$ (hard)

147. Let $f(x) = (\ln x)^x$. Find $f'(x)$.

A) x^{-x} B) $1/\left(x^{x-1} \right)$ C) $(\ln x)^x \ln x$
D) $(\ln x)^x \ln \ln x$ E) $(\ln x)^{x-1}$ F) $(\ln x)(\ln \ln x)$
G) $(\ln x)^x (\ln x + 1)$ H) $(\ln x)^x (\ln \ln x + (1/\ln x))$

Answer: $(\ln x)^x (\ln \ln x + (1/\ln x))$ (hard)

148. Find an equation of the tangent to the curve $y = e^{2x}$ that is perpendicular to the line $x + 4y = 3$.

A) $x - 4y = \ln 3$ B) $4x - y = 3$
C) $x + 2y = \ln 3$ D) $4x + y = \ln 3$
E) $4x - y = 2 \ln 2 - 2$ F) $4x + y = 3 + 3 \ln 3$
G) $4x - y = 2 + 4 \ln 3$ H) $4x - y = 1 + \ln 2$

Answer: $4x - y = 2 \ln 2 - 2$ (hard)

149. Let $f(x) = x^{\sqrt{x}}$. Find the value of $f'(4)$.

A) 2 B) 4 C) 8 D) 16
E) $2 + \ln 4$ F) $4 + \ln 2$ G) $8 + 4 \ln 4$ H) $16 + 4 \ln 2$

Answer: $8 + 4 \ln 4$ (medium)

150. Let R be the region bounded by $y = \ln x$, $y = 0$, and $x = e$. Find the area of R integrating with <u>respect</u> <u>to</u> y.

Answer: 1   (medium)

151. Mr. Spock has accidentally injected himself with the dangerous drug cordrazine. He quickly calculates that the concentration (y), in parts per million, of the drug in his blood t minutes after the injection is given by:
$$y = e^{-t} - e^{-2t}$$
a) At what time will the concentration reach its maximum value?
b) What will the maximum concentration be?

Answer: a) $t = \ln 2$ b) 0.25 ppm   (hard)

Chapter 6, Section 2*
The Natural Logarithmic Function

152. Find the domain of the function $f(x) = \ln(\ln(\ln x))$.

A) $(0, \infty)$ B) $[1, \infty)$ C) $(1, \infty)$ D) $[e, \infty)$
E) (e, ∞) F) $(-\infty, 0)$ G) $(-\infty, 1)$ H) $(-\infty, e)$

Answer: (e, ∞) (medium)

153. Let $f(x) = \frac{\ln x}{x}$. Find the interval on which f is concave upward.

A) $(1/2) \ln 2$ B) $1/\ln 2$ C) 2 D) $\ln 2$
E) $1/2$ F) 1 G) $2 \ln 2$ H) 0

Answer: $\ln 2$ (medium)

154. Find the value of the integral $\int_0^1 \frac{x}{1+x^2}\, dx$.

A) 1 B) $\frac{1}{2} \ln 2$ C) $2 \ln 2$ D) $1/\ln 2$
E) $\ln 2$ F) $1/2$ G) 2 H) 0

Answer: $\frac{1}{2} \ln 2$ (medium)

155. Let $f(x) = x \ln(x^2 - 3)$. Find the value of $f'(2)$.

A) 0 B) 2 C) 4 D) 6
E) 8 F) 10 G) 12 H) 14

Answer: 8 (medium)

156. Find the interval on which the graph of $f(x) = \ln(x^2 + 1)$ is concave upward.

A) $(-1, 1)$ B) $(-1, 2)$ C) $(-2, 1)$ D) $(-2, 2)$
E) $(-1, 3)$ F) $(-3, 2)$ G) $(-3, 3)$ H) $(-\infty, \infty)$

Answer: $(-1, 1)$ (medium)

157. Find y' if $y = \ln\sqrt{\frac{4x-7}{x^2+2x}}$.

Answer: $\frac{2}{4x-7} - \frac{x+1}{x^2+2x}$ (medium)

158. If $y = \frac{(x+3)\,(x^2+1)^3(x+1)^2}{(x^2+10)^{1/2}}$, find y' by logarithmic differentiation.

Answer: $\left(\frac{1}{x+3} + \frac{6x}{x^2+1} + \frac{2}{x+1} - \frac{x}{x^2+10}\right) \cdot \frac{(x+3)\,(x^2+1)^3(x+1)^2}{(x^2+10)^{1/2}}$ (hard)

159. Find $\frac{dy}{dx}$ if $y = \ln\left(\frac{\tan x}{x^2+1}\right)$.

Answer: $\frac{\sec^2 x}{\tan x} - \frac{2x}{x^2+1}$ (medium)

160. Find the derivative of $(\ln \sec x)^4$.

Answer: $4 \tan x(\ln \sec x)^3$ (medium)

161. Find the value of the limit $\lim\limits_{x \to \infty} \frac{\ln x}{\ln \sqrt{x+10}}$.

A) 1/2   B) ∞ C) 1/11   D) 0
E) 1/10   F) $\ln 2$ G) 2   H) 1

Answer: 2 (medium)

162. Find the value of the limit $\lim\limits_{x \to 0^+} \frac{\ln x}{x}$.

A) $-\infty$ B) -1 C) 0   D) $1/e$
E) 1   F) e G) $e^{1/e}$ H) ∞

Answer: $-\infty$ (medium)

163. Find the value of the limit $\lim\limits_{x \to 1^+} e^{1/(x-1)}$.

A) $-\infty$ B) -2 C) -1 D) 0
E) 1/2   F) 1   G) 3/2   H) ∞

Answer: ∞ (medium)

164. Make a rough sketch of the graph of $y = \ln\left(\frac{1}{x}\right)$. Do not use a calculator. Just use the graphs given in your text and any needed transformations.

Answer: 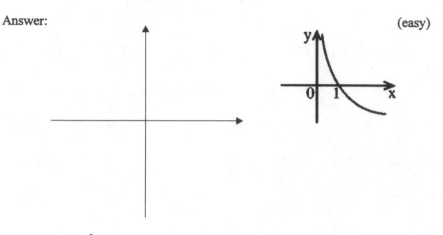 (easy)

165. Let $f(x) = \ln(x^2)$. Find the value of $f'(1)$.

A) 2^e B) e^2 C) $\ln(1/2)$ D) 2
E) $e^{-1/2}$ F) $1/\ln 2$ G) $1/2$ H) $e^{1/2}$

Answer: 2 (medium)

166. Let $f(x) = \ln(\ln(x))$. Find the value of $f'(e)$.

A) $1/e^2$ B) e^2 C) $1 + e$ D) $1/e$
E) $\ln 2$ F) 1   G) e H) 0

Answer: $1/e$ (medium)

167. Let $f(x) = \ln(\ln(x))$. Find the value of $f''(e)$.

A) $2e^{-1}$ B) e^{-1} C) $-e^{-1}$ D) $-e^{-2}$
E) $-2e^{-2}$ F) e^{-2} G) $-2e^{-1}$ H) $2e^{-2}$

Answer: $-2e^{-2}$ (hard)

168. Find the value of the integral $\int_1^e \frac{1}{x}\, dx$.

A) 1   B) e C) $1/2$ D) -1
E) -2 F) $-1/2$ G) $\sqrt{e}$ H) 2

Answer: 1 (easy)

169. Find the value of the integral $\int_1^{\sqrt{e}} \frac{1}{x}\, dx$.

A) 2   B) -2 C) $-1/2$ D) e
E) $\sqrt{e}$ F) 1   G) $1/2$ H) $\sqrt{e}/2$

Answer: $1/2$ (medium)

170. Find the value of $\int_e^{e^2} \frac{\ln x}{x} \, dx$.

A) $\ln 2$ B) $\frac{1}{2} \ln 2$ C) $1/2$ D) $3/2$

E) 1 F) $1/\ln 2$ G) 0 H) $2 \ln 2$

Answer: $3/2$ (medium)

171. Let $f(x) = \frac{\ln x}{x}$. Find the interval on which f is decreasing.

A) $(0, 1/e]$ B) $(0, 1]$ C) $(0, 2]$ D) $(1/e, 1]$

E) $[1/e, 2]$ F) $[1/e, e]$ G) $[1/e, \infty)$ H) $[e, \infty)$

Answer: $[e, \infty)$ (medium)

172. Let $f(x) = \frac{\ln x}{x}$. Find the maximum value of f.

A) 0 B) $1/e$ C) 1 D) e

E) $e^{1/e}$ F) e^e G) e^{-e} H) e^2

Answer: $1/e$ (medium)

173. Let $f(x) = \frac{\ln x}{x}$. Find the interval on which f is concave upward.

A) $(0, 1/e]$ B) $(0, 1)$ C) $(0, e)$ D) $(1/e, e)$

E) $(1, e)$ F) $(\sqrt{e}, \infty)$ G) (e, ∞) H) $\left(e^{3/2}, \infty\right)$

Answer: $\left(e^{3/2}, \infty\right)$ (hard)

174. Find the value of the integral $\int_{-e^2}^{-e} \frac{3}{x} \, dx$.

A) -3 B) $-e$ C) e^3 D) $1/3$

E) $\ln 2$ F) $-\ln 3$ G) $e - \ln 3$ H) $e^2 - \ln 3$

Answer: -3 (medium)

175. Find the value of the integral $\int_e^{e^4} \frac{dx}{x\sqrt{\ln x}}$.

A) 0 B) 1 C) 2 D) 3

E) 4 F) 5 G) 6 H) 7

Answer: 2 (medium)

176. Let $f(x) = \sqrt{x} \ln x$. Find the interval on which f is increasing.

A) $(0, \infty)$ B) $(0, 1]$ C) $[1, \infty)$ D) $(0, e^{-1}]$

E) $[e^{-1}, \infty)$ F) $(0, e^{-2}]$ G) $[e^{-2}, \infty)$ H) $(0, \sqrt{e})$

Answer: $[e^{-2}, \infty)$ (medium)

177. Let $f(x) = \sqrt{x} \ln x$. Find the interval on which f is concave upward.

   A) $(0, \infty)$ B) $(0, 1)$ C) $(1, \infty)$ D) $(0, e^{-1})$
   E) (e^{-1}, ∞) F) $(0, e^{-2})$ G) (e^{-2}, ∞) H) (e, ∞)

   Answer: $(0, 1)$ (hard)

178. Find the minimum value of the function $f(x) = x \ln x$.

   A) $-e$ B) -1 C) $-1/e$ D) 0
   E) e F) $e^{1/e}$ G) e^e H) e^{-e}

   Answer: $-1/e$ (medium)

179. Let $f(x) = \ln(\ln(\ln x))$. Find the value of $f'(e^2)$.

   A) $1/\ln 2$ B) $1/\ln 4$ C) $1/\ln 8$ D) $1/e$
   E) $1/e^2$ F) $1/(e^2 \ln 2)$ G) $1/(e^2 \ln 4)$ H) $1/(e^2 \ln 8)$

   Answer: $1/(e^2 \ln 4)$ (medium)

180. Use logarithmic differentiation to find $\frac{dy}{dx}$ if $y = x^{e^x}$.

   Answer: $x^{e^x}(e^x)\left(\frac{1}{x} + \ln x\right)$ (medium)

181. Find the area under the curve $y = \frac{1}{x}$ from $x = 1$ to $x = e^2$.

   Answer: 2 (medium)

182. Let $f(x) = \ln(3x^2 + 1 + e^{-x})$. Find the value of $f'(0)$.

   A) -1 B) 0 C) $1/2$ D) $-1/2$
   E) e^{-1} F) $\sqrt{e}$ G) $1 + \ln 2$ H) $3 \ln 2$

   Answer: $-1/2$ (medium)

183. Use the laws of logarithms to expand $\ln \sqrt{\frac{x^2 y^3}{z^4}}$.

   Answer: $\ln x + \frac{3}{2} \ln y - 2 \ln z$ (easy)

184. Use the laws of logarithms to expand $\ln \left(\frac{a^9}{b^3 c^4 d^4 e}\right)^{3/4}$.

   Answer: $\frac{27}{4} \ln a - \frac{9}{4} \ln b - 3 \ln c - 4 \ln d - \frac{3}{4} \ln e$ (medium)

185. Find the value of the integral $\int_0^{\pi/12} \frac{\sin(4x)}{\cos(4x)} \, dx$.

   Answer: $\frac{1}{4} \ln 2$ (medium)

186. Find the value of the integral $\int_{-\pi/6}^{\pi/6} \frac{\sec(4x)}{\csc(4x)} \, dx$.

Answer: 0 (hard)

187. Find the value of the integral $\int \frac{\csc^2 x}{3+\cot x} \, dx$.

Answer: $-\ln(3+\cot x)$ (medium)

188. Find y' if $y = \sqrt{\frac{(x-4)^3(x+5)^2}{(x+2)^2}}$.

Answer: $\frac{1}{2}\left(\frac{3}{x-4} + \frac{2}{x+5} - \frac{2}{x+2}\right)\sqrt{\frac{(x-4)^3(x+5)^2}{(x+2)^2}}$ (medium)

189. Find the integral $\int \frac{e^x}{e^x+4} \, dx$.

Answer: $\ln(e^x+4) + C$ (medium)

190. Find y' if $y = \sqrt[4]{\frac{x^2(x+3)^3}{(x-7)^2(x+5)^2}}$.

Answer: $\frac{1}{4}\left(\frac{2}{x} + \frac{3}{x+3} - \frac{2}{x-7} - \frac{2}{x+5}\right)\sqrt[4]{\frac{x^2(x+3)^3}{(x-7)^2(x+5)^2}}$ (medium)

Chapter 6, Section 3*
The Natural Exponential Function

191. Let $f(x) = e^{-x}$. Find the value of $f'(1)$.

A) $2e$ B) e C) $2e^{-1}$ D) $-2e$
E) e^{-1} F) $-e$ G) $-2e^{-1}$ H) $-e^{-1}$

Answer: $-e^{-1}$ (easy)

192. Let $f(x) = e^{-x^2}$. Find the value of $f'(1)$.

A) $2e^{-1}$ B) $2e$ C) $-2e$ D) $-e$
E) e F) $-2e^{-1}$ G) e^{-1} H) $-e^{-1}$

Answer: $-2e^{-1}$ (medium)

193. Let $f(x) = e^{x^2}$. Find the value of $f''(0)$.

A) e B) 1 C) -1 D) e^{-1}
E) -2 F) $2e^{-1}$ G) $2e$ H) 2

Answer: 2 (medium)

194. Let $f(x) = e^{\ln 2x}$. Find the value of $f'(\pi)$.

A) 1
B) 2
C) 2π
D) -1
E) -2π
F) 0
G) -2
H) π

Answer: 2 (medium)

195. Let $f(x) = e^{e^x}$. Find the value of $f'(1)$.

A) e^{e+2}
B) e^e
C) e^{e-1}
D) e^{e-2}
E) e
F) e^{e+1}
G) e^2
H) $2e^2$

Answer: e^{e+1} (hard)

196. Find the value of the integral $\int_0^1 xe^{-x^2}\,dx$.

A) $-e/2$
B) $e/2$
C) $(1-e^{-1})/2$
D) e
E) $-e$
F) $-e^{-1}$
G) $e^{-1}/2$
H) e^{-1}

Answer: $(1-e^{-1})/2$ (medium)

197. How many points of inflection does $f(x) = x^3 e^{-x}$ have?

A) 0
B) 1
C) 2
D) 3
E) 4
F) 5
G) 6
H) infinitely many

Answer: 3 (hard)

198. Find the absolute maximum of the function $f(x) = \frac{e^{-x}}{1+x^2}$.

A) 4/3
B) 1
C) e^{-1}
D) $e^{-1}/2$
E) 2
F) 1/2
G) 3/2
H) no absolute maximum

Answer: no absolute maximum (medium)

199. Find the interval on which $f(x) = xe^{-x}$ is increasing.

A) $(-\infty, 1]$
B) $(-\infty, 2]$
C) $(-\infty, 3]$
D) $[1, 2]$
E) $[1, e]$
F) $(-\infty, e]$
G) $(-\infty, \infty)$
H) $(-\infty, 1/e]$

Answer: $(-\infty, 1]$ (medium)

200. Find the interval on which $f(x) = xe^{-x}$ is concave upward.

A) $(-\infty, 0)$
B) $(-\infty, 1)$
C) $(-\infty, 2)$
D) $(0, 1)$
E) $(1, 2)$
F) $(1, \infty)$
G) $(2, \infty)$
H) $(-\infty, \infty)$

Answer: $(2, \infty)$ (medium)

201. Find the interval on which the function $f(x) = e^x/x$ is increasing.

A) $(-\infty, -1]$ B) $(-\infty, 0)$ C) $[-1, 1]$ D) $(0, 1/e]$
E) $[1/e, 1]$ F) $(0, e]$ G) $[1/e, \infty)$ H) $[1, \infty)$

Answer: $[1, \infty)$ (medium)

202. On the domain $(0, \infty)$ find the minimum value of $f(x) = e^x/x$.

A) 0 B) $1/e^2$ C) $1/e$ D) 1
E) $e - 1$ F) e G) $e^2 - 1$ H) e^2

Answer: e (medium)

203. Let $f(x) = e^x/x$. Find $f''(x)$.

A) $e^x(x+4)/x^4$ B) $e^x(x^2-1)/x^4$
C) $e^x(x^2+x)/x^4$ D) $e^x(x^2+3)/x^4$
E) $e^x(x-2)/x^3$ F) $e^x(x^2+5x)/x^3$
G) $e^x(x^2-2x+2)/x^3$ H) $e^x(x^3-4x^2+3)/x^3$

Answer: $e^x(x^2 - 2x + 2)/x^3$ (medium)

204. Find y' if $y = e^{\sqrt{x^3+1}}$.

Answer: $\dfrac{3x^2 e^{\sqrt{x^3+1}}}{2\sqrt{x^3+1}}$ (medium)

205. Find $\frac{dy}{dx}$ if $y = e^{xy} + e^{99}$

Answer: $\dfrac{dy}{dx} = \dfrac{ye^{xy}}{1 - xe^{xy}}$ (medium)

206. Find y' if $y = xe^{(x^2+7)}$.

Answer: $2x^2 e^{x^2+7} + e^{x^2+7}$ (medium)

207. Evaluate the integral: $\int xe^{x^2}\, dx$.

Answer: $\frac{1}{2} e^{x^2} + C$ (easy)

208. Evaluate the integral: $\int e^{\frac{1}{x}x^2}\, dx$

Answer: $-e^{\frac{1}{x}} + C$ (medium)

209. Evaluate the integral: $\int e^x \sin(e^x)\, dx$

Answer: $-\cos(e^x) + C$ (easy)

210. Find $f(x)$ if $f''(x) = 3e^x + 5\sin x$, $f(0) = 1$, and $f'(0) = 2$.

Answer: $f(x) = 3e^x - 5\sin x + 4x - 2$ (medium)

211. Find the value of the limit $\lim\limits_{x \to 0^-} e^{\cot x}$.

    A) $-\infty$ B) $-e$ C) -1 D) 0
    E) 1 F) e G) ∞ H) does not exist

Answer: 0 (medium)

212. Find the value of the limit $\lim\limits_{x \to -\infty} \frac{e^x}{x}$.

    A) $-\infty$ B) $-e$ C) -1 D) 0
    E) e^{-1} F) 1 G) e H) ∞

Answer: 0 (medium)

213. Find the value of the limit $\lim\limits_{x \to 0^+} \frac{e^x}{x}$.

    A) $-\infty$ B) $-e$ C) -1 D) 0
    E) e^{-1} F) 1 G) e H) ∞

Answer: ∞ (medium)

214. Find the value of the limit $\lim\limits_{x \to 0^-} \frac{e^x}{x}$.

    A) $-\infty$ B) $-e$ C) -1 D) 0
    E) e^{-1} F) 1 G) e H) ∞

Answer: $-\infty$ (medium)

215. Find the value of $\ln e$.

    A) -1 B) $1/\sqrt{e}$ C) e D) 0
    E) $\sqrt{e}$ F) $1/e$ G) 1 H) $-e$

Answer: 1 (easy)

216. Find the value of $\ln \sqrt{e^3}$.

    A) $2/3$ B) $\sqrt{e}$ C) $e^3/2$ D) $3/2$
    E) e^3 F) $e^3 - 2$ G) $2e/3$ H) $2/e^3$

Answer: $3/2$ (medium)

217. Find the value of $e^{\ln 8}$.

    A) 3 B) 8 C) 1 D) 2
    E) $1/8$ F) $1/3$ G) e^3 H) 4

Answer: 8 (easy)

218. Find the value of the limit $\lim\limits_{x \to \infty} \frac{e^x}{e^x + 10}$.

A) 1   B) ln 10   C) $1/\ln 10$ D) 10
E) $1/10$ F) 0   G) ln $(1/10)$ H) -1

Answer: 1 (medium)

219. Solve the equation $e^{2x-2} = 4$.

A) ln 2   B) $1 - \ln 2$ C) $1 + \ln 2$ D) $1 - 2\ln 2$
E) $1 + 2\ln 2$ F) $2 + \ln 2$ G) $2 - \ln 2$ H) $2 - 2\ln 2$

Answer: $1 + \ln 2$ (medium)

220. Solve the equation $e^{2x-4} = 16$.

A) ln 2   B) $-\ln 2$ C) $1 + \ln 2$ D) $1 - \ln 2$
E) $1 + 2\ln 2$ F) $1 - 2\ln 2$ G) $2 + 2\ln 2$ H) $2 - 2\ln 2$

Answer: $2 + 2\ln 2$ (medium)

221. Find the value of the limit $\lim\limits_{x \to 0^-} \frac{1}{1 + e^{1/x}}$.

A) 1   B) $1/2$ C) 0   D) ∞
E) $-\infty$ F) -1 G) $-1/2$ H) 2

Answer: 1 (medium)

222. Solve the equation $e^{x-2} = 4$.

A) ln 2   B) $-\ln 2$ C) $1 + \ln 2$ D) $1 - \ln 2$
E) $1 + 2\ln 2$ F) $1 - 2\ln 2$ G) $2 + 2\ln 2$ H) $2 - 2\ln 2$

Answer: $2 + 2\ln 2$ (medium)

223. Solve the equation $e^{x-1} = 4$.

A) ln 2   B) $-\ln 2$ C) $1 + \ln 2$ D) $1 - \ln 2$
E) $1 + 2\ln 2$ F) $1 - 2\ln 2$ G) $2 + 2\ln 2$ H) $2 - 2\ln 2$

Answer: $1 + 2\ln 2$ (medium)

224. Find $f^{-1}(x)$ for $f(x) = \sqrt{e^x + 2}$.

Answer: $f^{-1}(x) = \ln\left(x^2 - 2\right)$ (medium)

225. Find the range of the function $e^{\sin x}$.

A) $[-1, 1]$
B) $[e^{-\pi/2}, e^{\pi/2}]$
C) $[0, e]$
D) $[0, 1]$
E) $[-e, e]$
F) $[e^{-\pi}, e^{\pi}]$
G) $[e^{-1}, e]$
H) $[0, e^{\pi/2}]$

Answer: $[e^{-1}, e]$ (easy)

226. Find the value of the integral $\int_0^1 \frac{e^x}{e^x+1}\,dx$.

A) $e+1$
B) $\ln(e-1)$
C) $(e-1)/2$
D) $\ln[(e+1)/2]$
E) $\frac{1}{2}\ln(e-1)$
F) $(e+1)/2$
G) $\frac{1}{2}\ln(e+1)$
H) $e-1$

Answer: $\ln[(e+1)/2]$ (medium)

227. Find the value of $\int_0^{\ln 2} 3e^{4x}\,dx$.

A) $45/4$
B) 11
C) $43/4$
D) $21/2$
E) $41/4$
F) 10
G) $39/4$
H) $19/2$

Answer: $45/4$ (medium)

228. Find an equation of the tangent line to the curve $y = e^{-x}$ which is perpendicular to the line $2x - y = 8$.

A) $x + y = 1$
B) $x + y = 2$
C) $x + y = \ln 2$
D) $x + 2y = 1$
E) $x + 2y = 2$
F) $x + 2y = \ln 2$
G) $x + 2y = 1 + \ln 2$
H) $x + 2y = 2 + \ln 2$

Answer: $x + 2y = 1 + \ln 2$ (hard)

229. Find an equation of the tangent to the curve $y = e^{2x}$ that is perpendicular to the line $x + 4y = 3$.

A) $x - 4y = \ln 3$
B) $4x - y = 3$
C) $x + 2y = \ln 3$
D) $4x + y = \ln 3$
E) $4x - y = 2\ln 2 - 2$
F) $4x + y = 3 + 3\ln 3$
G) $4x - y = 2 + 4\ln 3$
H) $4x - y = 1 + \ln 2$

Answer: $4x - y = 2\ln 2 - 2$ (hard)

230. Let R be the region bounded by $y = \ln x$, $y = 0$, and $x = e$. Find the area of R integrating with <u>respect to</u> y.

Answer: 1 (medium)

231. Mr. Spock has accidentally injected himself with the dangerous drug cordrazine. He quickly calculates that the concentration (y), in parts per million, of the drug in his blood t minutes after the injection is given by:

$$y = e^{-t} - e^{-2t}$$

a) At what time will the concentration reach its maximum value?
b) What will the maximum concentration be?

Answer: a) $t = \ln 2$ b) 0.25 ppm (hard)

Chapter 6, Section 4[*]
General Logarithmic and Exponential Functions

232. For what value of x is $2^x = (1/2)^x$?

A) $\sqrt{2}$ B) 2   C) $-\sqrt{2}$ D) -2
E) 1   F) 0   G) $1/2$ H) -1

Answer: 0 (easy)

233. Find the minimum value of $2^{|x|}$.

A) $-\sqrt{2}$ B) $1/2$ C) 2   D) -2
E) 0   F) 1   G) -1 H) $\sqrt{2}$

Answer: 1 (easy)

234. Find the value of the limit $\lim\limits_{x \to \infty} (\pi/4)^x$.

A) π B) ∞ C) 0   D) -1
E) 1   F) $\pi/4$ G) $-\pi$ H) $-\infty$

Answer: 0 (medium)

235. Find the value of the limit $\lim\limits_{x \to \infty} 4^{(x+1)/x}$.

A) ∞ B) $-1/4$ C) $1/4$ D) 0
E) -4 F) 4   G) 2   H) -2

Answer: 4 (medium)

236. Find the value of the limit $\lim\limits_{x \to 0^+} 4^{(x+1)/x}$.

A) 0   B) -4 C) $1/4$ D) -2
E) 4   F) 2   G) ∞ H) $-1/4$

Answer: ∞ (medium)

237. Find the value of the limit $\lim\limits_{x \to 0^-} 4^{(x+1)/x}$.

A) 4   B) -2 C) ∞ D) $-1/4$
E) 1/4   F) -4 G) 2   H) 0

Answer: 0 (medium)

238. Find the value of the limit $\lim\limits_{x \to 3^-} 2^{1/(x-3)}$.

A) $-\infty$ B) -2 C) -1 D) 0
E) 1/2   F) 1   G) 3/2   H) ∞

Answer: 0 (medium)

239. If $0 < a < 1$, find the value of the limit $\lim\limits_{x \to \infty} a^x$.

A) ∞ B) 1   C) a D) $1/a$
E) $\sqrt{a}$ F) a^2 G) 0   H) $-\infty$

Answer: 0 (easy)

240. Find the value of the limit $\lim\limits_{x \to 2^+} 3^{1/(2-x)}$.

A) $-\infty$ B) -2 C) -1 D) 0
E) 1/2   F) 1   G) 3/2   H) ∞

Answer: 0 (medium)

241. Make a rough sketch of the graph of $y = (1.1)^x$. Do not use a calculator. Use the basic graphs from Section 6.1 and any needed transformations.

Answer: (easy)

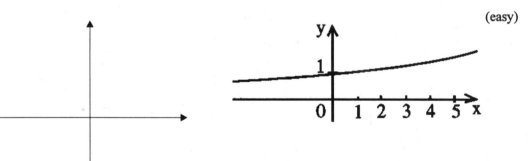

242. Make a rough sketch of the graph of $y = 2^{x+1}$. Do not use a calculator. Use the basic graphs from Section 6.1 and any needed transformations.

Answer: (easy)

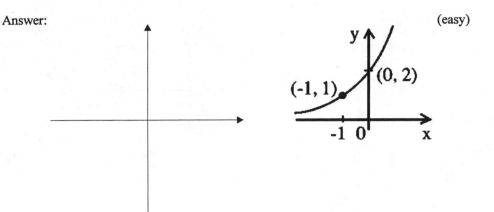

243. Make a rough sketch of the graph of $y = -3^x$. Do not use a calculator. Use the basic graphs from Section 6.1 and any needed transformations.

Answer: (medium)

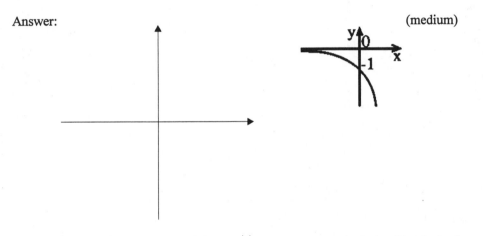

244. Make a rough sketch of the graph of $y = 2^{|x|}$. Do not use a calculator. Use the basic graphs from Section 6.1 and any needed transformations.

Answer: (medium)

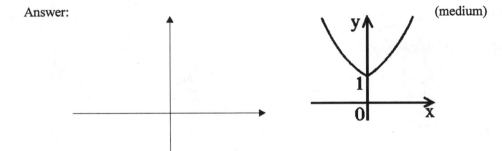

245. Make a rough sketch of the graph of $y = 2 + 5\left(1 - 10^{-x}\right)$. Do not use a calculator. Use the basic graphs from Section 6.1 and any needed transformations.

Answer: (medium)

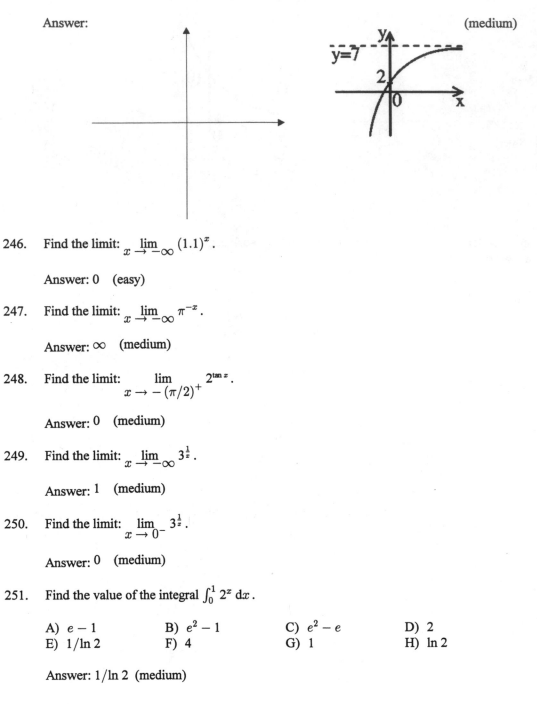

246. Find the limit: $\displaystyle \lim_{x \to -\infty} (1.1)^x$.

Answer: 0   (easy)

247. Find the limit: $\displaystyle \lim_{x \to -\infty} \pi^{-x}$.

Answer: ∞ (medium)

248. Find the limit: $\displaystyle \lim_{x \to -(\pi/2)^+} 2^{\tan x}$.

Answer: 0   (medium)

249. Find the limit: $\displaystyle \lim_{x \to -\infty} 3^{\frac{1}{x}}$.

Answer: 1   (medium)

250. Find the limit: $\displaystyle \lim_{x \to 0^-} 3^{\frac{1}{x}}$.

Answer: 0   (medium)

251. Find the value of the integral $\int_0^1 2^x \, dx$.

A) $e - 1$ B) $e^2 - 1$ C) $e^2 - e$ D) 2
E) $1/\ln 2$ F) 4   G) 1   H) $\ln 2$

Answer: $1/\ln 2$ (medium)

252. From the choices below, pick the limit whose value is e.

A) $\lim_{x \to 0} (1 + x)^x$

B) $\lim_{x \to 0} (1 + x)^{1/x}$

C) $\lim_{x \to 0} \left(1 + \frac{1}{x}\right)^x$

D) $\lim_{x \to 0} \left(1 + \frac{1}{x}\right)^{1/x}$

E) $\lim_{x \to 0} x^{1+(1/x)}$

F) $\lim_{x \to 0} x^{1/x}$

G) $\lim_{x \to 0} x^x$

H) $\lim_{x \to \infty} x^{\ln x}$

Answer: $\lim_{x \to 0} (1 + x)^{1/x}$ (medium)

253. Find the value of the limit $\lim_{x \to 0} (1 + x)^{1/x}$.

A) 1   B) $1/e$ C) $e - 1$ D) $e^2 - 1$
E) $e + 1$ F) e G) $1/(e - 1)$ H) $1/(e + 1)$

Answer: e (easy)

254. Find the value of $\log_2 1$.

A) -1 B) $-1/2$ C) 0   D) 10^2
E) 1   F) $1/2$ G) 2   H) -2

Answer: 0 (easy)

255. Find the value of $\log_2 16$.

A) $1/8$ B) 3   C) 2   D) 0
E) $1/4$ F) 4   G) 1   H) $1/2$

Answer: 4 (easy)

256. Find the value of $\log_{16} 2$.

A) $1/2$ B) 2   C) 4   D) 1
E) 3   F) 0   G) $1/8$ H) $1/4$

Answer: 1/4 (medium)

257. Find the value of $\log_2 e - \log_2 (e/16)$.

A) -2 B) e^{-2} C) 4   D) e^{16}
E) -4 F) e^2 G) 2   H) e^{-16}

Answer: 4 (medium)

258. Solve the equation $\log_2(\ln x) = 1$.

    A) 2^e B) $2e$ C) $e/2$ D) 1
    E) $\sqrt{e}$ F) $1/e$ G) $2/e$ H) e^2

Answer: e^2 (medium)

259. Find the value of $\log_{32} 8$.

Answer: $\frac{3}{5}$ (easy)

260. Find the value of $25^{\log_5 10}$.

Answer: 100 (easy)

261. Make a rough sketch of the graph of $y = 1 + \log_5(x - 1)$. Do not use a calculator. Just use the graphs given in your text and any needed transformations.

Answer: (easy)

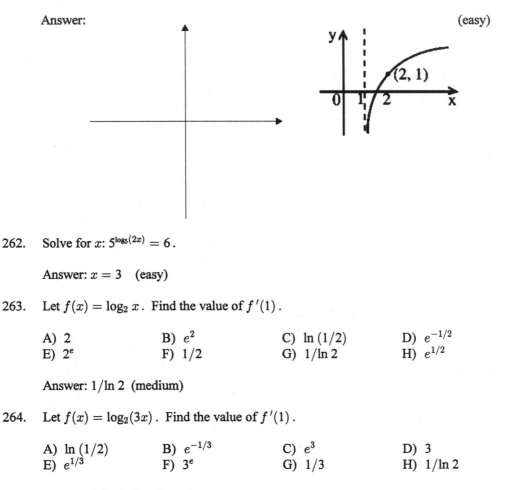

262. Solve for x: $5^{\log_5(2x)} = 6$.

Answer: $x = 3$ (easy)

263. Let $f(x) = \log_2 x$. Find the value of $f'(1)$.

    A) 2 B) e^2 C) $\ln(1/2)$ D) $e^{-1/2}$
    E) 2^e F) $1/2$ G) $1/\ln 2$ H) $e^{1/2}$

Answer: $1/\ln 2$ (medium)

264. Let $f(x) = \log_2(3x)$. Find the value of $f'(1)$.

    A) $\ln(1/2)$ B) $e^{-1/3}$ C) e^3 D) 3
    E) $e^{1/3}$ F) 3^e G) $1/3$ H) $1/\ln 2$

Answer: $1/\ln 2$ (hard)

265. Find y' if $y = (\sqrt{x})^x$, $x > 0$.

Answer: $\frac{(\sqrt{x})^x}{2}(1 + \ln x)$ (medium)

266. Find $\frac{dy}{dx}$ for $y = 3^{x^2} + e^\pi + (1 + x^2)^{\sqrt{2}}$

Answer: $3^{x^2} + \sqrt{2}(1 + x^2)^{(\sqrt{2}-1)}(2x)$ (medium)

267. Find $\frac{dy}{dx}$ for $y = (1 + x^2)^{x^3} + \sin x$.

Answer: $(1 + x^2)^{x^3}\left[3x^2 \ln(1 + x^2) + \frac{2x^4}{1+x^2}\right] + \cos x$ (hard)

268. Find the derivative y' for $y = 3^x$.

Answer: $(\ln 3) \cdot 3^x$ (easy)

269. Find the derivative y' for $y = x^x$.

Answer: $(1 + \ln x) \cdot x^x$ (medium)

270. Find y' if $y = (\ln x)^{\tan x}$.

Answer: $(\ln x)^{\tan x}\left[\frac{\tan x}{x \ln x} + \ln(\ln x) \sec^2 x\right]$ (hard)

271. Differentiate and simplify: $f(x) = x^{\sin x}$.

Answer: $f'(x) = x^{\sin x}\left(\frac{1}{x} \sin x + \ln x \cos x\right)$ (medium)

272. Let $f(x) = x^{2x}$. Find the value of $f'(1)$.

A) 2   B) $e - 1$ C) $e^e - 1$ D) $e + 1$
E) e F) e^{e+1} G) e^{e-1} H) e^2

Answer: 2 (hard)

273. Let $f(x) = x^{\ln x}$. Find $f'(x)$.

A) $x \ln x$ B) $(\ln x)/x$
C) $2x^{\ln x}(\ln x)/x$ D) $x^{\ln x}(1 + x \ln x)$
E) $x^{\ln x}(1 + (\ln x)/x)$ F) $x^{\ln x}(\ln x + \ln(\ln x))$
G) $x^{\ln x}(x + \ln x)$ H) $x^{\ln x}/\ln x$

Answer: $2x^{\ln x}(\ln x)/x$ (hard)

274. Let $f(x) = (\sin x)^x$. Find the value of $f'(\pi/2)$.

A) 0   B) 1   C) 2   D) $e^{\pi/2}$
E) e^π F) $\pi/2$ G) π H) 2π

Answer: $e^{\pi/2}$ (hard)

275. Let $f(x) = 2^{3^x}$. Find the value of $f'(1)$.

    A) $3 \ln 2$ B) $8 \ln 2$ C) $24 \ln 2$ D) $3 \ln 3$
    E) $8 \ln 3$ F) $24 \ln 3$ G) $8 \ln 2 \ln 3$ H) $24 \ln 2 \ln 3$

Answer: $24 \ln 2 \ln 3$ (hard)

276. Let $f(x) = x^{1/x}$. Find the value of $f'(e)$.

    A) 0 B) 1 C) 2 D) 3
    E) 4 F) 5 G) 6 H) 7

Answer: 0 (medium)

277. Let $f(x) = x^x$. Find the value of $f'(2)$.

    A) 1 B) 2 C) 4 D) $\ln 2$
    E) $1 + \ln 2$ F) $2(1 + \ln 2)$ G) $4(1 + \ln 2)$ H) $4(1 + \ln 4)$

Answer: $4(1 + \ln 2)$ (medium)

278. Find the absolute minimum of $f(x) = x^x$, $x > 0$.

    A) 0 B) 1 C) 4 D) e
    E) e^e F) $e^{1/e}$ G) $e^{-1/e}$ H) e^{-e}

Answer: $e^{-1/e}$ (medium)

279. Let $f(x) = 5^{\tan x}$. Find the value of $f'(\pi/4)$.

    A) 1 B) 2 C) 5 D) 10
    E) $\ln 5$ F) $2 \ln 5$ G) $5 \ln 5$ H) $10 \ln 5$

Answer: $10 \ln 5$ (medium)

280. Let $f(x) = x^{\tan x}$. Find the value of $f'(x)$.

    A) $x^{\tan x} \ln x$ B) $x^{\tan x} \sec^2 x$
    C) $x^{\tan x} \sec^2 x \ln x$ D) $x^{\tan x} \tan x$
    E) $x^{\tan x} \left(\sec^2 x \ln x + \tan x\right)$ F) $x^{\tan x} \left(\sec^2 x \ln x + (\tan x / x)\right)$
    G) $x^{\tan x} \left(\sec^2 x + \ln x\right)$ H) $x^{\tan x} \left(\sec^2 x + \ln x \tan x\right)$

Answer: $x^{\tan x} \left(\sec^2 x \ln x + (\tan x / x)\right)$ (hard)

281. Let $f(x) = (\ln x)^x$. Find $f'(x)$.

    A) x^{-x} B) $1/\left(x^{x-1}\right)$ C) $(\ln x)^x \ln x$
    D) $(\ln x)^x \ln \ln x$ E) $(\ln x)^{x-1}$ F) $(\ln x)(\ln \ln x)$
    G) $(\ln x)^x (\ln x + 1)$ H) $(\ln x)^x (\ln \ln x + (1/\ln x))$

Answer: $(\ln x)^x (\ln \ln x + (1/\ln x))$ (hard)

282. Let $f(x) = x^{\sqrt{x}}$. Find the value of $f'(4)$.

A) 2   B) 4   C) 8   D) 16

E) $2 + \ln 4$ F) $4 + \ln 2$ G) $8 + 4\ln 4$ H) $16 + 4\ln 2$

Answer: $8 + 4\ln 4$ (medium)

Chapter 6, Section 5
Exponential Growth and Decay

283. The radioactive isotope Bismuth-210 has a half-life of 5 days. How many days does it take for 87.5% of a given amount to decay?

A) 15   B) 8   C) 10   D) 13

E) 11   F) 9   G) 12   H) 14

Answer: 15 (medium)

284. A bacteria culture starts with 200 bacteria and triples in size every half hour. After 2 hours, how many bacteria are there?

A) 17800   B) 16200   C) 23500   D) 24000

E) 19300   F) 14800   G) 15700   H) 21000

Answer: 16200 (medium)

285. A bacteria culture starts with 200 bacteria and triples in size every half hour. After 45 minutes, how many bacteria are there?

A) $600\sqrt{3}$ B) $800\ln 2$ C) $800\ln 3$ D) 1800

E) $500\sqrt{2}$ F) 900   G) $45\ln 3$ H) $1200\ln(3/2)$

Answer: $600\sqrt{3}$ (medium)

286. A bacteria culture starts with 200 bacteria and in 1 hour contains 400 bacteria. How many hours does it take to reach 2000 bacteria?

A) $\ln 400$ B) $\ln 10$ C) 10   D) $\ln 1600$

E) $\ln 2000$ F) $\ln 200$ G) 5   H) $(\ln 10)/\ln 2$

Answer: $(\ln 10)/\ln 2$ (hard)

287. When a child was born, her grandparents placed $1,000 in a savings account at 10% interest compounded continuously, to be withdrawn at age 20 to help pay for college. How much money is in the account at the time of withdrawal?

A) $1000e$ B) $500e$ C) $500e^2$ D) $2000e^2$

E) $4000e$ F) $2000e$ G) $1000e^2$ H) $4000e^2$

Answer: $1000e^2$ (medium)

288. Radium has a half-life of 1600 years. How many years does it take for 90% of a given amount of radium to decay?

A) $1600/\ln 5$ B) $1600 \ln 2$ C) $1600(\ln 10)/\ln 2$
D) $1600 \ln 5$ E) $1600 \ln 10$ F) $1600/\ln 2$
G) $1600 \ln 10$ H) $1600(\ln 2)/\ln 10$

Answer: $1600 (\ln 10)/\ln 2$ (hard)

289. Carbon 14, with a half-life of 5700 years, is used to estimate the age of organic materials. What fraction of the original amount of carbon 14 would an object have if it were 2000 years old?

A) $\exp((-57/20) \ln 2)$ B) $(57/20) \ln 2$ C) $\exp((-20/57) \ln 2)$
D) $(20/57) \ln 2$ E) $\exp((57/20) \ln 2)$ F) $(1/57) \ln 20$
G) $\exp((20/57) \ln 2)$ H) $(1/20) \ln 57$

Answer: $\exp((-20/57) \ln 2)$ (hard)

290. An object cools at a rate (°C/min) equal to k times the difference between its temperature and the surrounding air. Suppose the object takes 10 minutes to cool from 60° C to 40° C in a room kept at 20° C. Find the value of k.

A) e^{-20} B) $\ln 2$ C) $10e^{-20}$
D) $40 \ln 10$ E) $1/2$ F) $e^{-1/20}$
G) $(1/10) \ln (1/2)$ H) $60 \ln (1/2)$

Answer: $(1/10) \ln (1/2)$ (medium)

291. An object cools at a rate (°C/min) equal to k times the difference between its temperature and the surrounding air. Suppose the object takes 10 minutes to cool from 60° C to 40° C in a room kept at 20° C. How many minutes would it take for the object to cool down from 60° C to 30° C?

A) $\ln 30$ B) 20 C) 15 D) $2 \ln 30$
E) $\ln (3/4)$ F) 30 G) $e^{30 \ln 2}$ H) 60

Answer: 20 (medium)

292. A bacteria culture starts with 1000 bacteria and grows at a rate proportional to its size. After 2 hours there are 3000 bacteria. After how many hours will there be 10,000 bacteria?

A) $\ln 2$ B) $\ln 10$ C) $\ln 100$
D) $\ln 1000$ E) $(\ln 2)/(\ln 3)$ F) $(\ln 10)/(\ln 3)$
G) $(\ln 100)/(\ln 3)$ H) $(\ln 1000)/(\ln 3)$

Answer: $(\ln 100)/(\ln 3)$ (medium)

293. A thermometer is taken from a room where the temperature is 20° C to the outdoors where the temperature is 5° C. After 1 minute the thermometer reads 12° C. After how many minutes will the thermometer read 6° C?

A) $\ln 15$ B) $\ln 7$ C) $(\ln 15)/(\ln 7)$
D) $\ln 15 - \ln 7$ E) $1/(\ln 15 - \ln 7)$ F) $\ln 15/(\ln 15 - \ln 7)$
G) $\ln 7/(\ln 15 - \ln 7)$ H) $(\ln 7)/(\ln 15)$

Answer: $\ln 15/(\ln 15 - \ln 7)$ (hard)

294. A bacteria population grows at a rate proportional to its size. The count was 400 after 2 hours and 25,600 after 6 hours. In how many minutes does the population double?

A) 20   B) 25   C) 30   D) 35
E) 40   F) 45   G) 50   H) 55

Answer: 40 (medium)

295. An object cools at a rate (in °C/min) equal to $1/10$ of the difference between its temperature and the surrounding air. If a room is kept at 20° C and the temperature of the object is 28° C, what is the temperature of the object 5 minutes later?

A) 22   B) 24   C) $20 + 5e^{-1/10}$
D) $20 + 8e^{-1/2}$ E) $20 + 5e^{-4/5}$ F) $20 + 8e^{-1/10}$
G) $28 - 8e^{-1/10}$ H) $28 - 10e^{-1/2}$

Answer: $20 + 8e^{-1/2}$ (medium)

296. In an experiment, a tissue culture has been subjected to ionizing radiation. It was found that the number A of undamaged cells depends on the exposure time, in hours, according to the following formula:
$$A = A_0 e^{kt}, \ t \geq 0$$
If 5000 cells were present initially and 3000 survived a 2 hour exposure, find the elapsed time of exposure after which only half the original cells survive.

Answer: 2.71 hours (medium)

297. A lettuce leaf collected from the salad bar at the college cafeteria contains $\frac{99}{100}$ as much carbon C^{14} as a freshly cut lettuce leaf. How old is it? (Use 5700 years for the half-life of C^{14}.)

Answer: about 83 years old (medium)

298. Assume that the rate of growth of a population of fruit flies is proportional to the size of the population at each instant of time. If 100 fruit flies are present initially and 200 are present after 5 days, how many will be present after 10 days?

Answer: 400 (easy)

299. A population of bacteria is known to grow exponentially. If 4 million are observed initially and 9 million after 2 days, how many will be present after 3 days?

Answer: $13\frac{1}{2}$ million (easy)

300. It takes money 20 years to triple at a certain rate of interest. How long does it take for money to double at this rate?

Answer: 12.62 years (medium)

301. What annual rate of interest will make an investment of P dollars double in five years if the interest is compounded continuously?

Answer: 13.9% (medium)

302. Suppose that the number of bacteria in a culture at time t is given by $x = 5^4 e^{3t}$. Use natural logarithms to solve for t in terms of x.

Answer: $t = \frac{\ln x - 4 \ln 5}{3}$ (medium)

303. In 1970, the Brown County groundhog population was 100. By 1980, there were 900 groundhogs in Brown County. If the rate of population growth of these animals is proportional to the population size, how many groundhogs might one expect to see in 1995?

Answer: $24,300$ (medium)

304. Given $f'(t) = k \cdot f(t)$, $f(0) = 35$ and $f(3) = 945$, find $f(4)$.

Answer: 2835 (medium)

305. In a certain medical treatment a tracer dye is injected into a human organ to measure its function rate and the rate of change of the amount of dye is proportional to the amount present at any time. If a physician injects 0.5g of dye and 30 minutes later 0.1g remains, how much dye will be present in $1\frac{1}{2}$ hours?

Answer: .004g (medium)

306. John deposits $\$100$ in a bank and at the same time Mary deposits $\$200$. If John's bank pays 10% interest compounded continuously and Mary's bank pays 8% interest, how long must John wait till his bank account exceeds Mary's? (Use $\ln 2 = 0.7$)

Answer: 35 years (medium)

Chapter 6, Section 6
Inverse Trigonometric Functions

307. Find the value of $\cos^{-1}(1/2)$.

A) $\pi/8$ B) $\pi/6$ C) $\pi/2$ D) $\pi/12$
E) $\pi/3$ F) π G) $3\pi/4$ H) $\pi/4$

Answer: $\pi/3$ (easy)

308. Find the value of $\cot^{-1}\sqrt{3}$.

A) $\pi/3$ B) $\pi/6$ C) π D) $\pi/4$
E) $\pi/12$ F) $\pi/2$ G) $\pi/4$ H) $\pi/8$

Answer: $\pi/6$ (medium)

309. Let $f(x) = \tan^{-1}x$. Find the value of $f'(1)$.

A) $-1/2$ B) $1/2$ C) $-1/3$ D) 1
E) $1/3$ F) $-1/4$ G) $1/4$ H) -1

Answer: $1/2$ (easy)

310. Let $f(x) = \sin^{-1}(2x)$. Find the value of $f'(0)$.

A) $-1/2$ B) 2 C) -2 D) 1
E) $1/2$ F) -1 G) 0 H) $-1/\sqrt{2}$

Answer: 2 (medium)

311. Find the value of $\sin(2\tan^{-1}4)$.

A) $4/17$ B) $2/17$ C) $8/17$ D) $4/15$
E) $1/15$ F) $8/15$ G) $1/17$ H) $2/15$

Answer: $8/17$ (medium)

312. Find the value of the integral $\int_0^1 \frac{1}{1+x^2}\,dx$.

A) $\pi/6$ B) $\frac{1}{2}\ln 2$ C) $\pi/4$ D) 1
E) $\pi/2$ F) $\pi/8$ G) -1 H) $-\frac{1}{2}\ln 2$

Answer: $\pi/4$ (easy)

313. Find the value of the integral $\int_0^1 \frac{x}{1+x^2}\,dx$.

A) $\pi/6$ B) $\pi/4$ C) $\frac{1}{2}\ln 2$ D) $-\frac{1}{2}\ln 2$
E) 1 F) $\pi/2$ G) -1 H) $\pi/8$

Answer: $\frac{1}{2}\ln 2$ (medium)

314. Find the value of the integral $\int_0^2 \frac{1}{4+x^2}\,dx$.

A) $\pi/8$ B) 1 C) $\pi/4$ D) -1
E) $\pi/2$ F) $\frac{1}{2}\ln 2$ G) $\pi/6$ H) $-\frac{1}{2}\ln 2$

Answer: $\pi/8$ (medium)

315. Find the value of the integral $\int_0^{1/2} \frac{1}{1+4x^2}\,dx$.

A) $\pi/2$ B) $\pi/6$ C) $\pi/8$ D) -1
E) $-\frac{1}{2}\ln 2$ F) $\pi/4$ G) 1 H) $\frac{1}{2}\ln 2$

Answer: $\pi/8$ (medium)

316. Find the value of the integral $\int_0^1 \frac{1}{\sqrt{4-x^2}}\,dx$.

A) $\pi/8$ B) $-\frac{1}{2}\ln 2$ C) $\frac{1}{2}\ln 2$ D) $\pi/6$
E) $\pi/4$ F) -1 G) 1 H) $\pi/2$

Answer: $\pi/6$ (hard)

317. Let $f(x) = \tan^{-1}\left(x^2+1\right)$. Find the value of $f'(1)$.

A) 0   B) 0.1   C) 0.2   D) 0.3
E) 0.4   F) 0.5   G) 0.6   H) 0.8

Answer: 0.4 (medium)

318. Find the value of the limit $\lim\limits_{x \to -2^+} \tan^{-1}\left(\frac{x}{x+2}\right)$.

A) $-\infty$ B) $-\pi$ C) $-\pi/2$ D) $-\pi/4$
E) 0 F) $\pi/4$ G) $\pi/2$ H) π

Answer: $-\pi/2$ (medium)

319. Find the domain of the function $f(x) = \sin^{-1}(3 - 2x)$.

A) $[0, 1]$ B) $[1, 2]$ C) $[0, 2]$ D) $[0, 3]$
E) $[1, 3]$ F) $[2, 3]$ G) $[-3, -1]$ H) $[-3, -2]$

Answer: $[1, 2]$ (medium)

320. Let $f(x) = \sin^{-1}(4/x)$. Find the value of $f'(8)$.

A) $-1/\left(8\sqrt{3}\right)$ B) $-1/\left(4\sqrt{3}\right)$ C) $-1/\left(2\sqrt{3}\right)$ D) $-1/\sqrt{3}$
E) $\pi/8$ F) $\pi/4$ G) $\pi/2$ H) π

Answer: $-1/(8\sqrt{3})$ (medium)

321. Find the value of the limit $\lim\limits_{x \to 1} \tan^{-1}\left(\frac{1}{(x-1)^2}\right)$.

A) 0   B) 1   C) 2   D) $\pi/4$
E) $\pi/2$ F) π G) ∞ H) does not exist

Answer: $\pi/2$ (easy)

322. Find the value of the integral $\int_0^1 \frac{\tan^{-1} x}{1+x^2}\, dx$.

A) $\pi^2/32$ B) $\pi^2/24$ C) $\pi^2/16$ D) $\pi^2/12$
E) $\pi^2/8$ F) $\pi^2/4$ G) $\pi^2/2$ H) π^2

Answer: $\pi^2/32$ (medium)

323. Find the value of the limit $\lim\limits_{x \to \infty} \tan^{-1}\left(x - x^2\right)$.

A) $-\infty$ B) $-\pi/2$ C) 0 D) $\pi/2$
E) 1 F) -1 G) ∞ H) does not exist

Answer: $-\pi/2$ (medium)

324. For $y = \frac{\arcsin x}{\sqrt{1-x^2}}$, $|x| < 1$, find y''. Simplify your answer.

Answer: $y'' = \dfrac{\left(1+2x^2\right)(\text{Arcsin } x)+3x\left(1-x^2\right)^{1/2}}{\left(1-x^2\right)^{5/2}}$ (hard)

325. Find the value of $\sin\left(2\cos^{-1}\left(-\frac{7}{8}\right)\right)$ correct to three decimal places.

Answer: -0.847 (medium)

326. Find the exact value of $\arcsin\left(\sin\left(\frac{9\pi}{7}\right)\right)$.

Answer: $\theta = -\frac{2\pi}{7}$ (easy)

327. Find the exact value of $\tan\left(\arccos\left(-\frac{1}{3}\right)\right)$.

Answer: $\tan\theta = -\sqrt{8}$ (easy)

328. If $x = \frac{1}{3}\cos\theta$, what is $\tan^2\theta$ in terms of x?

Answer: $\frac{1-9x^2}{9x^2}$ (easy)

329. Find the value of $\int_0^{1/\sqrt{3}} \frac{dx}{1+3x^2}$.

Answer: $\frac{\pi}{4\sqrt{3}}$ (medium)

330. Find $\sin\left(\sin^{-1} 3x\right)$.

Answer: $3x$ (easy)

331. Find $\cos\left(\sin^{-1} 3x\right)$.

Answer: $\sqrt{1 - 9x^2}$ (medium)

332. Find $\tan\left(\sin^{-1} 3x\right)$.

Answer: $\frac{3x}{\sqrt{1-9x^2}}$ (medium)

333. Differentiate $f(t) = \tan^{-1} t$.

Answer: $\frac{1}{1+t^2}$ (easy)

334. Differentiate $f(t) = \tan^{-1} \sqrt{1-t}$.

Answer: $\frac{-1}{(4-2t)\sqrt{1-t}}$ (medium)

Chapter 6, Section 7
Hyperbolic Functions

335. If $\sinh x = 2$, what is the value of $\cosh x$?

A) $\sqrt{3}$ B) $\sqrt{6}$ C) 1 D) 3
E) $\sqrt{8}$ F) $\sqrt{5}$ G) 2 H) $\sqrt{2}$

Answer: $\sqrt{5}$ (medium)

336. If $\tanh x = 1/2$, what is the value of $\cosh x$?

A) $\sqrt{5}/2$ B) $2/\sqrt{5}$ C) $\sqrt{5}$ D) $2\sqrt{5}$
E) $2\sqrt{3}$ F) $\sqrt{3}$ G) $2/\sqrt{3}$ H) $\sqrt{3}/2$

Answer: $2/\sqrt{3}$ (hard)

337. If $\cosh x = 2$, what is the value of $\cosh 2x$?

A) 3 B) 7 C) 9 D) 4
E) 8 F) 6 G) 5 H) 10

Answer: 7 (medium)

338. Let $f(x) = \sinh x$. Find the value of $f'(0)$.

A) $\sqrt{2}$ B) 1/2 C) 2 D) 1/3
E) 1 F) $1/\sqrt{2}$ G) 3 H) 0

Answer: 1 (easy)

339. Let $f(x) = \tanh(2x)$. Find the value of $f'(0)$.

A) 0 B) 1/3 C) 1/2 D) $\sqrt{2}$
E) 1 F) $1/\sqrt{2}$ G) 3 H) 2

Answer: 2 (medium)

340. Find the value of $\tanh^{-1} 1/2$.

A) $\frac{1}{2}\ln 3$ B) $\ln 3$ C) $2/\ln 3$ D) $3/\ln 2$
E) $\ln 2$ F) $\frac{1}{3}\ln 2$ G) $2\ln 3$ H) $3\ln 2$

Answer: $\frac{1}{2}\ln 3$ (medium)

341. Let $f(x) = \sinh^{-1} x$. Find the value of $f'(1)$.

A) $1/\sqrt{3}$ B) $\sqrt{2}/3$ C) $1/\sqrt{2}$ D) $1/\sqrt{5}$
E) $2/\sqrt{3}$ F) $2\sqrt{5}$ G) $3/\sqrt{5}$ H) $3/\sqrt{2}$

Answer: $1/\sqrt{2}$ (medium)

342. Find the value of $\int_{-1}^{1} \cosh x \, \mathrm{d}x$.

A) e^2 B) $1/e^2$ C) $e - 1/e$ D) $2e^2$
E) $2/e$ F) $1/e$ G) $2e$ H) $2/e^2$

Answer: $e - 1/e$ (medium)

343. Find the value of the integral $\int_0^1 \frac{1}{4-x^2} \, \mathrm{d}x$.

A) $(1/4)\ln 5$ B) $(1/3)\ln 2$ C) $(1/4)\ln 3$ D) $(1/5)\ln 4$
E) $(1/4)\ln 2$ F) $(1/2)\ln 2$ G) $(1/2)\ln 3$ H) $(1/3)\ln 4$

Answer: $(1/4)\ln 3$ (hard)

344. Find the value of the integral $\int_0^{3/4} \frac{1}{\sqrt{x^2+1}} \, \mathrm{d}x$.

A) $\sqrt{3/4}$ B) 2 C) $\ln 4$ D) $\ln(5/4)$
E) $\sqrt{5/4}$ F) $\ln 2$ G) $\sqrt{2}$ H) $\ln(3/4)$

Answer: $\ln 2$ (hard)

345. Find the value of $\tanh(\ln 3)$.

A) 0.2 B) 0.4 C) 0.6 D) 0.8
E) 1.0 F) 1.2 G) 1.4 H) 1.6

Answer: 0.8 (easy)

346. Find the value of the limit $\lim_{x \to \infty} \tanh x$.

A) $-\infty$ B) 0 C) 1 D) 2
E) e F) e^2 G) $\ln\sqrt{2}$ H) ∞

Answer: 1 (easy)

347. Find a simpler form for $\frac{1+\tanh(\ln x)}{1-\tanh(\ln x)}$.

A) $\sinh x$ B) $\cosh x$ C) $\operatorname{csch} x$ D) $\operatorname{sech} x$
E) $\coth x$ F) x G) x^2 H) x^3

Answer: x^2 (medium)

348. Find the value of $\sinh(\ln 2)$.

A) 0   B) 1/4   C) 1/2   D) 3/4
E) 2   F) 5/4   G) 3/2   H) 7/4

Answer: 3/4 (easy)

349. Find $\lim_{x \to \infty} \tanh x$.

Answer: 1

350. Show that $\sinh[\ln x] = \frac{x^2-1}{2x}$.

Answer: Since $\sinh(u) = \frac{e^u - e^{-u}}{2}$,

$$\sinh[\ln x] = \frac{e^{\ln x} - e^{-\ln x}}{2} = \frac{e^x - e^{\ln(1/x)}}{2}$$

$$= \frac{x - \frac{1}{x}}{2} = \frac{\frac{x^2-1}{x}}{2} = \frac{x^2-1}{2x} \quad \text{(hard)}$$

351. Find the exact coordinates of the two points of inflection of the graph of $y = \operatorname{sech} x$.

Answer: $\left(\pm \ln\left(1 + \sqrt{2}\right), \frac{\sqrt{2}}{2} \right)$ (medium)

352. Evaluate $\int \cosh(\ln x)\, dx$.

Answer: $\frac{x^2}{4} + \frac{1}{2} \ln x + C$ (medium)

353. Find an explicit formula for $\sinh^{-1} x$.

Answer: $\sinh^{-1} = y = \ln\left(x + \sqrt{1 + x^2}\right)$ (medium)

354. Find $\frac{dy}{dx}$ if $x \tanh^{-1}(y) + \frac{y}{x} = 0$.

Answer: $\frac{dy}{dx} = \frac{(1-y^2)\left[y - x^2 \tanh^{-1}(y)\right]}{x^3 + x - xy^2}$ (hard)

355. Find the derivative: $g(x) = e^x \sinh x$.

Answer: $e^x \sinh x + e^x \cosh x$ (medium)

356. Find the derivative: $y = \cos(\sinh x)$.

Answer: $y' = -\sin(\sinh x) \cosh x$ (medium)

357.   Find the derivative: $y = e^{\tanh x} \cosh(\cosh x)$.

Answer: $y' = e^{\tanh x} \operatorname{sech}^2 x \cosh(\cosh x) + e^{\tanh x} \sinh(\cosh x) \sinh x$ (medium)

358.   Evaluate the integral: $\int \operatorname{sech}^2 x \, dx$

Answer: $\tanh x + C$ (easy)

Chapter 6, Section 8
Indeterminate Forms and L'Hopital's Rule

359.   Find the value of the limit $\displaystyle\lim_{x \to 0^+} \frac{\cos x - 1}{x}$.

A) $1/4$ B) -2 C) ∞ D) $-1/2$
E) 2 F) 0 G) $1/2$ H) 4

Answer: 0 (easy)

360.   Find the value of the limit $\displaystyle\lim_{x \to 0^+} \frac{\cos x - 1}{x^2}$.

A) $-1/2$ B) $1/4$ C) 0 D) $1/2$
E) 2 F) ∞ G) 4 H) -2

Answer: $-1/2$ (medium)

361.   Find the value of the limit $\displaystyle\lim_{x \to 0^+} \frac{1 - \sin^2 x}{x^2}$.

A) 2 B) -2 C) ∞ D) $1/2$
E) $1/4$ F) 4 G) $-1/2$ H) 0

Answer: ∞ (medium)

362.   Find the value of the limit $\displaystyle\lim_{x \to 0^+} \frac{x}{\sin x + \tan x}$.

A) -2 B) 0 C) $-1/2$ D) $1/4$
E) 2 F) ∞ G) $1/2$ H) 4

Answer: $1/2$ (medium)

363.   Find the value of the limit $\displaystyle\lim_{x \to 1^+} \frac{\ln(2x)}{\ln x}$.

A) $1/4$ B) 2 C) 4 D) $1/2$
E) 0 F) -2 G) ∞ H) $-1/2$

Answer: ∞ (medium)

364. Find the value of the limit $\lim\limits_{x \to 0^+} \frac{e^x - 1}{x}$.

A) 0   B) 4   C) $-1/2$ D) 1/4

E) 1   F) 1/2   G) 2   H) -2

Answer: 1 (medium)

365. Find the value of the limit $\lim\limits_{x \to 0^+} \frac{e^{x^2} - 1}{x}$.

A) 4   B) 1/4   C) -2 D) ∞

E) 2   F) 0   G) 1/2   H) $-1/2$

Answer: 0 (medium)

366. Find the value of the limit $\lim\limits_{x \to 0^+} x^{2/x}$.

A) 1/2   B) ∞ C) 1   D) e

E) 0   F) 2   G) $\ln 2$ H) $\sqrt{2}$

Answer: 0 (hard)

367. Find the value of the limit $\lim\limits_{x \to \infty} x^{2/x}$.

A) 2   B) e C) $\ln 2$ D) 0

E) 1   F) ∞ G) 1/2   H) $\sqrt{2}$

Answer: 1 (hard)

368. Find the value of the limit $\lim\limits_{x \to \infty} x^{1/\ln x}$.

A) 0   B) 2   C) e D) ∞

E) $\ln 2$ F) 1/2   G) 1   H) $\sqrt{2}$

Answer: e (hard)

369. Find the value of the limit $\lim\limits_{x \to \infty} \left(1 + \frac{3}{x} + \frac{5}{x^2}\right)^x$.

A) 0   B) 1   C) 3   D) 5

E) e^3 F) e^5 G) $\ln 3$ H) $\ln 5$

Answer: e^3 (hard)

370. Find the value of the limit $\lim\limits_{x \to \infty} \frac{\ln x}{x}$.

A) $-\infty$ B) -1 C) 0   D) $1/e$

E) 1   F) e G) $e^{1/e}$ H) ∞

Answer: 0 (easy)

371. Sketch the curve $y = \frac{\ln x}{x}$.

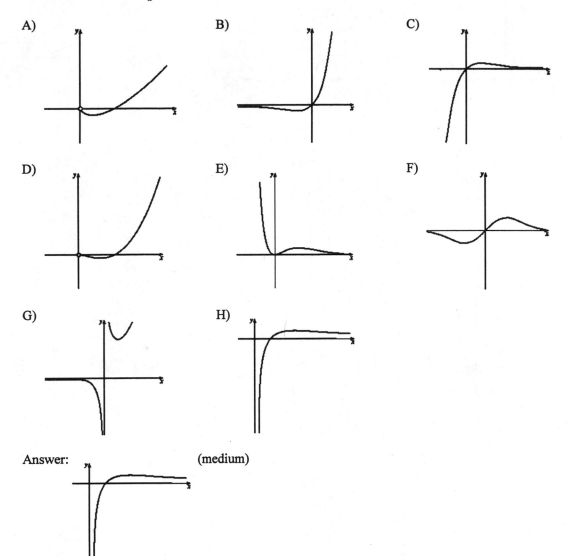

A)

B)

C)

D)

E)

F)

G)

H)

Answer: (medium)

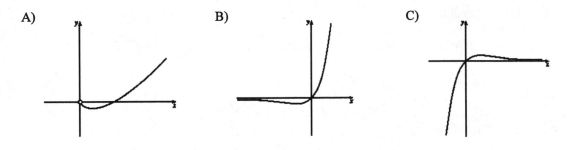

372. Sketch the curve $y = x \ln x$.

A)

B)

C)

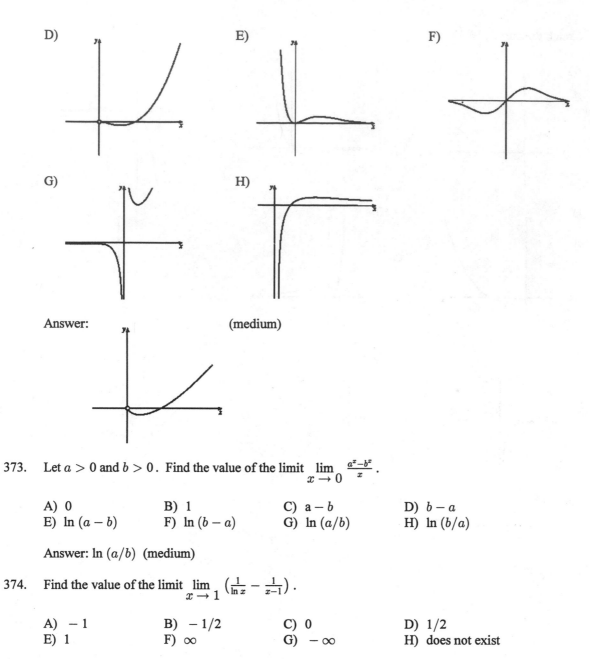

D)

E)

F)

G)

H)

Answer: (medium)

373.   Let $a > 0$ and $b > 0$. Find the value of the limit $\lim\limits_{x \to 0} \frac{a^x - b^x}{x}$.

A) 0   B) 1   C) $a - b$ D) $b - a$
E) $\ln(a - b)$ F) $\ln(b - a)$ G) $\ln(a/b)$ H) $\ln(b/a)$

Answer: $\ln(a/b)$ (medium)

374.   Find the value of the limit $\lim\limits_{x \to 1} \left(\frac{1}{\ln x} - \frac{1}{x-1} \right)$.

A) -1 B) $-1/2$ C) 0   D) $1/2$
E) 1   F) ∞ G) $-\infty$ H) does not exist

Answer: $1/2$ (medium)

375.   Let a, b, c, d all be positive constants. Find the value of the limit $\lim\limits_{x \to \infty} \frac{\ln(a + be^{cx})}{dx}$.

A) 0   B) a/d C) b/d D) c/d
E) b F) c G) d H) ∞

Answer: c/d (medium)

376. Find the value of the limit $\lim\limits_{x \to 0} \frac{1-\cos \lambda x}{x^2}$.

A) λ B) λ^2 C) $\lambda/2$ D) $\lambda^2/2$
E) $1/2$ F) $1/\lambda$ G) $3/\lambda^2$ H) ∞ .

Answer: $\lambda^2/2$ (medium)

377. Find the value of the limit $\lim\limits_{x \to 0} \frac{6^x - 2^x}{x}$.

A) 0   B) 1   C) 2   D) 3
E) 6   F) ln 2   G) ln 3   H) ln 4

Answer: ln 3 (medium)

378. Find the value of the limit $\lim\limits_{x \to \infty} \left(1 + \frac{2}{x}\right)^{3x}$.

A) e^2 B) e^3 C) e^5 D) e^6
E) ln 2   F) ln 3   G) ln 5   H) ln 6

Answer: e^6 (medium)

379. Find the value of the limit $\lim\limits_{x \to 0^+} \sqrt{x} \ln x$.

A) $-\infty$ B) -1 C) 0   D) 1
E) e F) ∞ G) $\sqrt{e}$ H) $-\sqrt{e}$

Answer: 0 (easy)

380. Find the value of the limit $\lim\limits_{x \to 0} \frac{e^x - 1 - x - (x^2/2)}{x^3}$.

A) 0   B) 1   C) $1/2$ D) $1/3$
E) $1/6$ F) ∞ G) $-1/2$ H) $-1/3$

Answer: $1/6$ (medium)

381. Sketch the curve $y = \frac{e^x}{x}$.

A)   B)   C)

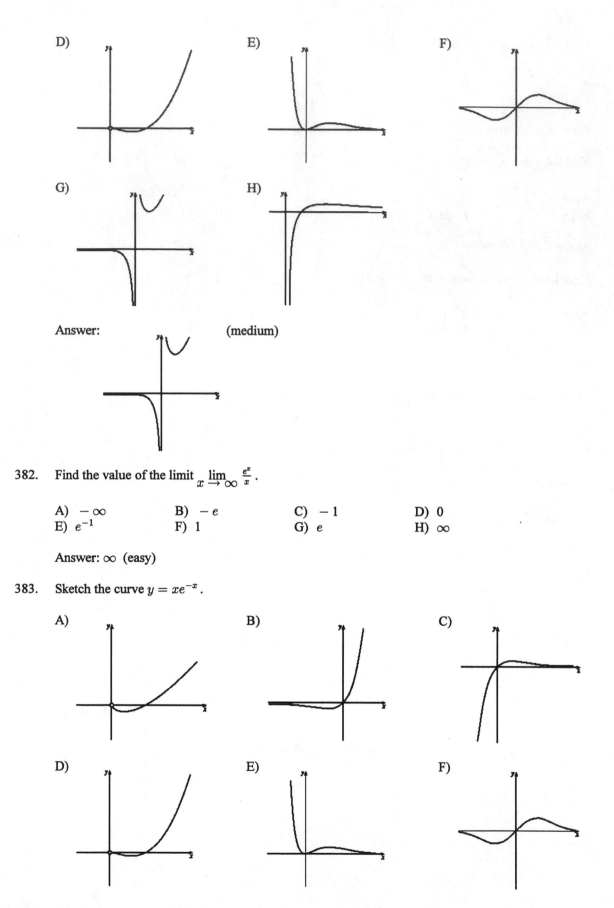

D)

E)

F)

G)

H)

Answer: (medium)

382.   Find the value of the limit $\lim\limits_{x \to \infty} \frac{e^x}{x}$.

A) $-\infty$ B) $-e$ C) -1 D) 0
E) e^{-1} F) 1   G) e H) ∞

Answer: ∞ (easy)

383.   Sketch the curve $y = xe^{-x}$.

A)

B)

C)

D)

E)

F)

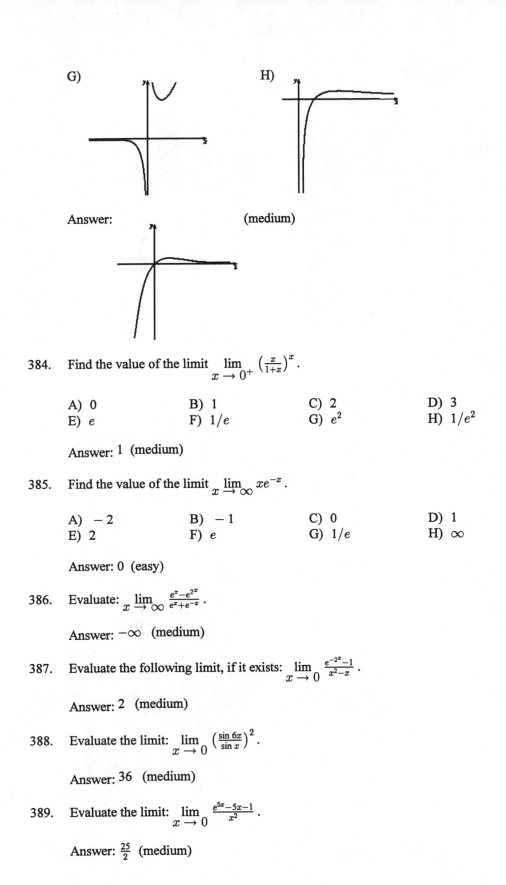

G)

H)

Answer: (medium)

384. Find the value of the limit $\lim\limits_{x \to 0^+} \left(\frac{x}{1+x}\right)^x$.

A) 0   B) 1   C) 2   D) 3
E) e F) $1/e$ G) e^2 H) $1/e^2$

Answer: 1 (medium)

385. Find the value of the limit $\lim\limits_{x \to \infty} xe^{-x}$.

A) -2 B) -1 C) 0   D) 1
E) 2   F) e G) $1/e$ H) ∞

Answer: 0 (easy)

386. Evaluate: $\lim\limits_{x \to \infty} \frac{e^x - e^{2x}}{e^x + e^{-x}}$.

Answer: $-\infty$ (medium)

387. Evaluate the following limit, if it exists: $\lim\limits_{x \to 0} \frac{e^{-2x} - 1}{x^2 - x}$.

Answer: 2 (medium)

388. Evaluate the limit: $\lim\limits_{x \to 0} \left(\frac{\sin 6x}{\sin x}\right)^2$.

Answer: 36 (medium)

389. Evaluate the limit: $\lim\limits_{x \to 0} \frac{e^{5x} - 5x - 1}{x^2}$.

Answer: $\frac{25}{2}$ (medium)

390. Evaluate the limit: $\lim\limits_{x \to 0} \frac{2e^x - x^2 - 2x - 2}{x^4 + x^3}$.

Answer: $\frac{1}{3}$ (medium)

391. Find $\lim\limits_{x \to 0} \frac{\ln(1+x)}{x^3}$, if it exists.

Answer: ∞ (medium)

392. Evaluate the limit: $\lim\limits_{x \to 0} (1 + \sin \pi x)^{1/x}$.

Answer: e^π (medium)

393. Evaluate the limit: $\lim\limits_{x \to 0^+} x^2 (\ln x)$.

Answer: 0 (medium)

394. Sketch the curve $y = x^2 \ln x$.

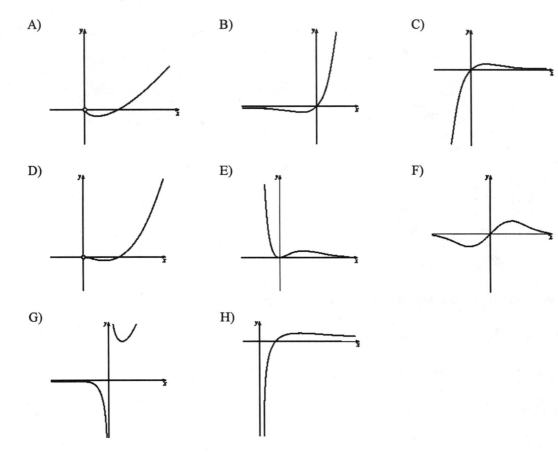

A)

B)

C)

D)

E)

F)

G)

H)

Answer: (medium)

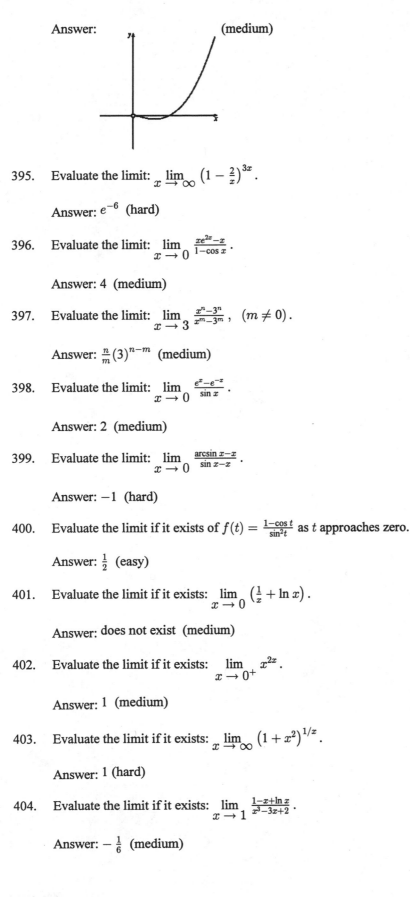

395. Evaluate the limit: $\lim\limits_{x \to \infty} \left(1 - \frac{2}{x}\right)^{3x}$.

Answer: e^{-6} (hard)

396. Evaluate the limit: $\lim\limits_{x \to 0} \frac{xe^{2x} - x}{1 - \cos x}$.

Answer: 4 (medium)

397. Evaluate the limit: $\lim\limits_{x \to 3} \frac{x^n - 3^n}{x^m - 3^m}$, $(m \neq 0)$.

Answer: $\frac{n}{m}(3)^{n-m}$ (medium)

398. Evaluate the limit: $\lim\limits_{x \to 0} \frac{e^x - e^{-x}}{\sin x}$.

Answer: 2 (medium)

399. Evaluate the limit: $\lim\limits_{x \to 0} \frac{\arcsin x - x}{\sin x - x}$.

Answer: -1 (hard)

400. Evaluate the limit if it exists of $f(t) = \frac{1 - \cos t}{\sin^2 t}$ as t approaches zero.

Answer: $\frac{1}{2}$ (easy)

401. Evaluate the limit if it exists: $\lim\limits_{x \to 0} \left(\frac{1}{x} + \ln x\right)$.

Answer: does not exist (medium)

402. Evaluate the limit if it exists: $\lim\limits_{x \to 0^+} x^{2x}$.

Answer: 1 (medium)

403. Evaluate the limit if it exists: $\lim\limits_{x \to \infty} \left(1 + x^2\right)^{1/x}$.

Answer: 1 (hard)

404. Evaluate the limit if it exists: $\lim\limits_{x \to 1} \frac{1 - x + \ln x}{x^3 - 3x + 2}$.

Answer: $-\frac{1}{6}$ (medium)

405. Evaluate the limit if it exists: $\lim\limits_{x \to \infty} \frac{x^3}{e^x}$.

Answer: 0 (medium)

406. Evaluate the limit if it exists: $\lim\limits_{x \to 0} (1 + \sinh x)^{3/x}$.

Answer: e^3 (hard)

407. Evaluate the limit if it exists: $\lim\limits_{x \to 0} \frac{x - \sin x}{x^3}$.

Answer: $\frac{1}{6}$ (medium)

408. Evaluate the limit if it exists: $\lim\limits_{x \to 0} \frac{\ln \sec^4 x}{x^2}$.

Answer: 2 (medium)

Calculus, 3rd Edition
by James Stewart
Chapter 7, Section 1
Integration by Parts

1. Find the value of the integral $\int_1^e \ln x \, dx$.

   A) 1   B) e^2 C) $e - 1$ D) 2
   E) $e^2 - e$ F) $e - 2$ G) $e - 1/2$ H) e

   Answer: 1 (medium)

2. Find the value of the integral $\int_0^1 xe^x \, dx$.

   A) 2   B) $e^2 - e$ C) 1   D) e^2
   E) e F) $e - 1$ G) $e - 2$ H) $(e - 1)/2$

   Answer: 1 (medium)

3. Find the value of the integral $\int_1^e \ln x^2 \, dx$.

   A) e^2 B) e C) 2   D) $e^2 - e$
   E) $e - 2$ F) 1   G) $e - 1$ H) $(e - 1)/2$

   Answer: 2 (medium)

4. Find the value of the integral $\int_0^1 xe^{x^2} \, dx$.

   A) 2   B) e C) 1   D) $e - 1$
   E) $e^2 - e$ F) e^2 G) $(e - 1)/2$ H) $e - 2$

   Answer: 2 (medium)

5. Find the value of the integral $\int_0^\pi x \sin x \, dx$.

   A) $4\pi - 2$ B) $2\pi - 2$ C) $\pi/2$ D) $4\pi - 4$
   E) $\pi - 2$ F) π G) 2π H) 4π

   Answer: π (medium)

6. Find the value of the integral $\int_0^{\pi/2} e^x \cos x \, dx$.

   A) $(e^{\pi/4} + 1)/2$ B) $(e^{\pi/2} + 1)/2$ C) $(e^{\pi/4} + 1)/4$
   D) $(e^{\pi/2} - 1)/4$ E) $(e^{\pi/4} - 1)/4$ F) $(e^{\pi/4} - 1)/2$
   G) $(e^{\pi/2} + 1)/4$ H) $(e^{\pi/2} - 1)/2$

   Answer: $(e^{\pi/2} - 1)/2$ (hard)

7. Find the value of the integral $\int_0^1 e^{\sqrt{x}}\, dx$.

A) e B) $2e - 1$ C) $2e - 2$ D) $2e$
E) $e - 2$ F) $e - 1$ G) 1 H) 2

Answer: 2 (hard)

8. Find the value of the integral $\int_0^1 x \tan^{-1} x\, dx$.

A) $\pi/4$ B) $\pi - 2$ C) $\pi/2$ D) $(\pi - 2)/2$
E) $(\pi - 2)/4$ F) $\pi - 1$ G) $(\pi - 1)/2$ H) $(\pi - 1)/4$

Answer: $(\pi - 2)/4$ (hard)

9. Find the value of the integral $\int_0^\pi x \cos x\, dx$.

A) π B) 2π C) 2 D) 0
E) -2 F) 1 G) $1/2$ H) $\pi/2$

Answer: -2 (medium)

10. Find the value of the integral $\int_0^1 2xe^x\, dx$.

A) 0 B) 1 C) 2 D) 3
E) e F) $e - 1$ G) $2e - 1$ H) $2e$

Answer: 2 (medium)

11. Find the value of the integral $\int_1^4 \sqrt{t} \ln t\, dt$.

A) $4 \ln 4$ B) $\frac{4}{3} \ln 4$ C) $\frac{8}{3} \ln 4 - \frac{22}{9}$

D) $\frac{16}{3} \ln 4 - \frac{28}{9}$ E) $\frac{22}{3} \ln 4 - 3$ F) $\frac{25}{3} \ln 4 - \frac{35}{9}$

G) $\frac{32}{3} \ln 4 - \frac{16}{9}$ H) $12 \ln 4 - \frac{25}{9}$

Answer: $\frac{16}{3} \ln 4 - \frac{28}{9}$ (hard)

12. Find the value of the integral $\int_0^1 xe^{2x}\, dx$.

A) $1 - e^2$ B) $e + e^2$ C) $(1 - e)/2$
D) $(e^2 + 3)/2$ E) $(2 - e^2)/3$ F) $(e^2 + 1)/4$
G) $(e^2 - 3)/4$ H) $(1 - e^2)/8$

Answer: $(e^2 + 1)/4$ (medium)

13. Find the value of the integral $\int_1^2 x^3 \ln x \, dx$.

    A) $\pi/16$ B) $3\pi - \frac{1}{4}$ C) $8 \ln 2 - \frac{3}{4}$

    D) $2 \ln 2 - 1$ E) $4 \ln 2 - \frac{15}{16}$ F) $\ln 4 - \frac{7}{8}$

    G) $3 \ln 4 - \frac{\pi}{16}$ H) $5 \ln 4 - \frac{3\pi}{4}$

    Answer: $4 \ln 2 - \frac{15}{16}$ (medium)

14. Evaluate the following integral: $\int x \cot^{-1}(x) \, dx$.

    Answer: $\frac{1}{2} x^2 \cot^{-1}(x) + \frac{1}{2} x - \frac{1}{2} \tan^{-1}(x) + C$ (hard)

15. Evaluate the following integral: $\int \ln \left[(e^x \ln x)^{1/x} \right] dx$.

    Answer: $\ln x \left[\ln(\ln x) - 1 \right]$ (hard)

16. Determine a reduction formula for $\int_1^e x(\ln x)^n \, dx$.

    Answer: $I_n = \frac{e^2}{2} - \frac{n}{2} I_{n-1}$ where $I_{n-1} = \int_1^e x(\ln x)^{n-1} \, dx$ (hard)

17. Find $\int x^2 e^{2x} \, dx$.

    Answer: $\frac{1}{2} x^2 e^{2x} - \frac{1}{2} x e^{2x} + \frac{1}{4} e^{2x} + C$ (hard)

18. Evaluate the following integral: $\int (\ln x)^3 \, dx$.

    Answer: $x(\ln x)^3 - 3x(\ln x)^2 + 6x \ln x - 6x + C$ (hard)

19. Evaluate the following integral: $\int_1^e (\ln x)^2 \, dx$.

    Answer: $e - 2$ (medium)

20. Find the area of the region bounded by the curve $y = \tan^{-1} x$, the x-axis and the line $x = 1$.

    Answer: $\frac{\pi - \ln 4}{4}$ (medium)

21. Evaluate the following integral: $\int \frac{\ln 2x \, dx}{x}$.

    Answer: $\ln 2(\ln x) + \frac{1}{2} (\ln x)^2 + C$ (medium)

22. Evaluate the following integral: $\int x^2 \cos x \, dx$.

    Answer: $x^2 \sin x + 2x \cos x - 2 \sin x + C$ (hard)

23. Evaluate the following integral: $\int \sec^3 x \, dx$.

    Answer: $\frac{\sec x \tan x}{2} + \frac{\ln |\sec x + \tan x|}{2} + \frac{C}{2}$ (hard)

24. Evaluate the following integral: $\int x^3 e^{3x}\, dx$.

Answer: $\frac{1}{3}x^3 e^{3x} - \frac{1}{3}x^2 e^{3x} + \frac{2}{9}x e^{3x} - \frac{2}{27}e^{3x} + C$ (hard)

25. Evaluate the following integral: $\int x e^{3x}\, dx$.

Answer: $\frac{1}{3}x e^{3x} - \frac{1}{9}e^{3x} + C$ (medium)

26. Evaluate the following integral: $\int x^3 e^{x^2}\, dx$.

Answer: $\frac{1}{2}x^2 e^{x^2} - \frac{1}{2}e^{x^2} + C$ (medium)

27. Evaluate the following integral: $\int x^2 \cos 2x\, dx$.

Answer: $\frac{x^2}{2}\sin 2x + \frac{x}{2}\cos 2x - \frac{1}{4}\sin 2x + C$ (medium)

Chapter 7, Section 2
Trigonometric Integrals

28. Find the value of the integral $\int_0^\pi \sin^2 x\, dx$.

A) $2\pi - 4$ B) $\pi - 2$ C) $\pi - 1$ D) π
E) $\pi/2$ F) 2π G) $2\pi - 2$ H) $(\pi/2) - 1$

Answer: $\pi/2$ (easy)

29. Find the value of the integral $\int_0^\pi \sin^3 x\, dx$.

A) 1   B) 4/3   C) 0   D) 8π
E) $2\pi/3$ F) $4\pi/3$ G) 2/3   H) 8/3

Answer: 4/3 (medium)

30. Find the value of the integral $\int_0^\pi \sin^2 x \cos x\, dx$.

A) 4/3   B) 1   C) 0   D) 2/3
E) $4\pi/3$ F) $2\pi/3$ G) $8\pi/3$ H) 8/3

Answer: 0 (easy)

31. Find the value of the integral $\int_0^\pi \cos^2 x \sin x\, dx$.

A) 0   B) $8\pi/3$ C) 8/3   D) 4/3
E) 2/3   F) 1   G) $2\pi/3$ H) $4\pi/3$

Answer: 2/3 (medium)

32. Find the value of the integral $\int_0^\pi \sin 2x \cos x \, dx$.

A) 1/2   B) $\pi/4$ C) 1   D) $3\pi/4$
E) 4/3   F) 2/3   G) $\pi/2$ H) 0

Answer: 4/3 (medium)

33. Find the value of the integral $\int_0^{\pi/4} \sin 4x \, dx$.

A) 1   B) 0   C) 1/4   D) $\pi/2$
E) $\pi/4$ F) $3\pi/4$ G) 3/4   H) 1/2

Answer: 1/2 (easy)

34. Find the value of the integral $\int_0^{\pi/4} \sec^2 x \, dx$.

A) 1/2   B) $\pi/4$ C) 3/4   D) $3\pi/4$
E) $\pi/2$ F) 1/4   G) 1   H) 0

Answer: 1 (easy)

35. Find the value of the integral $\int_0^{\pi/4} \tan x \sec^2 x \, dx$.

A) 1/2   B) $\pi/4$ C) $3\pi/4$ D) 1
E) $\pi/2$ F) 1/4   G) 0   H) 3/4

Answer: 1/2 (medium)

36. Find the value of the integral $\int_0^{\pi/3} \sec^3 x \tan x \, dx$.

A) 5/3   B) 7/3   C) $\pi^2/27$ D) $\sqrt{3/2}$
E) $3\sqrt{3}/8$ F) 3/7   G) 3/5   H) $\pi^3/27$

Answer: 7/3 (medium)

37. Find the value of the integral $\int_0^{\pi/4} \tan^2 x \sec^4 x \, dx$.

A) 2/15   B) 4/15   C) 2/5   D) 8/15
E) 2/3   F) 4/5   G) 14/15   H) 16/15

Answer: 8/15 (medium)

38. Find the value of the integral $\int_0^{\pi/2} \sin^2 x \cos^3 x \, dx$.

A) 2/15   B) 4/15   C) 2/5   D) 8/15
E) 2/3   F) 4/5   G) 14/15   H) divergent

Answer: 2/15 (medium)

39. Find the integral $\int \sin^3 x \, dx$.

A) $\frac{\cos^3 x}{3} + C$ B) $\frac{\sin^3 x}{3} + C$ C) $-\cos x + \frac{\cos^3 x}{3} + C$

D) $\sin x - \frac{\sin^3 x}{3} + C$ E) $\frac{\cos^4 x}{4} + C$ F) $\frac{\sin^4 x}{4} + C$

G) $\cos x - \frac{\sin^3 x}{3} + C$ H) $\sin x - \frac{\cos^3 x}{3} + C$

Answer: $-\cos x + \frac{\cos^3 x}{3} + C$ (easy)

40. Find the value of the integral $\int_0^\pi \cos^2 \theta \, d\theta$.

A) 1/3   B) 2/3   C) 1/2   D) 1
E) $\pi/3$ F) $2\pi/3$ G) $\pi/2$ H) π

Answer: $\pi/2$ (easy)

41. Find the integral $\int \frac{\tan^2 x}{\cos^2 x} \, dx$.

Answer: $\frac{1}{3} \tan^3 x + C$ (easy)

42. Evaluate the following integral: $\int_{\pi/6}^{\pi/2} \cos^3 x \sqrt{\sin x} \, dx$.

Answer: $\frac{32\sqrt{2}-25}{84\sqrt{2}}$ (hard)

43. Find the following integral: $\int \sin^4 x \cos^3 x \, dx$.

Answer: $\frac{1}{5} \sin^5 x - \frac{1}{7} \sin^7 x + C$ (medium)

44. Find the following integral: $\int \frac{\sin^5 x + \sin^3 x}{\cos^4 x} \, dx$.

Answer: $\frac{-2}{3\cos^3 x} + \frac{3}{\cos x} + \cos x + C$ (hard)

45. Find $\int \sec^4(3x) \, dx$.

Answer: $\frac{\tan(3x)}{3} + \frac{\tan^3(3x)}{9} + C$ (medium)

46. Evaluate $\int \cos(2x) \tan x \, dx$.

Answer: $-\frac{1}{2} \cos(2x) + \ln|\cos x| + C$ (medium)

47. Find the area under the curve $y = 5 \sec^2(2x)$ and above the interval $\left[\frac{\pi}{8}, \frac{\pi}{6}\right]$.

Answer: $\frac{5}{2}(\sqrt{3} - 1)$ (medium)

48. Integrate: $\int \frac{dx}{\sin \frac{1}{2} x}$.

Answer: $2 \ln|\csc \frac{1}{2} x - \cot \frac{1}{2} x| + C$ (medium)

49. Integrate: $\int \cos^3 t \, dt$.

Answer: $\sin t - \frac{\sin^3 t}{3} + C$ (medium)

50. Evaluate the integral: $\int \sqrt{\cos x} \sin^3 x \, dx$.

Answer: $-\frac{2}{3} (\cos x)^{3/2} + \frac{2}{7} (\cos x)^{7/2} + C$ (medium)

Chapter 7, Section 3
Trigonometric Substitution

51. Find the value of the integral $\int_0^1 \frac{1}{1+x^2} \, dx$.

A) 1   B) 3/4   C) $\pi/2$ D) $3\pi/4$
E) 1/4   F) 0   G) $\pi/4$ H) 1/2

Answer: $\pi/4$ (easy)

52. Find the value of the integral $\int_0^1 \frac{dx}{\sqrt{x^2+1}}$.

A) 1   B) $\ln\left(\sqrt{2}-1\right)$ C) $\ln\left(\sqrt{3}+1\right)$ D) $\ln 2$

E) 0   F) $\ln\left(\sqrt{2}+1\right)$ G) $\ln\left(\sqrt{3}-1\right)$ H) $\ln 3$

Answer: $\ln\left(\sqrt{2}+1\right)$ (medium)

53. Find the value of the integral $\int_0^1 \sqrt{x^2+1} \, dx$.

A) $\left(\sqrt{2}+\ln\left(\sqrt{2}-1\right)\right)/2$ B) $\left(\sqrt{2}-\ln\left(\sqrt{2}-1\right)\right)/2$

C) $\left(\sqrt{2}-\ln\left(\sqrt{2}+1\right)\right)/2$ D) $\left(\sqrt{3}+\ln\left(\sqrt{3}-1\right)\right)/2$

E) $\left(\sqrt{3}-\ln\left(\sqrt{3}+1\right)\right)/2$ F) $\left(\sqrt{3}+\ln\left(\sqrt{3}+1\right)\right)/2$

G) $\left(\sqrt{3}-\ln\left(\sqrt{3}-1\right)\right)/2$ H) $\left(\sqrt{2}+\ln\left(\sqrt{2}+1\right)\right)/2$

Answer: $\left(\sqrt{2}+\ln\left(\sqrt{2}+1\right)\right)/2$ (hard)

54. Find the value of the integral $\int_0^1 \sqrt{1-x^2} \, dx$.

A) $3\pi/4$ B) 3/4   C) 1/2   D) $\pi/4$
E) 0   F) 1   G) $\pi/2$ H) 1/4

Answer: $\pi/4$ (medium)

55. Find the value of the integral $\int_0^1 \sqrt{2x - x^2}\, dx$.

A) $\pi/4$ B) $1/2$ C) 1 D) $3\pi/4$
E) $1/4$ F) $3/4$ G) 0 H) $\pi/2$

Answer: $\pi/4$ (hard)

56. Find the value of the integral $\int_{1/2}^1 \frac{1}{\sqrt{1-x^2}}\, dx$.

A) $\pi/2$ B) $\pi/6$ C) 0 D) $3\pi/2$.
E) $3\pi/4$ F) π G) $2\pi/3$ H) $\pi/3$

Answer: $\pi/3$ (medium)

57. Find the value of the integral $\int_0^{3/4} \frac{x}{\sqrt{x^2+1}}\, dx$.

A) 1 B) $3/4$ C) $\pi/2$ D) $1/4$
E) $\pi/4$ F) $3\pi/4$ G) 0 H) $1/2$

Answer: $1/4$ (medium)

58. Find the value of the integral $\int_0^3 \frac{dx}{\sqrt{9+x^2}}$.

A) $\sqrt{2}$ B) $3\sqrt{2}$ C) $1 + \sqrt{2}$

D) $3 + \sqrt{2}$ E) $\ln\left(1 + \sqrt{2}\right)$ F) $\ln\left(3 + \sqrt{2}\right)$

G) $\ln\left(\sqrt{2} - 1\right)$ H) $\ln\left(3 - \sqrt{2}\right)$

Answer: $\ln\left(1 + \sqrt{2}\right)$ (medium)

59. Find the value of the integral $\int_0^2 \frac{x^3}{\sqrt{x^2+4}}\, dx$.

A) $\frac{8}{3}\left(2 - \sqrt{2}\right)$ B) $\frac{10}{3}\left(2 + \sqrt{2}\right)$ C) $4\left(3 - 2\sqrt{2}\right)$

D) $\frac{14}{3}\left(2\sqrt{2} - 1\right)$ E) $\frac{16}{3}\left(5 - 2\sqrt{2}\right)$ F) $6\left(4 - \sqrt{2}\right)$

G) $\frac{20}{3}\left(4 + \sqrt{2}\right)$ H) $12\left(5 + \sqrt{2}\right)$

Answer: $\frac{8}{3}\left(2 - \sqrt{2}\right)$ (medium)

60. Find the integral $\int \frac{dx}{x^2 \sqrt{x^2+4}}$.

A) $\sqrt{x^2+4} + C$ B) $x\sqrt{x^2+4} + C$ C) $-\frac{\sqrt{x^2+4}}{4x} + C$

D) $-\frac{\sqrt{x^2+4}}{x^2} + C$ E) $\frac{1}{\sqrt{x^2+4}} + C$ F) $\frac{x}{\sqrt{x^2+4}} + C$

G) $-\frac{1}{4x\sqrt{x^2+4}} + C$ H) $-\frac{x^2}{\sqrt{x^2+4}} + C$

Answer: $-\frac{\sqrt{x^2+4}}{4x} + C$ (medium)

61. Find the value of the integral $\int_0^3 x^2 \sqrt{9-x^2}\, dx$.

A) 1/8   B) 3/16   C) 5/32   D) 9/64
E) $27\pi/8$ F) $81\pi/16$ G) $243\pi/32$ H) $9\pi/64$

Answer: $81\pi/16$ (medium)

62. Find the integral $\int \frac{3x^2\, dx}{\sqrt{4-x^2}}$.

Answer: $6 \arcsin\left(\frac{x}{2}\right) - \frac{3}{2} x\sqrt{4-x^2} + C$ (medium)

63. If an integral involves the quantity $\sqrt{x^2+1}$, a good substitution to consider is:

A) $x = \sin u$ B) $x = \tan u$ C) $x = \sec u$ D) $x = e^u$
E) $x = \ln u$

Answer: $x = \tan u$ (easy)

64. Find the integral $\int \frac{\sqrt{x^2-4}}{x}\, dx$.

Answer: $\sqrt{x^2-4} - 2 \operatorname{arc sec}\left(\frac{x}{2}\right) + C$ (hard)

65. Find the integral $\int_0^2 \frac{x^2}{(4+x^2)^2}\, dx$.

Answer: $\frac{\pi-2}{16}$ (medium)

66. Find the integral $\int \sqrt{1-x^2}\, dx$.

Answer: $\frac{1}{2} \sin^{-1} x + \frac{1}{2} x\sqrt{1-x^2} + C$ (hard)

67. Find the integral $\int \frac{1}{x\,(x^2+1)^{\frac{3}{2}}}\, dx$.

Answer: $\ln\left| \frac{\sqrt{x^2+1}}{x} - \frac{1}{x} \right| + \frac{1}{\sqrt{x^2+1}} + C$ (hard)

68. Find the integral $\int \sqrt{x^2+5}\, dx$.

Answer: $\frac{x\sqrt{x^2+5}}{2} + \frac{5}{2} \log\left(\sqrt{x^2+5}+x\right) + C$ (hard)

69. Find the integral $\int \frac{dx}{\sqrt{x^2+2x+2}}$.

Answer: $\ln \left| \sqrt{x^2 + 2x + 2} + (x+1) \right| + C$ (medium)

70. Find the integral $\int \frac{dx}{2x\sqrt{9-x^2}}$.

Answer: $\frac{1}{6} \ln \left| \frac{3-\sqrt{9-x^2}}{x} \right| + C$ (medium)

Chapter 7, Section 4
Integration of Rational Functions by Partial Fractions

71. In the partial fraction decomposition $\frac{1}{x^2-1} = \frac{A}{x+1} + \frac{B}{x-1}$ find the value of A.

A) -1 B) $1/2$ C) 2 D) -2
E) 1 F) $3/4$ G) $-1/2$ H) $-3/4$

Answer: $-1/2$ (easy)

72. In the partial fraction decomposition $\frac{x}{x^2-1} = \frac{A}{x+1} + \frac{B}{x-1}$ find the value of A.

A) $-3/4$ B) 1 C) -1 D) $1/2$
E) 2 F) -2 G) $3/4$ H) $-1/2$

Answer: $1/2$ (easy)

73. Find the value of the integral $\int_0^{1/2} \frac{1}{x^2-1} \, dx$.

A) $\frac{1}{2} \ln \frac{3}{4}$ B) $\ln \frac{3}{4}$ C) $\frac{1}{2} \ln \frac{4}{3}$ D) $\frac{1}{2} \ln \frac{2}{3}$
E) $\frac{1}{2} \ln 2$ F) $\frac{1}{2} \ln \frac{1}{3}$ G) $\frac{1}{2} \ln 3$ H) $\ln \frac{1}{3}$

Answer: $\frac{1}{2} \ln \frac{1}{3}$ (medium)

74. Find the value of the integral $\int_0^{1/2} \frac{x}{x^2-1} \, dx$.

A) $\frac{1}{2} \ln \frac{3}{4}$ B) $\ln \frac{3}{4}$ C) $\ln 3$ D) $\ln \frac{1}{3}$
E) $\frac{1}{2} \ln \frac{1}{3}$ F) $\frac{1}{2} \ln 3$ G) $\frac{1}{2} \ln 2$ H) $\frac{1}{2} \ln \frac{2}{3}$

Answer: $\frac{1}{2} \ln \frac{3}{4}$ (medium)

75. Find the value of the integral $\int_0^{1/2} \frac{x^2}{x^2-1} \, dx$.

A) $\frac{1}{2} (1 - \ln 3)$ B) $\ln 3$ C) $1 - \ln \frac{3}{4}$ D) $1 + \ln \frac{3}{4}$
E) $1 + \ln 3$ F) $-\frac{1}{2} \ln 3$ G) $1 - \ln 3$ H) $\frac{1}{2} \ln 3$

Answer: $\frac{1}{2} (1 - \ln 3)$ (medium)

76. In the partial fraction decomposition of $\frac{1}{x^2(x+1)}$ find the numerator of the fraction whose denominator is x^2.

   A) $1/2$ B) -1 C) -3 D) 2
   E) 3 F) -2 G) $-1/2$ H) 1

   Answer: 1 (medium)

77. Find the value of the integral $\int_0^1 \frac{1}{x^2-2x+2}\,dx$.

   A) $\ln\frac{1}{2}$ B) 0 C) $3\pi/4$ D) $\pi/2$
   E) $\ln\frac{3}{4}$ F) $\ln\frac{1}{4}$ G) $\pi/4$ H) 1

   Answer: $\pi/4$ (medium)

78. Find the value of the integral $\int_0^1 \frac{2x^2\,dx}{(x+1)(x^2+1)}$.

   A) $5\sqrt{5}-1$ B) $3\pi/2$ C) $\frac{\pi}{2}\left(3\sqrt{3}-1\right)$

   D) $\frac{\ln 2}{3}$ E) $\frac{3}{2}\ln 2 - \frac{\pi}{4}$ F) $\ln 8 - \frac{\pi}{2}$

   G) $\frac{\pi}{2}(\ln 3 - 1)$ H) $\ln 2 - \frac{\sqrt{3}}{2}$

   Answer: $\frac{3}{2}\ln 2 - \frac{\pi}{4}$ (hard)

79. Find the value of the integral $\int_2^3 \frac{dx}{x(x-1)}$.

   A) $3/2$ B) $4/3$ C) $\ln 2$ D) $\ln 3$
   E) $\ln(3/2)$ F) $\ln(4/3)$ G) $\ln(2/3)$ H) $\frac{3}{2}\ln 2$

   Answer: $\ln(4/3)$ (medium)

80. Find the value of the integral $\int_0^1 \frac{x}{x+1}\,dx$.

   A) $1 - \ln 2$ B) $1 + \ln 2$ C) $\ln 2$ D) $-\ln 2$
   E) $2 - \ln 2$ F) $2 + \ln 2$ G) $2 + 2\ln 2$ H) $2 - 2\ln 2$

   Answer: $1 - \ln 2$ (medium)

81. Find the value of the integral $\int_1^2 \frac{1}{x^3+x}\,dx$.

   A) $3\ln 2 - \ln 3$ B) $\ln 2 - 2\ln 3$ C) $\ln 2 - \ln 5$

   D) $3\ln 2 - \ln 5$ E) $\frac{3\ln 2-\ln 3}{2}$ F) $\frac{\ln 2-2\ln 3}{2}$

   G) $\frac{\ln 2-\ln 5}{2}$ H) $\frac{3\ln 2-\ln 5}{2}$

   Answer: $\frac{3\ln 2-\ln 5}{2}$ (medium)

82. Find the value of the integral $\int_2^4 \frac{dx}{x^2-1}$.

A) $\ln 2$ B) $\ln 3$ C) $\ln 4$

D) $\ln 5$ E) $\ln 4 - \ln 3$ F) $2 \ln 5 - \ln 4$

G) $\frac{1}{5} \ln 5 - \frac{1}{3} \ln 3$ H) $\ln 3 - \frac{1}{2} \ln 5$

Answer: $\ln 3 - \frac{1}{2} \ln 5$ (medium)

83. Find the value of the integral $\int_0^1 \frac{x+1}{x^2+1} \, dx$.

A) π B) $1 - 2 \ln 2$ C) $\frac{\pi}{2} - 1$ D) $\frac{\ln 6}{2}$

E) $\frac{4-\pi}{2}$ F) $\frac{\pi + 2 \ln 2}{4}$ G) $\frac{4 \ln 2 - \pi}{6}$ H) $\frac{\pi - \ln 2}{8}$

Answer: $\frac{\pi + 2 \ln 2}{4}$ (medium)

84. Find the value of the integral $\int_3^4 \frac{dx}{(x-1)(x-2)}$.

A) $\ln 2$ B) $\ln 3$ C) $\ln 4$ D) $\ln 8$

E) $\ln(1/2)$ F) $\ln(2/3)$ G) $\ln(4/3)$ H) $\ln(8/3)$

Answer: $\ln(4/3)$ (medium)

85. Evaluate the integral $\int \frac{5x^2+26x+29}{(x+2)(x+1)(x+3)} \, dx$.

Answer: $3 \ln |x+2| + 4 \ln |x+1| - 2 \ln |x+3| + C$ (hard)!

86. Evaluate the integral $\int \frac{2x+1}{(x^2+1)(3x-1)} \, dx$.

Answer: $-\frac{1}{4} \ln(x^2+1) + \frac{1}{2} \arctan x + \frac{1}{2} \ln |3x-1| + C$ (hard)

87. Evaluate the integral $\int \frac{12+21x-8x^2}{4x^2-x^3} \, dx$.

Answer: $-\frac{3}{x} + 2 \ln |x^3(4-x)| + C$ (hard)

88. Evaluate the integral $\int \frac{25}{x^4+2x^3+5x^2} \, dx$.

Answer: $\ln \left(\frac{x^2+2x+5}{x^2} \right) - \frac{5}{x} - \frac{3}{2} \tan^{-1} \frac{x+1}{2} + C$ (hard)

89. Evaluate the integral $\int \frac{(2x+1)}{(x^2-1)(x^2+1)} \, dx$.

Answer: $\frac{3}{4} \ln |x+1| + \frac{1}{4} \ln |x-1| - \frac{1}{2} \ln |x^2+1| - \frac{1}{2} \arctan x + C$ (hard)

90. Evaluate the integral $\int \frac{1}{x^3-x^2+x-1} \, dx$.

Answer: $-\frac{1}{2} \arctan x + \frac{1}{2} \ln(x-1) + C$ (hard)

91. Use the method of partial fractions to evaluate $\int_0^1 \frac{3x+4}{x^3-2x-4}\ dx$.

Answer: $\ln 10^{-1/2}$ (hard)

92. Evaluate the integral $\int \frac{2x^2+5x-4}{x(x+2)(x-1)}\ dx$.

Answer: $2\ln|x| - \ln|x+2| + \ln|x-1| + C$ (hard)

93. Evaluate the integral $\int \frac{6x^3+3x+1}{x^2(x^2+1)}\ dx$.

Answer: $3\ln|x| - \frac{1}{x} + \frac{3}{2}\ln(x^2+1) - \tan^{-1}x + C$ (hard)

94. Evaluate the integral $\int \frac{x^2+x+4}{(x+1)(x^2+3)}\ dx$.

Answer: $\ln|x+1| + \frac{1}{\sqrt{3}}\tan^{-1}\frac{x}{\sqrt{3}} + C$ (hard)

95. Evaluate the integral $\int \frac{dx}{x^3+2x^2+x}$

Answer: $\ln\left|\frac{x}{x+1}\right| + \frac{1}{x+1} + C$ (medium)

96. Evaluate the integral $\int \frac{x}{(x-2)(x+3)}\ dx$.

Answer: $\frac{2}{5}\ln|x-2| + \frac{3}{5}\ln|x+3| + C$ (medium)

97. Evaluate the integral $\int \frac{2x}{(x^2+1)(x+1)^2}\ dx$.

Answer: $\tan^{-1}x + \frac{1}{x+1} + C$ (medium)

Chapter 7, Section 5
Rationalizing Substitutions

98. Find the value of the integral $\int_0^1 \frac{x}{\sqrt{x+1}}\ dx$.

A) $\frac{2}{3}\left(2+\sqrt{2}\right)$ B) $\frac{4}{3}\left(\sqrt{2}+1\right)$ C) $\frac{2}{3}\left(\sqrt{2}+1\right)$ D) $\frac{2}{3}\left(2-\sqrt{2}\right)$

E) $\frac{4}{3}\left(2-\sqrt{2}\right)$ F) $\frac{2}{3}\left(\sqrt{2}-1\right)$ G) $\frac{4}{3}\left(2+\sqrt{2}\right)$ H) $\frac{4}{3}\left(\sqrt{2}-1\right)$

Answer: $\frac{2}{3}\left(2-\sqrt{2}\right)$ (medium)

99. Find the value of the integral $\int_0^1 \frac{1}{1+\sqrt{x}}\ dx$.

A) $3(1-\ln 2)$ B) $\frac{2}{3}(1-\ln 2)$ C) $\frac{3}{2}(1-\ln 2)$

D) $2(1+\ln 2)$ E) $2(1-\ln 2)$ F) $\frac{2}{3}(1+\ln 2)$

G) $\frac{3}{2}(1+\ln 2)$ H) $3(1+\ln 2)$

Answer: $2(1-\ln 2)$ (medium)

100. Find the value of the integral $\int_3^8 \frac{\sqrt{x+1}}{x}\,dx$.

   A) $\frac{1}{2}\ln\frac{4}{3}$ B) $\ln\frac{2}{3}$ C) $\frac{1}{2}\ln\frac{8}{3}$ D) $2-\ln\frac{3}{2}$

   E) $\frac{1}{2}\ln\frac{1}{3}$ F) $\ln\frac{8}{3}$ G) $\ln\frac{1}{3}$ H) $\ln\frac{4}{3}$

   Answer: $2-\ln\frac{3}{2}$ (hard)

101. Find the value of the integral $\int_3^8 \frac{1}{x\sqrt{x+1}}\,dx$.

   A) $\ln(3/2)$ B) $\ln(5/2)$ C) $\ln(11/5)$ D) $\ln(4/3)$
   E) $\ln(8/3)$ F) $\ln(11/3)$ G) $\ln(5/3)$ H) $\ln(11/2)$

   Answer: $\ln(3/2)$ (hard)

102. Find the value of the integral $\int_0^{\pi/2} \frac{1}{1+\sin x}\,dx$.

   A) 3   B) 2   C) 4/3   D) 1
   E) 5/3   F) 2/3   G) 8/3   H) 7/3

   Answer: 1 (hard)

103. Find the value of the integral $\int_1^4 \frac{x+1}{\sqrt{x}}\,dx$.

   A) 23/3   B) 8   C) 7   D) 20/3
   E) 22/3   F) 19/3   G) 25/3   H) 6

   Answer: 20/3 (easy)

104. Find the value of the integral $\int_2^6 \frac{\sqrt{x-2}}{x+2}\,dx$.

   A) 1   B) 2   C) $4-\pi$ D) $\pi/2$
   E) $2+\pi$ F) $3\ln 2$ G) $2\ln 2 - 1$ H) $4-\ln 2$

   Answer: $4-\pi$ (hard)

105. Find the value of the integral $\int_0^3 \frac{x}{\sqrt{x+1}}\,dx$.

   A) $\tan^{-1}3$ B) $\ln 2$ C) 8/3   D) 3π
   E) 3   F) 3/2   G) $\pi/\sqrt{3}$ H) $\frac{1}{2}\ln 3$

   Answer: 8/3 (medium)

106. Find the integral $\int \frac{\sqrt{x+2}-1}{\sqrt{x+2}+1}\,dx$.

   Answer: $x+2-4\sqrt{x+2}+4\log\left|\sqrt{x+2}+1\right|+C$ (hard)

107. Find the integral $\int \frac{2+\sqrt[3]{x}}{\sqrt[3]{x}+\sqrt{x}}\,dx$.

Answer: $\frac{6}{5}x^{5/6} - \frac{3}{2}x^{2/3} + 6x^{1/2} - 9x^{1/3} + 18x^{1/6} - 18\ln\left|x^{1/6}+1\right| + C$ (hard)

108. The substitution $x = u^{12}$ changes $\int \frac{1}{\sqrt[3]{x}+\sqrt[4]{x}}\,dx$ into:

A) $\int \frac{1}{u^4+u^3}\,du$ B) $\int \frac{12u^8}{u+1}\,du$ C) $\int \frac{u^9}{u+1}\,du$

D) $\int \frac{1}{u^2+u}\,du$ E) $\int \frac{12u}{u^2+1}\,du$

Answer: $\int \frac{12u^8}{u+1}\,du$ (easy)

109. Find the integral $\int \frac{\sqrt[6]{x}}{\sqrt{x}+\sqrt[3]{x}}\,dx$.

Answer: $\frac{3}{2}x^{2/3} - 2\sqrt{x} + 3\sqrt[3]{x} - 6\sqrt[6]{x} + 6\ln\left(\sqrt[6]{x}+1\right) + C$ (hard)

110. Find the value of the integral $\int_0^1 \frac{1}{1+\sqrt[3]{x}}\,dx$.

Answer: $3\left(\ln 2 - \frac{1}{2}\right)$

111. Find the integral $\int \frac{1}{x\sqrt{x+1}}\,dx$.

Answer: $\ln\left|\frac{\sqrt{x+1}-1}{\sqrt{x+1}+1}\right| + C$

112. Find the integral $\int \frac{1}{x-\sqrt{x+2}}\,dx$.

Answer: $\frac{2}{3}\left[2\ln\left|\sqrt{x+2}-2\right| + \ln(\sqrt{x+2}+1)\right] + C$

113. Evaluate the integral $\int_1^3 \frac{\sqrt{x-1}}{x+1}\,dx$.

Answer: $2\sqrt{2}(1-\pi/4)$

114. Find the integral $\int \frac{\sqrt[3]{x}+1}{\sqrt[3]{x}-1}\,dx$.

Answer: $x + 3x^{2/3} + 6\sqrt[3]{x} + 6\ln\left|\sqrt[3]{x}-1\right| + C$

115. Find the integral $\int \frac{x}{x^2-\sqrt[3]{x^2}}\,dx$.

Answer: $\frac{3}{4}\ln\left|x^{4/3}-1\right| + C$

116. Find the integral $\int \frac{1}{\sqrt[3]{x}+\sqrt[4]{x}}\,dx$.

Answer: $\frac{3}{2}x^{2/3} - \frac{12}{7}x^{7/12} + 2\sqrt{x} - \frac{12}{5}x^{5/12} + 3\sqrt[3]{x} - 4\sqrt[4]{x} + 6\sqrt[6]{x} - 12\sqrt[12]{x} +$
$12\ln\left(\sqrt[12]{x}+1\right) + C$

117. Find the integral $\int \sqrt{\frac{x-1}{x}} \, dx$.

Answer: $\sqrt{x(x-1)} - \ln\sqrt{x} + \sqrt{(x-1)} + C$

118. Find the integral $\int \frac{\sin x}{\cos^2 x + \cos x - 6} \, dx$.

Answer: $\frac{1}{5} \ln \left| \frac{\cos x + 3}{\cos x - 2} \right| + C$

119. Find the integral $\int \frac{e^{3x}}{e^{2x}-1} \, dx$.

Answer: $e^x + \frac{1}{2} \ln \left| \frac{e^x - 1}{e^x + 1} \right| + C$

120. Find the integral $\int \frac{dx}{3 - 5\sin x}$.

Answer: $\frac{1}{4} \ln \left| \frac{\tan(x/2) - 3}{3\tan(x/2) - 1} \right| + C$

121. Find the integral $\int \frac{\sec x}{1 + \sin x} \, dx$.

Answer: $\frac{1}{2} \ln \left| \frac{1 + \tan(x/2)}{1 - \tan(x/2)} \right| + \frac{1}{1 + \tan(x/2)} - \frac{1}{[1 + \tan(x/2)]^2} + C$

Chapter 7, Section 6
Strategy for Integration

122. Find the value of the integral $\int_0^{\pi/4} \frac{1}{\cos^2 x} \, dx$.

A) $\pi/3$ B) $1/2$ C) $\pi/2$ D) $\sqrt{3}/2$
E) $2\pi/3$ F) 1 G) π H) $\sqrt{3}/4$

Answer: 1 (easy)

123. Find the value of the integral $\int_0^{\pi/3} \frac{\sin x}{\cos^2 x} \, dx$.

A) 1 B) $\pi/3$ C) $1/2$ D) π
E) $\sqrt{3}/4$ F) $\pi/2$ G) $2\pi/3$ H) $\sqrt{3}/2$

Answer: 1 (easy)

124. Find the value of the integral $\int_1^4 e^{-\sqrt{x}} \, dx$.

A) $(2e+1)/(6e)$ B) $(2e+1)/(6e^2)$ C) $(2e-1)/(12e)$

D) $(2e+1)/(12e^2)$ E) $(2e-1)/(12e^2)$ F) $(4e-6)/e^2$
G) $(4e-6)/e$ H) $(2e+1)/(12e)$

Answer: $(4e-6)/e^2$ (medium)

125. Find the value of the integral $\int_1^e \frac{(\ln x)^3}{x}\, dx$.

A) 1   B) $e/2$ C) $1/3$ D) $1/2$
E) e F) $e/3$ G) $1/4$ H) $e/4$

Answer: 1/4 (medium)

126. Find the value of the integral $\int_0^1 \frac{x}{x^2+1}\, dx$.

A) $\frac{1}{2}\ln 2$ B) $3/4$ C) 1   D) $\ln 2$
E) $1/4$ F) $3/2$ G) $\frac{1}{4}\ln 2$ H) $1/2$

Answer: $\frac{1}{2}\ln 2$ (easy)

127. Find the value of the integral $\int_0^{\pi/4} \tan^2 x\, dx$.

A) $2+(\pi/2)$ B) $1-(\pi/2)$ C) $2+(\pi/4)$ D) $1+(\pi/4)$
E) $2-(\pi/4)$ F) $1-(\pi/4)$ G) $2-(\pi/2)$ H) $1+(\pi/2)$

Answer: $1-(\pi/4)$ (medium)

128. Find the value of the integral $\int_0^1 \frac{x^2}{x+1}\, dx$.

A) $\ln 2 - \frac{1}{2}$ B) $\ln 2 - \frac{1}{4}$ C) $\ln 2 + \frac{1}{4}$ D) $\frac{1}{2}\ln 2 + \frac{1}{2}$
E) $\frac{1}{2}\ln 2 - \frac{1}{2}$ F) $\frac{1}{2}\ln 2 + \frac{1}{4}$ G) $\ln 2 + \frac{1}{2}$ H) $\frac{1}{2}\ln 2 - \frac{1}{4}$

Answer: $\ln 2 - \frac{1}{2}$ (medium)

129. Find the value of the integral $\int_0^1 x^7 e^{-x^4}\, dx$.

A) $\frac{1}{4}(2+1/e)$ B) $\frac{1}{2}(2+2/e)$ C) $\frac{1}{2}(2-1/e)$

D) $\frac{1}{4}(1+1/e)$ E) $\frac{1}{4}(2-1/e)$ F) $\frac{1}{4}(1-2/e)$

G) $\frac{1}{2}(2+1/e)$ H) $\frac{1}{2}(2-2/e)$

Answer: $\frac{1}{4}(1-2/e)$ (hard)

130. Find the value of the integral $\int_0^1 \ln(1+x^2)\, dx$.

A) $\ln 2$ B) $\pi/8$ C) $\pi/2 - 2 + \ln 2$

D) $2 - \ln 2$ E) $\pi/4 + \ln 2$ F) $\pi - 4$

G) $\pi - 2$ H) $\pi - \ln 2$

Answer: $\pi/2 - 2 + \ln 2$ (hard)

131. Find the value of the integral $\int \frac{1+\ln x}{x \ln x} dx$.

A) $\ln x + C$ B) $\ln \ln x + C$ C) $x + \ln x + C$
D) $\ln x + \ln \ln x + C$ E) $x/\ln x + C$ F) $\ln x/(x + \ln x) + C$
G) $x \ln x + C$ H) $x \ln \ln x + C$

Answer: $\ln x + \ln \ln x + C$ (medium)

132. Find the value of the integral $\int \cos \sqrt{x}\, dx$.

A) $2 \sin \sqrt{x} + C$ B) $2 \sqrt{x} \cos \sqrt{x} + C$

C) $\sqrt{x}\, (\cos \sqrt{x} + \sin \sqrt{x}) + C$ D) $\frac{\cos \sqrt{x} + \sin \sqrt{x}}{\sqrt{x}} + C$

E) $2(\sqrt{x} \sin \sqrt{x} + \cos \sqrt{x}) + C$ F) $2(\sqrt{x} \cos \sqrt{x} + \sin \sqrt{x}) + C$

G) $\sqrt{x} \cos \sqrt{x} + \frac{\sin \sqrt{x}}{\sqrt{x}} + C$ H) $\sqrt{x} \sin \sqrt{x} + \frac{\cos \sqrt{x}}{\sqrt{x}} + C$

Answer: $2\,(\sqrt{x} \sin \sqrt{x} + \cos \sqrt{x}) + C$ (hard)

133. Evaluate the following integral $\int \frac{4\sqrt{x}}{6+x} dx$.

Answer: $8\sqrt{x} - 8\sqrt{6} \tan^{-1}\left(\sqrt{\frac{x}{6}}\right) + C$ (medium)

134. Evaluate the following integral $\int_0^{1/4} \sec(\pi u) \tan(\pi u)\, du$.

Answer: $\frac{1}{\pi}\left(\sqrt{2} - 1\right)$ (easy)

135. Evaluate the following integral $\int x(1 + x^3)^2 dx$.

Answer: $\frac{x^2}{2} + \frac{2x^5}{5} + \frac{x^8}{8} + C$ (medium)

136. $\int \sin^5 x \cos x\, dx$ is:

A) $\frac{1}{12} \sin^6 x \cos^2 x + C$ B) $\frac{1}{6} \sin^6 x \cos x + C$
C) $-\sin^6 x + 5 \sin^4 x \cos^2 x + C$ D) $\frac{1}{6} \sin^6 x + C$
E) $\frac{1}{6} \sin^7 x + C$

Answer: $\frac{1}{6} \sin^6 x + C$ (easy)

137. Integrate $\int \frac{1}{\sqrt{9-4x^2}} dx$.

Answer: $\frac{1}{2} \sin^{-1}\left(\frac{2}{3} x\right) + C$ (medium)

138. Integrate $\int t \sin t\, dt$.

Answer: $-t \cos t + \sin t$ (medium)

139. Integrate $\int \frac{x^3 + 2x}{\sqrt{x^2 - 2}} \, dx$.

Answer: $\frac{1}{3} \left(x^2 - 2\right)^{3/2} + 4 \left(x^2 - 2\right)^{1/2} + C$ (medium)

140. Integrate $\int \frac{e^x + e^{-x}}{e^x - e^{-x}} \, dx$.

Answer: $\ln\left(e^x + e^{-x}\right) + C$ (medium)

141. Evaluate the following integral $\int \frac{x^3 + 4x^2 + 13x + 3}{x^2 + 4x + 13} \, dx$.

Answer: $\frac{1}{2}x^2 + \tan^{-1}\left(\frac{x+2}{3}\right) + C$ (hard)

142. Give the integration technique most likely to work for the following integral. It is not necessary to do the integration.
$$\int x \sin x \, dx$$

Answer: Integration by parts. The two factors, x and $\sin x$, are dissimilar. (easy)

143. Give the integration technique most likely to work for the following integral. It is not necessary to do the integration.
$$\int \frac{x+1}{x^2 - 4} \, dx$$

Answer: Partial fractions. The integrand is a rational function, and the denominator factors.

(easy)

144. Give the integration technique most likely to work for the following integral. It is not necessary to do the integration.
$$\int \frac{t}{\sqrt{t+2}} \, dt$$

Answer: Substitution, such as $u^2 = t + 2$, to remove the radical. (easy)

145. Give the integration technique most likely to work for the following integral. It is not necessary to do the integration.
$$\int \frac{x^3 + x^2 + 1}{x - 3} \, dx$$

Answer: Long division. The fraction is improper, since the numerator is of higher degree than

the denominator. After division, integrate the quotient and remainder using basic

formulas. (medium)

146. Give the integration technique most likely to work for the following integral. It is not necessary to do the integration.
$$\int \sqrt{1 - x^2} \, dx$$

Answer: Trigonometric substitution $x = \sin \theta$ to remove the radical. $x = \cos \theta$ would work as

well. (medium)

147. Give the integration technique most likely to work for the following integral. It is not necessary to do the integration.

$$\int \ln(2x - 3)\ dx$$

Answer: Integration by parts with $u = \ln(2x - 3)$ and $dv = dx$ to change the form

of the integral. (easy)

148. Evaluate the integral $\int \frac{x^5}{\sqrt{1+x^3}}\ dx$.

Answer: $\frac{2}{9}\left(1 + x^3\right)^{3/2} - \frac{2}{3}\left(1+x^3\right)^{1/2} + C$ (medium)

Chapter 7, Section 7
Using Tables of Integrals and Computer Algebra Systems

149. Find the value of the integral $\int_{-1}^{1} \sqrt{1 - u^2}\ du$.

A) 2   B) 1   C) $\pi/4$ D) 1/4
E) 1/2   F) π G) $\pi/2$ H) 2π

Answer: $\pi/2$ (easy)

150. Find the value of the integral $\int_{-1}^{1} \sqrt{2 - u^2}\ du$.

A) $2 - (\pi/2)$ B) $2 + (\pi/4)$ C) $1 - (\pi/4)$ D) $1 + (\pi/4)$
E) $(\pi/2) - 1$ F) $2 - (\pi/4)$ G) $1 + (\pi/2)$ H) $2 + (\pi/2)$

Answer: $1 + (\pi/2)$ (medium)

151. Find the value of the integral $\int_{\pi/4}^{\pi/2} \csc u\ du$.

A) $-\frac{1}{2}\ln\left(\sqrt{2} - 1\right)$ B) $\ln\left(2 - \sqrt{2}\right)$ C) $\frac{1}{2}\ln\left(\sqrt{2} - 1\right)$

D) $-\ln\left(2 - \sqrt{2}\right)$ E) $\ln\left(\sqrt{2} - 1\right)$ F) $-\frac{1}{2}\ln 2 - \left(\sqrt{2}\right)$

G) $\frac{1}{2}\ln 2 - \left(\sqrt{2}\right)$ H) $-\ln\left(\sqrt{2} - 1\right)$

Answer: $-\ln\left(\sqrt{2} - 1\right)$ (medium)

152. Find the value of the integral $\int_{1}^{2} \sqrt{u^2 - 1}\ du$.

A) $\sqrt{3} + \frac{1}{2}\ln\left(4 - \sqrt{3}\right)$ B) $\sqrt{3} - \frac{1}{2}\ln\left(2 + \sqrt{3}\right)$ C) $\sqrt{3} - \frac{1}{2}\ln\left(4 + \sqrt{3}\right)$

D) $\sqrt{3} + \frac{1}{2}\ln\left(2 - \sqrt{3}\right)$ E) $\sqrt{3} - \frac{1}{2}\ln\left(4 - \sqrt{3}\right)$ F) $\sqrt{3} + \frac{1}{2}\ln\left(4 + \sqrt{3}\right)$

G) $\sqrt{3} + \frac{1}{2}\ln\left(2 + \sqrt{3}\right)$ H) $\sqrt{3} - \frac{1}{2}\ln\left(2 - \sqrt{3}\right)$

Answer: $\sqrt{3} - \frac{1}{2}\ln\left(2 + \sqrt{3}\right)$ (medium)

153. Find the value of the integral $\int_0^1 \tan^{-1} u \, du$.

A) $\frac{\pi}{4} - \ln 2$ B) $\frac{\pi}{2} + \frac{1}{2}\ln 2$ C) $\frac{\pi}{2} - \ln 2$ D) $\frac{\pi}{2} + \ln 2$

E) $\frac{\pi}{4} + \ln 2$ F) $\frac{\pi}{2} - \frac{1}{2}\ln 2$ G) $\frac{\pi}{4} - \frac{1}{2}\ln 2$ H) $\frac{\pi}{4} + \frac{1}{2}\ln 2$

Answer: $\frac{\pi}{4} - \frac{1}{2}\ln 2$ (medium)

154. Find the value of the integral $\int_0^{\pi/12} \sin^2 u \, du$.

A) $(\pi - 3)/18$ B) $(\pi - 3)/16$ C) $(\pi - 3)/24$
D) $(\pi - 3)/72$ E) $(\pi - 3)/36$ F) $(\pi - 3)/12$
G) $(\pi - 3)/48$ H) $(\pi - 3)/60$

Answer: $(\pi - 3)/24$ (easy)

155. Find the value of the integral $\int_1^e u^{10} \ln u \, du$.

A) $\left(10e^{10} + 1\right)/121$ B) $\left(10e^{10} - 1\right)/121$ C) $\left(11e^{10} + 1\right)/121$

D) $\left(11e^{10} - 1\right)/121$ E) $\left(10e^{11} + 1\right)/121$ F) $\left(11e^{11} + 1\right)/121$

G) $\left(11e^{11} - 1\right)/121$ H) $\left(10e^{11} - 1\right)/121$

Answer: $\left(10e^{11} + 1\right)/121$ (medium)

156. Evaluate the integral $\int \csc^3\left(\frac{x}{2}\right) dx$.

Answer: $-\csc\left(\frac{x}{2}\right)\cot\left(\frac{x}{2}\right) + \ln\left|\csc\left(\frac{x}{2}\right) - \cot\left(\frac{x}{2}\right)\right| + C$ (medium)

157. Evaluate the integral $\int \frac{\sqrt{4 - 3x^2}}{x} dx$.

Answer: $\sqrt{4 - 3x^2} - 2\ln\left|\frac{2 + \sqrt{4 - 3x^2}}{x}\right| + C$ (medium)

158. Evaluate the integral $\int \frac{\sin x \cos x}{\sqrt{1 + \sin x}} dx$.

Answer: $-\frac{2}{3}(2 - \sin x)\sqrt{1 + \sin x} + C$ (medium)

159. Evaluate the integral $\int x^3 \sin^{-1}\left(x^2\right) dx$.

Answer: $\frac{2x^4 - 1}{8}\sin^{-1}\left(x^2\right) + \frac{x^2\sqrt{1 - x^2}}{8} + C$ (medium)

160. Evaluate the integral $\int \frac{x^5}{x^2 + \sqrt{2}} dx$.

Answer: $\frac{1}{4}x^4 - \frac{1}{\sqrt{2}}x^2 + \ln\left(x^2 + \sqrt{2}\right) + C$ (medium)

161. Evaluate the integral $\int \sin^6 2x \, dx$.

Answer: $-\frac{1}{12}\sin^5 2x \cos 2x - \frac{5}{48}\sin^3 2x \cos 2x - \frac{5}{64}\sin 4x + \frac{5}{16}x + C$ (hard)

162. Evaluate the integral $\int \frac{x}{\sqrt{x^2-4x}}\, dx$.

Answer: $\sqrt{x^2 - 4x} + 2\ln\left|x - 2 + \sqrt{x^2 - 4x}\right| + C$ (medium)

163. Evaluate the integral $\int_0^\infty x^4 e^{-x}\, dx$.

Answer: 24 (medium)

Chapter 7, Section 8
Approximate Integration

164. Use the Trapezoidal Rule with $n = 1$ to approximate the integral $\int_0^1 \sqrt{x}\, dx$.

A) 1/2   B) 9/16   C) 7/16   D) 1/4
E) 3/8   F) 2/3   G) 1/3   H) 5/8

Answer: 1/2 (easy)

165. Use Simpson's Rule with $n = 2$ to approximate the integral $\int_0^1 x^3\, dx$.

A) 5/8   B) 1/3   C) 3/8   D) 2/3
E) 7/16   F) 1/4   G) 9/16   H) 1/2

Answer: 1/4 (easy)

166. Use the Trapezoidal Rule with $n = 2$ to approximate the integral $\int_0^1 x^3\, dx$.

A) 5/16   B) 1/4   C) 1/2   D) 5/8
E) 1/3   F) 7/16   G) 2/3   H) 3/8

Answer: 5/16 (medium)

167. Use Simpson's Rule with $n = 4$ to approximate the integral $\int_1^5 \frac{1}{x}\, dx$.

A) 73/45   B) 71/48   C) 61/35   D) 73/48
E) 61/36   F) 59/36   G) 59/35   H) 71/45

Answer: 73/45 (medium)

168. Use the Midpoint Rule with $n = 5$ to approximate $\int_1^2 \frac{1}{x}\, dx$.

A) 0.6909   B) 0.6913   C) 0.6919   D) 0.6925
E) 0.6928   F) 0.6932   G) 0.6937   H) 0.6945

Answer: 0.6919 (medium)

169. Use the Midpoint Rule with $n = 4$ to approximate $\int_0^{\pi/4} \tan x \, dx$.

    A) 0.2914   B) 0.3160   C) 0.3289   D) 0.3317
    E) 0.3450   F) 0.3601   G) 0.3764   H) 0.3844

    Answer: 0.3450 (medium)

170. Suppose using $n = 10$ to approximate the integral of a certain function by the Trapezoidal Rule results in an upper bound for the error equal to $1/10$. What will the upper bound become if we change to $n = 20$?

    A) 1/10000   B) 1/100   C) 1/80   D) 1/160
    E) 1/1000   F) 1/20   G) 1/40   H) 1/100000

    Answer: 1/40 (easy)

171. Suppose using $n = 10$ to approximate the integral of a certain function by Simpson's Rule results in an upper bound for the error equal to $1/10$. What will the upper bound become if we change to $n = 20$?

    A) 1/100   B) 1/10000   C) 1/40   D) 1/1000
    E) 1/160   F) 1/20   G) 1/100000   H) 1/80

    Answer: 1/160 (easy)

172. Evaluate $\int_0^2 \sqrt{x^3 + 2} \, dx$ using Simpson's Rule with $n = 6$.

    Answer: approximately 3.86 (medium)

173. Use Simpson's rule with $n = 10$ to approximate $\int_0^1 \frac{1}{1+x^2} \, dx$.

    Answer: approximately 0.7846 (medium)

174. Use the midpoint rule with 2 equal subdivisions to get an approximation for $\ln 5$.

    Answer: 1.5 (easy)

175. Use (a) the Trapezoidal Rule and (b) Simpson's Rule to approximate the given integral with the given value of n. (Round your answers to six decimal places.)
$$\int_0^2 e^x \, dx, \quad n = 8$$

    Answer: (a) $T = 6.422298$ (b) $S = 6.389194$

176. Use (a) the Trapezoidal Rule and (b) Simpson's Rule to approximate the given integral with the given value of n. (Round your answers to six decimal places.)
$$\int_0^1 \frac{1}{1+x^2} \, dx, \quad n = 10$$

    Answer: (a) $T = -.784981$ (b) $S = 0.785398$

177. Use (a) the Trapezoidal Rule and (b) Simpson's Rule to approximate the given integral with the given value of n. (Round your answers to six decimal places.)
$$\int_{-1}^{2} xe^x \, dx, \quad n = 12$$

Answer: (a) $T = 8.240073$ (b) $S = 8.125593$

178. Use (a) the Trapezoidal Rule and (b) Simpson's Rule to approximate the given integral with the given value of n. (Round your answers to six decimal places.)
$$\int_0^1 \cos(x^2) \, dx, \quad n = 4$$

Answer: (a) $T = 0.895759$ (b) $S = 0.904501$

179. Use (a) the Trapezoidal Rule and (b) Simpson's Rule to approximate the given integral with the given value of n. (Round your answers to six decimal places.)
$$\int_0^{\pi/4} x \tan x \, dx, \quad n = 6$$

Answer: (a) $T = 0.189445$ (b) $S = 0.904501$

180. Use (a) the Trapezoidal Rule, (b) the Midpoint Rule, and (c) Simpson's Rule to approximate the given integral with the given value of n. (Round your answers to six decimal places.)
$$\int_0^2 \frac{1}{\sqrt{1+x^3}} \, dx, \quad n = 10$$

Answer: (a) $T = 1.401435$ (b) $M = 1.402556$ (c) $S = 1.402206$

181. Use (a) the Trapezoidal Rule and (b) Simpson's Rule to approximate the given integral with the given value of n. (Round your answers to six decimal places.)
$$\int_2^3 \frac{1}{\ln x} \, dx, \quad n = 10$$

Answer: (a) $T = 1.119061$ (b) $S = 1.118428$

182. Use (a) the Trapezoidal Rule and (b) Simpson's Rule to approximate the given integral with the given value of n. (Round your answers to six decimal places.)
$$\int_0^1 \ln(1 + e^x) \, dx, \quad n = 8$$

Answer: (a) $T = 0.984120$ (b) $S = 0.983819$

183. The widths (in meters) of a kidney-shaped swimming pool were measured at 2-m intervals as indicated in the figure. Use Simpson's Rule to estimate the area of the pool.

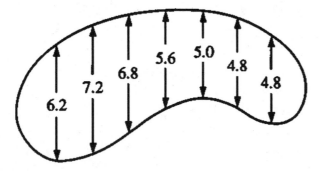

Answer: 84 m^2

Chapter 7, Section 9
Improper Integrals

184. Evaluate the improper integral $\int_1^\infty x^{-2}\,dx$.

   A) 1/4   B) 1   C) 2   D) 4
   E) 1/2   F) 3   G) 1/3   H) divergent

   Answer: 1 (medium)

185. Evaluate the improper integral $\int_0^1 x^{-2}\,dx$.

   A) 3   B) 1/4   C) 4   D) 2
   E) 1/3   F) 1/2   G) 1   H) divergent

   Answer: divergent (easy)

186. Evaluate the improper integral $\int_1^\infty x^{-1/2}\,dx$.

   A) 4   B) 3   C) 1/4   D) 1/3
   E) 1/2   F) 2   G) 1   H) divergent

   Answer: divergent (easy)

187. Evaluate the improper integral $\int_0^1 x^{-1/2}\,dx$.

   A) 1/3   B) 1/2   C) 1   D) 2
   E) 1/4   F) 3   G) 4   H) divergent

   Answer: 2 (medium)

188. Evaluate the improper integral $\int_1^\infty \frac{\ln x}{x}\,dx$.

   A) 2   B) $\frac{1}{2}\ln 2$ C) $\frac{1}{4}\ln 2$ D) 1

   E) $\ln 2$ F) 1/2   G) $2\ln 2$ H) divergent

   Answer: divergent (medium)

189. Evaluate the improper integral $\int_0^1 \frac{\ln x}{x}\,dx$.

   A) 1/2   B) 1   C) $\ln 2$ D) $\frac{1}{4}\ln 2$
   E) $\frac{1}{2}\ln 2$ F) $2\ln 2$ G) 2   H) divergent

   Answer: divergent (medium)

190. Evaluate the improper integral $\int_{-\infty}^{\infty} xe^{-x^2}\,dx$.

A) e   B) $e^2 - 1$ C) 0   D) e^2
E) e^{-1} F) e^{-2} G) 1   H) $1 - e^{-2}$

Answer: 0 (medium)

191. Evaluate the improper integral $\int_{-1}^{1} x^{-2}\,dx$.

A) 1   B) 2   C) 4   D) 1/4
E) 1/3   F) 3   G) 1/2   H) divergent

Answer: divergent (easy)

192. Evaluate the improper integral $\int_0^2 \frac{dx}{(2x-3)}$.

A) $-2/3$ B) $-1/3$ C) 0   D) 1/3
E) 2/3   F) 1   G) 2   H) divergent

Answer: divergent (easy)

193. Evaluate the improper integral $\int_{-\infty}^{0} e^{3x}\,dx$.

A) 3   B) 1/3   C) $-1/3$ D) 1
E) -1 F) -3 G) 0   H) divergent

Answer: 1/3 (medium)

194. Evaluate the improper integral $\int_0^{\infty} xe^{-x^2}\,dx$.

A) 0   B) 1   C) e   D) e^{-1}
E) $e - 1$ F) 1/2   G) 2   H) divergent

Answer: 1/2 (medium)

195. Evaluate the improper integral $\int_1^{\infty} \frac{\ln x}{x^3}\,dx$.

A) 1/4   B) 1/3   C) 1/2   D) 1
E) ln 2   F) ln 3   G) ln 4   H) divergent

Answer: 1/4 (medium)

196. Evaluate the improper integral $\int_0^e \frac{dx}{x-1}$.

A) $\ln(e-1)$ B) e C) 0   D) 1
E) $-\ln(e-1)$ F) e^{-1} G) e^2 H) divergent

Answer: divergent (easy)

197. Evaluate the improper integral $\int_0^1 \frac{1}{3x-2}\, dx$.

A) 2   B) 3   C) $\frac{\ln 2}{3}$ D) $-\frac{\ln 2}{3}$

E) $\frac{\ln 4}{3}$ F) $-\frac{\ln 3}{2}$ G) $\frac{\ln 3}{2}$ H) divergent

Answer: divergent (easy)

198. Evaluate the improper integral $\int_1^\infty \frac{1}{(1+x)^4}\, dx$.

A) 1   B) 1/2   C) 1/4   D) 1/8
E) 1/16   F) 1/24   G) 1/32   H) divergent

Answer: 1/24 (medium)

199. Evaluate the improper integral $\int_1^\infty \frac{\ln x}{x^2}\, dx$.

A) 0   B) 1/4   C) 1/3   D) 1/2
E) 1   F) 2   G) 3   H) divergent

Answer: 1 (medium)

200. Evaluate the improper integral $\int_{-\infty}^\infty \frac{1}{1+x^2}\, dx$.

A) 1   B) 2   C) 3   D) π
E) 2π F) 3π G) $2/\pi$ H) $3/\pi$

Answer: π (medium)

201. Determine whether the improper integral is convergent or divergent. If it is convergent, evaluate it.
$$\int_{-\infty}^2 \frac{1}{x^2+4}\, dx$$

Answer: $\frac{3\pi}{8}$ (medium)

202. Determine whether the improper integral is convergent or divergent. If it is convergent, evaluate it.
$$\int_0^\infty e^{-4x}\, dx$$

Answer: $\frac{1}{4}$ (easy)

203. Determine whether the improper integral is convergent or divergent. If it is convergent, evaluate it.
$$\int_0^5 \left(\frac{1}{\sqrt{x}} + \frac{1}{\sqrt{5-x}} \right) dx$$

Answer: 6 (medium)

204. Determine whether the improper integral is convergent or divergent. If it is convergent, evaluate it.
$$\int_3^\infty \frac{1}{x^{3/2}}\, dx$$

Answer: $\frac{2}{\sqrt{3}}$ (medium)

205. Determine whether the improper integral is convergent or divergent. If it is convergent, evaluate it.
$$\int_0^1 \frac{1}{(x-1)^2}\, dx$$

Answer: divergent (medium)

206. Determine whether the improper integral is convergent or divergent. If it is convergent, evaluate it.
$$\int_0^2 \frac{1}{(x-1)^2}\, dx$$

Answer: divergent (medium)

207. $\int_{-1}^3 \frac{1}{x}\, dx$ is:

A) $\frac{8}{9}$ 　　　　　　　 B) $\ln 3$ 　　　　　　　 C) $-1 + \ln 3$

D) $-\frac{10}{9}$ 　　　　　　 E) $\frac{12}{17}$ 　　　　　　 F) $\ln 9$

G) $1 + \ln 9$ 　　　　　 H) a divergent improper integral

Answer: a divergent improper integral (easy)

208. Determine whether the improper integral is convergent or divergent. If it is convergent, evaluate it.
$$\int_3^\infty \frac{1}{x^2}\, dx$$

Answer: $\frac{1}{3}$ (easy)

209. Determine whether the improper integral is convergent or divergent. If it is convergent, evaluate it.
$$\int_{-1}^3 \frac{1}{x^2}\, dx$$

Answer: divergent (easy)

210. Determine whether the improper integral is convergent or divergent. If it is convergent, evaluate it.
$$\int_0^\infty \frac{x}{(x^2+5)^2}\, dx$$

Answer: $\frac{1}{10}$ (medium)

211. Determine whether the improper integral is convergent or divergent. If it is convergent, evaluate it.
$$\int_1^3 \frac{2}{(x-2)^{4/3}}\, dx$$

Answer: divergent (medium)

212. Determine whether the improper integral is convergent or divergent. If it is convergent, evaluate it.
$$\int_1^\infty x^{-5/4}\, dx$$

Answer: 4 (medium)

213. Determine whether the improper integral is convergent or divergent. If it is convergent, evaluate it.
$$\int_0^\infty \frac{8}{x^2+4}\, dx$$

Answer: 2π (medium)

214. Sketch $f(x) = \frac{1+\ln x}{x}$ and determine the area enclosed between the curve and the x-axis, as x approaches ∞.

Answer:

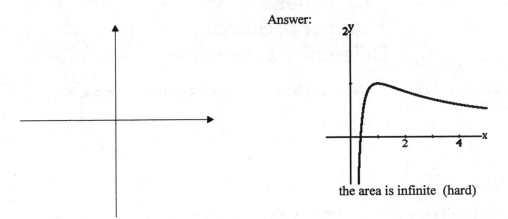

the area is infinite (hard)

Calculus, 3rd Edition
by James Stewart
Chapter 8, Section 1
Differential Equations

1. Solve the differential equation $y' = x^2$ subject to the initial condition $y(0) = 2$. From your solution find the value of $y(1)$.

   A) 7/2   B) 7/3   C) 10/3   D) 8/3

   E) 9/2   F) 5/2   G) 4   H) 3

   Answer: 7/3 (easy)

2. Solve the differential equation $y' = 5y(1000 - y)$ subject to the initial condition $y(0) = 500$. From your solution find the value of the limit $\lim_{t \to \infty} y(t)$.

   A) 5000   B) 2500   C) 1000   D) 2000

   E) 200   F) 20000   G) 100   H) 500

   Answer: 1000 (medium)

3. Solve the differential equation $y' = y$ subject to the initial condition $y(0) = 0$. From your solution find the value of $y(e)$.

   A) e^e B) e C) $e^e - 1$ D) $\ln 2$

   E) $e^e - e$ F) 0 G) e^2 H) 1

   Answer: 0 (medium)

4. Solve the differential equation $y' = e^{x-y}$ subject to the initial condition $y(0) = 2$. From your solution find the value of $y(1)$.

   A) $\ln\left(e^2 - e - 1\right)$ B) $\ln\left(e^2 - e + 1\right)$ C) $\ln\left(e^2 + e + 1\right)$

   D) $\ln\left(e^2 - e + 2\right)$ E) $\ln\left(e^2 + e - 1\right)$ F) $\ln\left(e^2 + e + 2\right)$

   G) $\ln\left(e^2 - e - 2\right)$ H) $\ln\left(e^2 + e - 2\right)$

   Answer: $\ln\left(e^2 + e - 1\right)$ (hard)

5. A tank contains 100 L of brine with 5 kg of dissolved salt. Pure water enters the tank at a rate of 10 L/min. The solution is kept thoroughly mixed and drains from the tank at the same rate. How much salt is in the tank after 6 minutes?

   A) $5e^6$ B) $5e^{-6}$ C) $5e^{-0.6}$ D) $5e^{0.006}$

   E) $5e^{-0.006}$ F) $5e^{-0.06}$ G) $5e^{0.06}$ H) $5e^{0.6}$

   Answer: $5e^{-0.6}$ (hard)

6. A tank contains 100 L of pure water. Brine that contains 0.1 kg of salt per liter enters the tank at a rate of 10 L/min. The solution is kept thoroughly mixed and drains from the tank at the same rate. How much salt is in the tank after 6 minutes?

    A) $100e^{-0.06}$
    D) $10e^{-0.06}$
    G) $10 - 10e^{-0.6}$

    B) $100e^{-0.6}$
    E) $10 - e^{-0.06}$
    H) $10e^{-0.6}$

    C) $10 - 10e^{-0.06}$
    F) $10 - e^{-0.6}$

    Answer: $10 - 10e^{-0.6}$ (hard)

7. Find the solution of the initial-value problem $y' = \frac{\ln x}{xy}$, $y(1) = 2$.

    A) $y = \frac{1+x}{1+\ln x}$
    D) $y = \sqrt{4 + (\ln x)^2}$
    G) $y = x + \sqrt{1 + \ln x}$

    B) $y = \frac{8x}{(1+x)^2}$
    E) $y = x \ln x + 2x$
    H) $y = \sqrt{x}(1 + x)$

    C) $y = 2 + 2\ln x$
    F) $y = x(1 + x^2)$

    Answer: $\sqrt{4 + (\ln x)^2}$ (medium)

8. Solve the differential equation $y' = xy$.

    Answer: $y = Ke^{x^2/2}$, where $K = \pm e^C$ is a constant (medium)

9. Find the equation of the curve that passes through the point $(1, 1)$ and whose slope at (x, y) is y^2/x^3.

    Answer: $y = \frac{2x^2}{1+x^2}$ (medium)

10. Solve the differential equation: $\frac{dx}{dt} = 1 + t - x - tx$.

    Answer: $x = 1 + Ae^{-(t^2/2+t)}$ where $A = \pm e^C$ or 0 (medium)

11. Solve the differential equation: $\frac{dy}{dx} = \frac{x + \sin x}{3y^2}$.

    Answer: $y = \sqrt[3]{(x^2/2) - \cos x + C}$ (easy)

12. Find a particular solution to the separable differential equation $x^2 y' = y^3$, $y(1) = 1$.

    Answer: $y = \frac{x}{2-x}$ (medium)

13. Obtain a general solution of the following differential equation $\csc x \, dy + y^4 \, dx = 0$.

    Answer: $\frac{1}{3y^2} = \cos x + C = 0$ (medium)

14. Solve the differential equation $\frac{dz}{dt} = 2z^2 t \sqrt{1+t^2}$, if $z = 1$ when $t = 0$.

    Answer: $-\frac{1}{z} = \frac{2}{3}(1 + t^2)^{3/2} - \frac{5}{3}$ (hard)

15. Find the general solution of the following differential equation $\frac{dy}{dx} = \frac{(3x+1)^2\sqrt{2-y^2}}{y}$.

Answer: $\frac{1}{9}(3x+1)^3 + \frac{1}{\sqrt{2-y^2}} + C$ (medium)

16. Solve the differential equation $e^{-y}y' + \cos x = 0$.

Answer: $y = -\ln|\sin x + C|$

17. Solve the differential equation $y' = \frac{\ln x}{xy + xy^3}$.

Answer: $y^2 + 1 = \sqrt{2(\ln x)^2 + K}$

18. Solve $xy' = \sqrt{1-y^2}$, $x > 0$, given $y(1) = 0$.

Answer: $y = \sin(\ln x)$

19. Solve $\frac{dy}{dx} = \frac{1+x}{xy}$ $x > 0$ given $y(1) = -4$.

Answer: $y^2 = 2\ln x + 2x + 14$

20. Solve $\frac{dy}{dx} = e^{x-y}$ given $y(0) = 1$.

Answer: $y = \ln(e^x + e - 1)$

21. Solve $x\,dx + 2y\sqrt{x^2+1}\,dy = 0$ given $y(0) = 1$.

Answer: $y^2 = 2 - \sqrt{x^2+1}$

22. Solve $\frac{dy}{dx} = \frac{ty+3t}{t^2+1}$, given $y(2) = 2$.

Answer: $y = -3 + \sqrt{5t^2+5}$

Chapter 8, Section 2
Arc Length

23. Find the arc length of the curve $3y = 4x$ from $(3, 4)$ to $(9, 12)$.

| A) 13 | B) 10 | C) 8 | D) 14 |
| E) 9 | F) 15 | G) 11 | H) 12 |

Answer: 10 (easy)

24. Find the arc length of the curve $y^2 = x^3$ from $(0, 0)$ to $(1/4, 1/8)$.

| A) 65/216 | B) 29/108 | C) 59/216 | D) 37/108 |
| E) 61/216 | F) 31/108 | G) 35/108 | H) 71/216 |

Answer: 61/216 (medium)

25. Find the arc length of the curve $y = \frac{x^3}{6} + \frac{1}{2x}$, $2 \le x \le 3$.

A) 15/4   B) 7/2   C) 19/4   D) 9/2
E) 5   F) 4   G) 17/4   H) 13/4

Answer: 13/4 (medium)

26. Find the arc length of the curve $y = \sqrt{4 - x^2}$, $0 \le x \le 2$.

A) 2π B) $3\pi/4$ C) π D) $7\pi/4$
E) $3\pi/2$ F) $\pi/2$ G) $9\pi/4$ H) $5\pi/4$

Answer: π (medium)

27. Find the arc length of the curve $y = \ln(\cos x)$, $0 \le x \le \pi/3$.

A) $\ln\left(2 + \sqrt{2}\right)$ B) $\ln\left(1 + \sqrt{3}\right)$ C) $\ln\left(2 - \sqrt{2}\right)$ D) $\ln\left(2 - \sqrt{3}\right)$

E) $\ln\left(1 + \sqrt{2}\right)$ F) $\ln\left(2 + \sqrt{3}\right)$ G) $\ln\left(\sqrt{3} - 1\right)$ H) $\ln\left(\sqrt{2} - 1\right)$

Answer: $\ln\left(2 + \sqrt{3}\right)$ (medium)

28. Find the arc length of the curve $y = x^2/2$, $0 \le x \le 1$.

A) $\left(\sqrt{2} + 1 - \ln\left(\sqrt{2} + 1\right)\right)/2$ B) $\left(\sqrt{2} + 1 - \ln\left(\sqrt{2} - 1\right)\right)/2$

C) $\left(\sqrt{2} - \ln\left(\sqrt{2} - 1\right)\right)/2$ D) $\left(\sqrt{2} - \ln\left(\sqrt{2} + 1\right)\right)/2$

E) $\left(\sqrt{2} + \ln\left(\sqrt{2} + 1\right)\right)/2$ F) $\left(\sqrt{2} + 1 + \ln\left(\sqrt{2} + 1\right)\right)/2$

G) $\left(\sqrt{2} + \ln\left(\sqrt{2} - 1\right)\right)/2$ H) $\left(\sqrt{2} + 1 + \ln\left(\sqrt{2} - 1\right)\right)/2$

Answer: $\left(\sqrt{2} + \ln\left(\sqrt{2} + 1\right)\right)/2$ (hard)

29. Find the length of the curve $y = x^3$, $0 \le x \le 1$.

A) $\sqrt{2}$ B) $1 + \left(1/\sqrt{3}\right)$ C) $\sqrt{3/2}$

D) $2 - \left(1/\sqrt{2}\right)$ E) $\int_0^1 \left(1 + x^3\right) dx$ F) $\int_0^1 \sqrt{1 + 9x^4}\, dx$

G) $\int_0^1 \sqrt{4 + x^2}\, dx$ H) $\int_0^1 \sqrt{9 + x^3}\, dx$

Answer: $\int_0^1 \sqrt{1 + 9x^4}\, dx$ (easy)

30. Find the length of the curve $y = \frac{2}{3} x^{3/2}$, $0 \le x \le 3$.

A) 13/3   B) 14/3   C) 5   D) 16/3
E) 17/3   F) 6   G) 19/3   H) 20/3

Answer: 14/3 (medium)

31. Find the length of the curve $y = \ln(\cos x)$, $0 \le x \le \pi/4$.

A) $\sqrt{2}$ B) $\sqrt{2} - 1$ C) $1 - \left(1/\sqrt{2}\right)$ D) $\left(\sqrt{2} - 1\right)/2$

E) $\ln\left(1/\sqrt{2}\right)$ F) $\ln\left(1 + \sqrt{2}\right)$ G) $\ln\left(\sqrt{2}\right) - 1$ H) $\ln\left(\sqrt{2}\right) - (1/2)$

Answer: $\ln\left(1 + \sqrt{2}\right)$ (medium)

32. Find the length of the curve $y = xe^x$, $0 \le x \le 1$.

A) e B) $\int_0^1 \sqrt{1 + (x+1)^2\, e^{2x}}\, dx$ C) $\int_0^1 \sqrt{1 + x^2\, e^{2x}}\, dx$

D) $\int_0^1 xe^x\, dx$ E) π F) $\int_0^1 \left(1 + x^2\, e^{2x}\right) dx$

G) $\int_0^1 (x+1)^2\, e^{2x}\, dx$ H) $\int_0^1 x^2\, e^{2x}\, dx$

Answer: $\int_0^1 \sqrt{1 + (x+1)^2\, e^{2x}}\, dx$ (medium)

33. Find the length of the arc of the curve $9y^2 = 4(x - 1)^3$ from $(1, 0)$ to $(5, 16/3)$.

Answer: $\frac{10\sqrt{5} - 2}{3}$ (hard)

34. Find the arc length of the curve $y = 2x^{3/2}$ between $x = 0$ and $x = 3$.

Answer: $\frac{2}{27}\left(28^{3/2} - 1\right)$ (medium)

35. Find the length of the curve $y = \frac{8}{3}\, x^{3/2}$ from the point $(1, 8/3)$ to the point $(4, 64/3)$.

Answer: $\frac{1}{24}\left(65^{3/2} - 17^{3/2}\right)$ (medium)

36. Set up, but do not evaluate, the equations and/or integrals to find the perimeter of the region bounded by the curve $y = x^2 - 2x$ and the x-axis.

Answer: $P = 2 + \int_0^2 \sqrt{1 + (2x - 2)^2}\, dx$ (medium)

37. Use Simpson's Rule with $n = 10$ to estimate the arc length of $y = x^4$, $0 \le x \le 2$.

Answer: 16.65 (medium)

38. Find the length of the arc of $y = 1 - x^{2/3}$ from $A(-8, -3)$ to $B(-1, 0)$.

Answer: $\frac{1}{27}\left(80\sqrt{10} - 13\sqrt{13}\right)$

39. Find the length of $y = \frac{x^3}{6} + \frac{1}{2x}$ for $1 \le x \le 2$.

Answer: $\frac{17}{12}$

40. Find the length of $y = \frac{x^2}{2} - \frac{\ln x}{4}$ for $2 \le x \le 4$.

Answer: $6 + \frac{\ln 2}{4}$

41. Find the length of $y = \ln(\sin x)$ for $\pi/6 \le x \le \pi/3$.

Answer: $\ln\left(1 = 2/\sqrt{3}\right)$

42. Set up, but do not evaluate, an integral for the length of $y = x^4 - x^2$, $-1 \le x \le 2$.

Answer: $L = \int_{-1}^{2} \sqrt{16x^6 - 16x^4 + 4x^2 + 1}\ dx$

43. Set up, but do not evaluate, an integral for the length of $y = \tan x$, $0 < x < \pi/4$.

Answer: $L = \int_0^{\pi/4} \sqrt{1 + \sec^4 x}\ dx$

44. The figure shows a telephone wire hanging between two poles at $x = -b$ and $x = b$. It takes the shape of a catenary with equation $y = a \cosh(x/a)$. Find the length of the wire.

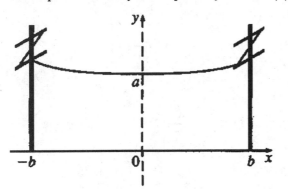

Answer: $2a \sinh(b/a)$

Chapter 8, Section 3
Area of a Surface of Revolution

45. Find the area of the surface obtained by rotating the curve $y = 2x$, $0 \le x \le 1$, about the x-axis.

A) $4\pi\sqrt{5}$ B) $\pi/\sqrt{5}$ C) $2\pi\sqrt{5}$ D) $4\pi/\sqrt{5}$
E) $\pi\sqrt{5}$ F) $6\pi/\sqrt{5}$ G) $2\pi/\sqrt{5}$ H) $6\pi\sqrt{5}$

Answer: $2\pi\sqrt{5}$ (easy)

46. Find the area of the surface obtained by rotating the curve $y = 2x$, $0 \le x \le 1$, about the y-axis.

A) $6\pi/\sqrt{5}$ B) $4\pi\sqrt{5}$ C) $4\pi/\sqrt{5}$ D) $\pi\sqrt{5}$
E) $\pi/\sqrt{5}$ F) $6\pi\sqrt{5}$ G) $2\pi\sqrt{5}$ H) $2\pi/\sqrt{5}$

Answer: $\pi\sqrt{5}$ (easy)

47. Find the area of the surface obtained by rotating the curve $y = x^2/2$, $0 \le x \le 1$, about the y-axis.

A) $\left(4\sqrt{2} - 2\right)\pi/3$

B) $\left(2\sqrt{2} - 2\right)\pi/3$

C) $\left(4\sqrt{2} + 2\right)\pi/3$

D) $\left(2\sqrt{2} + 2\right)\pi/3$

E) $\left(2\sqrt{2} - 1\right)\pi/3$

F) $\left(4\sqrt{2} + 1\right)\pi/3$

G) $\left(4\sqrt{2} - 1\right)\pi/3$

H) $\left(2\sqrt{2} + 1\right)\pi/3$

Answer: $\left(4\sqrt{2} - 2\right)\pi/3$ (medium)

48. Find the area of the surface obtained by rotating the curve $y = e^x$, $0 \le x \le \ln 2$, about the x-axis.

A) $\pi\left(2\sqrt{5} - \sqrt{2} + \ln\left(\frac{\sqrt{5}+2}{\sqrt{2}+1}\right)\right)$

B) $\pi\left(2\sqrt{5} + \sqrt{2} + \ln\left(\frac{2\sqrt{5}+2}{\sqrt{2}+1}\right)\right)$

C) $\pi\left(2\sqrt{5} + \sqrt{2} + \ln\left(\frac{\sqrt{5}+2}{\sqrt{2}+1}\right)\right)$

D) $\pi\left(2\sqrt{5} - \sqrt{2} - \ln\left(\frac{2\sqrt{5}+2}{\sqrt{2}+1}\right)\right)$

E) $\pi\left(2\sqrt{5} + \sqrt{2} - \ln\left(\frac{\sqrt{5}+2}{\sqrt{2}+1}\right)\right)$

F) $\pi\left(2\sqrt{5} - \sqrt{2} + \ln\left(\frac{2\sqrt{5}+2}{\sqrt{2}+1}\right)\right)$

G) $\pi\left(2\sqrt{5} - \sqrt{2} - \ln\left(\frac{2\sqrt{5}+2}{\sqrt{2}+1}\right)\right)$

H) $\pi\left(2\sqrt{5} - \sqrt{2} - \ln\left(\frac{\sqrt{5}+2}{\sqrt{2}+1}\right)\right)$

Answer: $\pi\left(2\sqrt{5} - \sqrt{2} + \ln\left(\frac{\sqrt{5}+2}{\sqrt{2}+1}\right)\right)$ (hard)

49. Find the area of the surface obtained by rotating the curve $y = \frac{x^3}{6} + \frac{1}{2x}$, $1 \le x \le 2$, about the y-axis.

A) $(15 + 2\ln 2)\pi/8$

B) $(15 + 4\ln 2)\pi/4$

C) $(15 + 4\ln 2)\pi/8$

D) $(31 + 2\ln 2)\pi/4$

E) $(31 + 4\ln 2)\pi/8$

F) $(31 + 2\ln 2)\pi/8$

G) $(31 + 4\ln 2)\pi/4$

H) $(15 + 2\ln 2)\pi/4$

Answer: $(15 + 4\ln 2)\pi/4$ (medium)

50. Find the area of the surface obtained by rotating the curve $y = \sqrt[3]{x}$, $0 \le x \le 1$, about the y-axis.

A) $26\pi/3$

B) $\pi\left(2\sqrt{2} - 1\right)/3$

C) $\pi\left(3\sqrt{3} - 1\right)/3$

D) $\pi\left(3\sqrt{3} - 1\right)/9$

E) $\pi\left(10\sqrt{10} - 1\right)/9$

F) $\pi\left(2\sqrt{2} - 1\right)/27$

G) $\left(3\sqrt{3} - 1\right)/27$

H) $\pi\left(10\sqrt{10} - 1\right)/27$

Answer: $\pi\left(10\sqrt{10} - 1\right)/27$ (hard)

51. The curve $y = \sqrt{x}$, $1 \le x \le 2$, is rotated about the x-axis. Find the area of the resulting surface.

A) $\pi \left(6\sqrt{6} - 1\right)/3$

B) $\pi \left(8 - 2\sqrt{2}\right)/3$

C) $\pi \left(5\sqrt{5} - 2\sqrt{2}\right)/3$

D) $\pi \left(3\sqrt{3} - 1\right)/3$

E) $\pi \left(7\sqrt{7} - 3\sqrt{3}\right)/6$

F) $\pi \left(27 - 5\sqrt{5}\right)/6$

G) $\pi \left(10\sqrt{10} - 16\sqrt{2}\right)/6$

H) $\pi \left(17\sqrt{17} - 27\right)/6$

Answer: $\pi \left(27 - 5\sqrt{5}\right)/6$ (hard)

52. The curve $y = x^3$, $0 \le x \le 1$, is rotated about the x-axis. Find the surface area of the resulting surface of revolution.

A) $26\pi/3$

B) $\pi \left(2\sqrt{2} - 1\right)/3$

C) $\pi \left(3\sqrt{3} - 1\right)/3$

D) $\pi \left(3\sqrt{3} - 1\right)/9$

E) $\pi \left(10\sqrt{10} - 1\right)/9$

F) $\pi \left(2\sqrt{2} - 1\right)/27$

G) $\left(3\sqrt{3} - 1\right)/27$

H) $\pi \left(10\sqrt{10} - 1\right)/27$

Answer: $\pi \left(10\sqrt{10} - 1\right)/27$ (hard)

53. Show that the surface obtained by rotating $y = \frac{1}{x}$ ($0 < x \le 1$) about the y-axis has infinite surface area, but encloses a finite volume.

Answer: $S.A. = \int_0^1 2\pi x \sqrt{1 + \left(\frac{-1}{x}\right)^2}\, dx = \infty$; $V = \int_1^\infty \frac{\pi}{y^2}\, dy = \pi$ (hard)

54. Find the surface area when the graph of $f(x) = 3\sqrt{x}$, $0 \le x \le 2$, is rotated about the x-axis.

Answer: $\frac{\pi}{2} \left(17^{3/2} - 27\right)$ (hard)

55. Find the surface area generated when the quarter-circle $x^2 + y^2 = 4$ in the first octant is rotated around the y-axis.

Answer: 8π (medium)

56. Find the area of the surface generated by rotating the portion of the curve $y = \cosh x$, over the interval $0 \le x \le \ln 2$, about the x-axis.

Answer: $\pi \left(\frac{15}{16} + \ln 2\right)$ (hard)

57. A standard formula for a sphere of radius r is
$$\text{Surface area} = 4\pi r^2.$$
Regarding the sphere as a solid of revolution, prove this formula.

Answer: Rotate the circle of radius r with center at the origin to get the sphere.

An equation of the circle is $x^2 + y^2 = r^2$.

Then, $2x + 2y \frac{dy}{dx} = 0$, $\frac{dy}{dx} = -\frac{x}{y}$,

$1 + \left(\frac{dy}{dx}\right)^2 = 1 + \frac{x^2}{y^2} = \frac{y^2 + x^2}{y^2} = \frac{r^2}{y^2}$

Therefore,

$$\text{Surface area} = \int_b^a 2\pi y \sqrt{1 + \left(\frac{dy}{dx}\right)^2}\, dx = \ldots = 4\pi r^2 \quad \text{(hard)}$$

58. Find the surface area generated when the curve $y = \cosh x$, $0 \leq x \leq 1$, is rotated around the y-axis.

Answer: $2\pi \left(1 - \frac{1}{e}\right)$ (hard)

59. Find the area of the surface obtained by rotating $y^2 = 4x + 4$, $0 \leq x \leq 8$ about the x-axis.

Answer: $\frac{8\pi}{3}\left(10\sqrt{10} - 2\sqrt{2}\right)$

60. Find the area of the surface obtained by rotating $y = x^3$, $0 \leq x \leq 2$ about the x-axis.

Answer: $\frac{\pi}{27}\left(145\sqrt{145} - 1\right)$

61. Find the area of the surface obtained by rotating $y = \frac{x^2}{4} - \frac{\ln x}{2}$, $1 \leq x \leq 4$ about the x-axis.

Answer: $\pi\left[\frac{315}{16} - 8\ln 2 - (\ln 2)^2\right]$

62. Find the area of the surface obtained by rotating $y = \cos x$, $0 \leq x \leq \pi/3$ about the x-axis.

Answer: $\pi\left[\frac{\sqrt{21}}{4} + \ln\left(\frac{\sqrt{7} + \sqrt{3}}{2}\right)\right]$

63. Find the area of the surface obtained by rotating $x = \sqrt{2y - y^2}$, $0 \leq y \leq 1$ about the y-axis.

Answer: 2π

64. Find the area of the surface obtained by rotating $4x + 3y = 19$, $1 \leq x \leq 4$ about the y-axis.

Answer: 25π

65. Find the area of the surface obtained by rotating $x = a\cosh(y/a)$, $-a \leq y \leq a$ about the y-axis.

Answer: $2\pi a^2\left[1 + \frac{1}{2}\sinh 2\right]$

66.   If the infinite curve $y = e^{-x}$, $x \geq 0$, is rotated about the x-axis, find the area of the resulting surface.

Answer: $\pi \left[\sqrt{2} + \ln\left(1 + \sqrt{2}\right) \right]$

Chapter 8, Section 4
Moments and Centers of Mass

67.   Find the moment M_y of a system consisting of a mass $m_1 = 1$ at $(1, 0)$ and a mass $m_2 = 2$ at $(2, 0)$.

A) 5   B) 3   C) 1   D) 6
E) 10   F) 2   G) 4   H) 0

Answer: 5 (easy)

68.   Find the x-coordinate $\overline{x}$ at the center of mass of a system consisting of a mass $m_1 = 1$ at $(1, 0)$ and a mass $m_2 = 2$ at $(2, 0)$.

A) 5/4   B) 11/6   C) 7/6   D) 1/2
E) 7/4   F) 0   G) 5/3   H) 4/3

Answer: 5/3 (easy)

69.   Consider a flat plate of uniform density $\rho = 1$ bounded by the curves $y = x^2$ and $y = 1$. Find the moment M_x.

A) 1.0   B) 0.6   C) 1.3   D) 0.7
E) 1.1   F) 0.8   G) 1.2   H) 0.9

Answer: 0.8 (medium)

70.   Find the y-coordinate of the centroid of the region bounded by the curves $y = x^2$ and $y = 1$.

A) 0.85   B) 0.70   C) 0.60   D) 0.50
E) 0.75   F) 0.55   G) 0.80   H) 0.65

Answer: 0.60 (hard)

71.   Find the x-coordinate $\overline{x}$ of the centroid of the region bounded by the x-axis and the lines $y = x$ and $x = 2$.

A) 4/3   B) 7/6   C) 10/7   D) 5/3
E) 11/7   F) 11/6   G) 5/4   H) 7/4

Answer: 4/3 (medium)

72. Find the volume obtained when a circle of radius 1 with center at $(1, 0)$ is rotated about the y-axis.

   A) $3\pi^2$ B) $2\pi^2$ C) 3π D) 8π
   E) $8\pi^2$ F) $4\pi^2$ G) 4π H) 2π

   Answer: $2\pi^2$ (medium)

73. Find the volume obtained when the square bounded by the lines $x = 0$, $x = 2$, $y = 1$, $y = -1$ is rotated about the y-axis.

   A) 8π B) $3\pi^2$ C) $4\pi^2$ D) 3π
   E) $8\pi^2$ F) 2π G) $2\pi^2$ H) 4π

   Answer: 8π (medium)

74. By Pappus' Theorem, the volume of the solid obtained by revolving the circle of radius 2 and center $(3, 7)$ about the x-axis is:

   A) 28π B) 42π C) $56\pi^2$ D) $84\pi^2$
   E) $19\pi^2$ F) $38\pi^3$ G) $76\pi^3$ H) $40\pi^{3/2}$

   Answer: $56\pi^2$ (medium)

75. Find the center of mass of the lamina of uniform density δ bounded by $y = 4 - x^2$ and the x-axis.

   Answer: $\left(0, \frac{8}{5}\right)$ (medium)

76. Determine the centroid of the region bounded by the equation $y^2 - 9x = 0$ in the first quadrant between $x = 1$ and $x = 4$.

   Answer: $(2.65, 2.41)$ (medium)

77. Find the center of mass of a homogeneous lamina of density k in the shape of the region bounded by $y = x^2$, $y = 0$, $x = 2$.

   Answer: $\left(\frac{3}{2}, \frac{6}{5}\right)$ (medium)

78. Find the centroid of the region bounded by the curves $y = 4x - x^2$ and $y = x$ in the xy-plane.

   Answer: $\left(\frac{3}{2}, \frac{12}{5}\right)$ (hard)

79. The masses m_i are located at the points P_i: $m_1 = 2$, $m_2 = 3$, $m_3 = 5$; $P_1(5, 1)$, $P_2(3, -2)$, $P_3(-2, 4)$. Find the moments M_x and M_y and the center of mass of the system.

   Answer: $M_x = 0$, $M_y = 17$; $(\bar{x}, \bar{y}) = \left(\frac{17}{6}, 0\right)$

80. Find the centroid of the region bounded by $y = 1 - x^2$ and $y - 0$.

   Answer: $(\bar{x}, \bar{y}) = \left(0, \frac{2}{5}\right)$

81. Find the centroid of the region bounded by $y = \sqrt{x}$, $y = 0$ and $x = 4$.

Answer: $(\bar{x}, \bar{y}) = \left(\frac{12}{5}, \frac{3}{4}\right)$

82. Find the centroid of the region bounded by $y = \sin x$, $y = 0$, $x = 0$, and $x = \pi/2$.

Answer: $(\bar{x}, \bar{y}) = \left(1, \frac{\pi}{8}\right)$

83. Find the centroid of the region bounded by $y = \ln x$, $y = 0$ and $x = e$.

Answer: $(\bar{x}, \bar{y}) = \left(\frac{e^2+1}{4}, \frac{e-2}{2}\right)$ (hard)

84. Calculate the moments M_x and M_y and the center of mass of a lamina with $\rho = 5$ and shape given in the figure below.

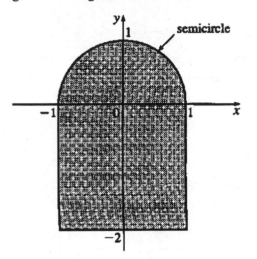

Answer: $M_x = \frac{2r^3}{3}$, $M_y = \frac{2r^3}{3}$, $(\bar{x}, \bar{y}) = \left(\frac{4r}{3\pi}, \frac{4r}{3\pi}\right)$

Chapter 8, Section 5
Hydrostatic Pressure and Force

85. An aquarium 1 foot high, 1 foot wide, and 2 feet long is filled with water. For simplicity, take the density of water to be 60 lb/ft³. Find the hydrostatic pressure on the bottom of the aquarium in lb/ft².

A) 30   B) 60   C) 14   D) 336
E) 28   F) 120   G) 168   H) 240

Answer: 60 (easy)

86. An aquarium 1 foot high, 1 foot wide, and 2 feet long is filled with water. For simplicity, take the density of water to be 60 lb/ft^3. Find the hydrostatic force in pounds on one of the 1 foot by 2 foot sides of the aquarium.

A) 336   B) 30   C) 168   D) 240
E) 60   F) 120   G) 28   H) 14

Answer: 60 (easy)

87. A gate in an irrigation canal is in the form of a trapezoid 3 feet wide at the bottom, 5 feet wide at the top, with height equal to 2 feet. It is placed vertically in the canal, with the water extending to its top. For simplicity, take the density of water to be 60 lb/ft^3. Find the hydrostatic force in pounds on the gate.

A) 360   B) 380   C) 440   D) 420
E) 400   F) 460   G) 500   H) 480

Answer: 440 (medium)

88. A right circular cylinder tank of height 1 foot and radius 1 foot is full of water. Taking the density of water to be a nice round 60 pounds per cubic foot, find the hydrostatic force in pounds on the side of the tank.

A) 30π B) 60   C) 240π D) 240
E) 30   F) 120π G) 60π H) 120

Answer: 60π (medium)

89. A right circular conical tank of height 1 foot and radius 1 foot at the top is full of water. Taking the density of water to be a nice round 60 pounds per cubic foot, find the hydrostatic force in pounds on the tank.

A) $60\sqrt{2}\pi$ B) $30\sqrt{2}$ C) $30\sqrt{2}\pi$ D) $20\sqrt{2}\pi$
E) $40\sqrt{2}\pi$ F) $60\sqrt{2}$ G) $40\sqrt{2}$ H) $20\sqrt{2}$

Answer: $20\sqrt{2}\pi$ (hard)

90. A swimming pool 24 feet long and 15 feet wide has a bottom that is an inclined plane, the shallow end having a depth of 3 feet, and the deep end 10 feet. The pool is filled with water. For simplicity, take the density of water to be 60 lbs/ft^3. Find the hydrostatic force in pounds on the bottom of the pool.

A) 145750   B) 146250   C) 147000   D) 147250
E) 146500   F) 147500   G) 146750   H) 146000

Answer: 146250 (hard)

91. A swimming pool 24 feet long and 15 feet wide has a bottom that is an inclined plane, the shallow end having a depth of 3 feet, and the deep end 10 feet. The pool is filled with water. For simplicity, take the density of water to be 60 lbs/ft^3. Find the hydrostatic force in pounds on one of the sides of the pool.

A) 33360   B) 40720   C) 39240   D) 36720
E) 40240   F) 40960   G) 40480   H) 39960

Answer: 33360 (hard)

92. Find the total force on a submerged vertical plate in the form of an isosceles triangle with a base of 10 feet that lies 3 feet beneath the water surface and an altitude of 12 feet.

Answer: $F = 26,208$ (medium)

93. Find the total hydraulic force on a dam in the shape of an equilateral triangle with a vertex down, if the side of the triangle is 100 feet and the water is even with the top.

Answer: $3906\frac{1}{4}$ tons (medium)

94. Assume water weighs 62.5 lb per cubic ft. Find the force due to water pressure on one side of a vertically submerged triangular plate having vertices at $(0, 0)$, $(1, 0)$, and $(1, 1)$ with the water surface at $y = 7$.

Answer: approximately 204.3 lb (hard)

95. A cylindrical barrel whose end has a diameter of 4 feet is submerged horizontally in seawater (64.3 lb/ft^3). Find the total force due to water pressure at one end if the center of the barrel is at a depth of 12 feet.

Answer: 3086.4π (hard)

96. A flat plate of negligible thickness is in the shape of a right triangle with base 5' and height 10'. The plate is submerged in a tank of water. Find the force on the face of the plate under the following conditions. (Use 62.4 lb/ft^3 as the density of water.) The plate is submerged horizontally so that it rests flat on the bottom of the tank at a depth of 14'.

Answer: 1560 lb (easy)

97. A flat plate of negligible thickness is in the shape of a right triangle with base 5' and height 10'. The plate is submerged in a tank of water. Find the force on the face of the plate under the following conditions. (Use 62.4 lb/ft^3 as the density of water.) The plate is submerged vertically, base edge up and base at a depth of 3'.

Answer: 9880 lb (medium)

98. A swimming pool 5 m wide, 10 m long, and 3 m deep is filled with seawater of density 1030 kg/m^3 to a depth of 2.5 m. Find (a) the hydrostatic pressure at the bottom of the pool, (b) the hydrostatic force on the bottom, and (c) the hydrostatic force on one end of the pool.

Answer: (a) 25.2 kPa (b) $1.26 \times 10^6 \text{ N}$ (c) $1.58 \times 10^5 \text{ N}$

99. A tank contains water. The end of the tank is vertical and has the shape below. Find the hydrostatic force against the end of the tank.

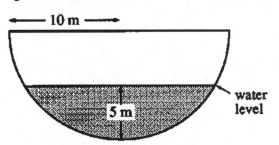

Answer: $1.23 \times 10^6 \text{ N}$

100. A tank contains water. The end of the tank is vertical and has the shape below. Find the hydrostatic force against the end of the tank.

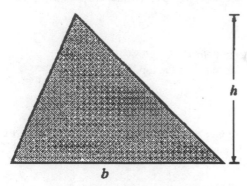

Answer: $1000gbh^2/3$ (metric units assumed)

101. A tank contains water. The end of the tank is vertical and has the shape below. Find the hydrostatic force against the end of the tank.

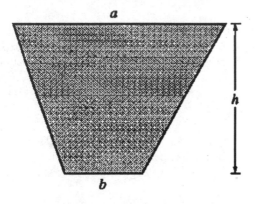

Answer: $\frac{500}{3} gh^2(a + 2b)$ N

102. A vertical dam has a semicircular gate as shown in the figure. Find the hydrostatic force against the gate.

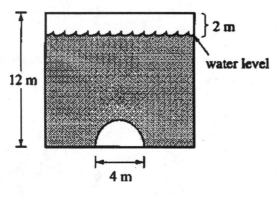

Answer: 5.63×10^5 N

103.   A dam is inclined at an angle of 30° from the vertical and has the shape of an isosceles trapezoid 100 ft wide at the top and 50 ft wide at the bottom and with a slant height of 70 ft. Find the hydrostatic force on the dam when it is full of water.

Answer: 7.71×10^6 lb

Chapter 8, Section 6
Applications to Economics and Biology

104.   The marginal revenue from selling x items is $90 - 0.02x$. The revenue from the sale of the first 100 items is $\$8800$. What is the revenue from the sale of the first 200 items?

Answer: $\$177,000$ (easy)

105.   The demand function for a certain commodity is $p = 5 - \frac{x}{10}$. Find the consumer's surplus when the sales level is 30. Illustrate by drawing the demand curve and identifying the consumer's surplus as an area.

Answer:

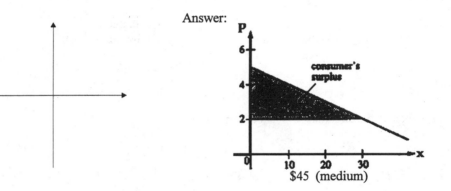

$\$45$ (medium)

106.   A trust fund pays $\$2000$ a year for 5 years, starting immediately. The interest rate is 12% per year compounded continuously. Find the present value of the trust fund.

Answer: $\$7519.81$ (medium)

107.   A baseball player signs a salary contract whereby he receives a sum that increases continuously and linearly from a starting salary of $\$1,000,000$ a year and reaches $\$3,000,000$ a year after 4 years. Thus his salary after t years (in millions of dollars) is $f(t) = 1 + \frac{1}{2}t$. Find the present value of the contract assuming an interest rate of 8% per year compounded continuously.

Answer: $\$4.72$ million (hard)

108.   An animal population is increasing at a rate of $200 + 50t$ per year (where t is measured in years). By how much does the animal population increase between the fourth and tenth years?

Answer: 3300 (medium)

109.   Use Poiseuille's Law to calculate the rate of flow in a typical human artery where we can take $\eta = 0.027$, $R = 0.008$ cm, $l = 2$ cm, and $P = 4000$ dynes/cm^2.

Answer: see 8.6 #17 in the second edition (medium)

Calculus, 3rd Edition
by James Stewart
Chapter 9, Section 1
Curves Defined by Parametric Equations

1. Eliminate the parameter in the equations $x = t^2$, $y = t^4$.

   A) $y = x^2$ for $x \geq 0$ B) $y = \sqrt{x}$ for $x \geq 0$
   C) $y = 2x^2$ for $x \geq 0$ D) $y = \sqrt{2x}$ for $x \geq 0$
   E) $y = 2\sqrt{x}$ for $x \geq 0$ F) $y = x^2/2$ for $x \geq 0$
   G) $y = \sqrt{x}/2$ for $x \geq 0$ H) $y = \sqrt{x/2}$ for $x \geq 0$

   Answer: $y = x^2$ for $x \geq 0$ (easy)

2. Describe the curve defined by $x = \sin 2t$, $y = -\cos 2t$.

   A) circle   B) parabola   C) hyperbola
   D) cycloid   E) hypocycloid   F) involute
   G) trochoid   H) cardioid

   Answer: circle (easy)

3. Eliminate the parameter in the equations $x = \sin t$, $y = \sin^3 t$.

   A) $y = x^3, 0 \leq x \leq 1$ B) $y = x^3, -1 \leq x \leq 1$

   C) $y = x^3, -1 \leq x \leq 0$ D) $y = \sqrt[3]{x}, 0 \leq x \leq 1$

   E) $y = \sqrt[3]{x}, -1 \leq x \leq 1$ F) $y = \sqrt[3]{x}, -1 \leq x \leq 0$

   G) $y = x^{3/2}, 0 \leq x \leq 1$ H) $y = x^{2/3}, -1 \leq x \leq 1$

   Answer: $y = x^3$, $-1 \leq x \leq 1$ (medium)

4. Describe the curve defined by $x = \sin t$, $y = \sin^2 t$.

   A) circle   B) semicircle
   C) quarter circle   D) parabola
   E) portion of parabola   F) hyperbola
   G) single branch of hyperbola   H) portion of branch of hyperbola

   Answer: portion of parabola (medium)

5. At how many places does the curve $x = \cos t$, $y = \sin 2t$ cross over the x-axis?

   A) 5   B) 4   C) 7   D) 6
   E) 0   F) 1   G) 3   H) 2

   Answer: 3 (hard)

6.   What kind of curve do the parametric equations $x = 2t - 3$, $y = 3t + 2$ describe?

A) a straight line   B) a circle   C) a cycloid
D) a parabola   E) an ellipse   F) a conchoid
G) a lemniscate   H) a spiral

Answer: a straight line (easy)

7.   Sketch the curve represented by $x = \frac{t}{2}$, $y = 1 - t$.

Answer:

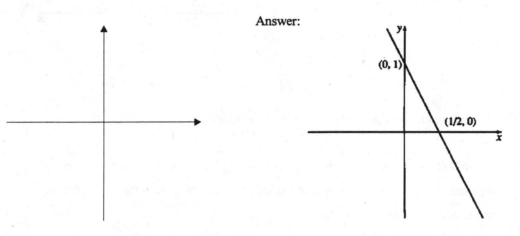

8.   Sketch the curve represented by $x = \frac{1}{2} - \frac{1}{2} t^2$, $y = t^2$.

Answer:

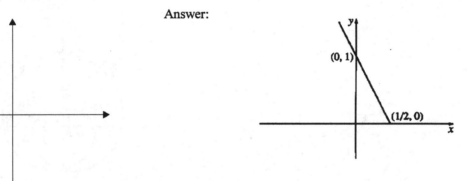

9.   Sketch the curve represented by $x = \frac{1}{2}\cos^2 t$, $y = \sin^2 t$.

Answer:

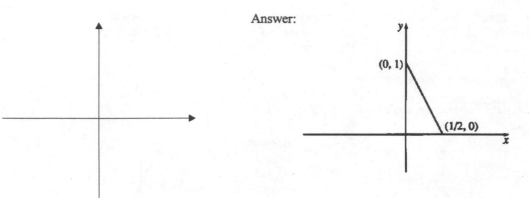

10.   Describe the motion of a particle with position (x, y) as t varies in the given interval.
$$x = 2 + \cos t, \quad y = 3 + \sin t, \quad 0 \le t \le 2\pi$$

Answer: the motion takes place on a unit circle centered at $(2, 3)$. As t goes from 0 to 2π,

the particle makes one complete counterclockwise rotation around the circle, starting

and ending at $(3, 3)$. (medium)

11.   Sketch the curve represented by $x = t\cos t$, $y = t\sin t$.

Answer:

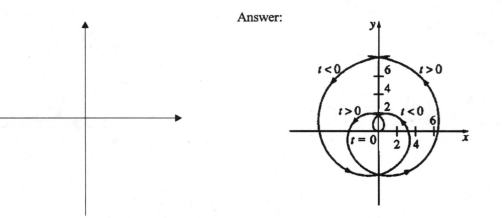

12.   If a projectile is fired with an initial velocity of v_0 meters per second at an angle α above the horizontal, then
its position after t seconds is given by the parametric equations
$$x = (v_0 \cos\alpha)\, t \qquad y = (v_0 \sin\alpha)\, t - \frac{1}{2} g t^2$$
a) If a gun is fired with $\alpha = 30°$ and $v_0 = 500$ m/s, when will the bullet hit the ground?
b) How far from the gun will it hit the ground?

Answer: a) $t = 0$ and $t \doteq 51$ s; b) $x \doteq 22092$ m (hard)

13.   If a bullet is fired with an initial velocity of v_0 meters per second at an angle α above the horizontal, then its position after t seconds is given by the parametric equations
$$x = (v_0 \cos \alpha)\, t \qquad y = (v_0 \sin \alpha)\, t - \tfrac{1}{2}\, gt^2$$
What is the maximum height reached by the bullet?

Answer: 3189 m (medium)

14.   If a projectile is fired with an initial velocity of v_0 meters per second at an angle α above the horizontal, then its position after t seconds is given by the parametric equations
$$x = (v_0 \cos \alpha)\, t \qquad y = (v_0 \sin \alpha)\, t - \tfrac{1}{2}\, gt^2$$
Show that the path is parabolic by eliminating the parameter.

Answer: $y = (\tan \alpha)\, x - \frac{g}{2v_0^2 \cos^2 \alpha} \cdot x^2$ which is the equation of a parabola. (hard)

Chapter 9, Section 2
Tangents and Areas

15.   Find the slope of the tangent to the curve $x = \sin t$, $y = \cos t$ when $t = \pi/3$.

A) $-1/\sqrt{3}$ B) $1/\sqrt{2}$ C) $1/\sqrt{3}$ D) 1
E) -1 F) $-\sqrt{3}$ G) $\sqrt{3}$ H) $-1/\sqrt{2}$

Answer: $-\sqrt{3}$ (medium)

16.   Find the slope of the tangent to the curve $x = t^3$, $y = t^4$ when $t = 3$.

A) 9/4   B) 3/16   C) 4/9   D) 4/3
E) 3   F) 3/4   G) 16/3   H) 4

Answer: 4 (easy)

17.   Find the slope of the tangent to the curve $x = \cos t$, $y = \cos^2 t$ when $t = 0$.

A) $-1/2$ B) -2 C) 1   D) 1/2
E) ∞ F) -1 G) 0   H) 2

Answer: 2 (easy)

18.   At what value of t does the curve $x = t^2 - t$, $y = t^2 + t$ have a vertical tangent?

A) $-1/3$ B) 1/2   C) -2 D) 1
E) $-1/2$ F) -3 G) -1 H) 2

Answer: 1/2 (easy)

19.   At what value of t does the curve $x = t^2 - t$, $y = t^2 + t$ have a horizontal tangent?

A) $-1/2$ B) -2 C) 1/2   D) 2
E) $-1/3$ F) 1   G) -3 H) -1

Answer: $-1/2$ (easy)

20.   Given $x = e^t$, $y = \sin t$, find the value of d^2y/dx^2 when $t = 0$.

A) $-1/\sqrt{2}$ B) -2 C) $1/\sqrt{2}$ D) $1/2$
E) -1 F) 2 G) 1 H) $-1/2$

Answer: -1 (medium)

21.   Find the slope of the tangent to the curve with parametric equations $x = 2 \ln t$, $y = t\, e^t$ at the point where $t = 1$.

A) 1 B) 2 C) 3 D) 4
E) e F) $2e$ G) $3e$ H) $4e$

Answer: e (medium)

22.   Find the slope of the tangent to the curve with parametric equations $x = t + t^2$, $y = t + e^t$ at the point $(0,\ 1)$.

A) -3 B) -2 C) -1 D) 0
E) 1 F) 2 G) 3 H) 4

Answer: 2 (medium)

23.   Find the slope of the tangent to the curve with parametric equations $x = \ln t$, $y = t^3$ at the point where $t = 1$.

A) 1 B) 2 C) 3 D) $1/2$
E) 4 F) 5 G) 6 H) 7

Answer: 3 (medium)

24.   Find the slope of the tangent to the astroid with parametric equations $x = \cos^3 t$, $y = \sin^3 t$ at the point where $t = \pi/4$.

A) 1 B) -1 C) 3 D) $1/3$
E) -3 F) $-1/3$ G) $\pi/4$ H) 0

Answer: -1 (medium)

25.   Find the slope of the tangent line to the curve with parametric equations $x = 1 + \ln t$, $y = t^2 - 3t$ at the point where $t = 3$.

A) 1 B) 3 C) 5 D) 7
E) 9 F) 11 G) 13 H) 15

Answer: 9 (medium)

26.   Consider the curve given by $x = t^2 + 3$ and $y = 2t^3 - t$. Find $\frac{dy}{dx}$ at the point corresponding to $t = 2$.

Answer: $\frac{23}{4}$ (easy)

27. Consider the curve given by $x = t^2 + 3$ and $y = 2t^3 - t$. Find $\frac{d^2y}{dx^2}$ at the point corresponding to $t = 2$.

Answer: $\frac{25}{32}$ (medium)

28. Find an equation in x and y for the tangent line to the curve $x = e^t$, $y = e^{-t}$ at the point $\left(\frac{1}{3}, 3\right)$.

Answer: $y = -9x + 6$ (medium)

29. Find $\frac{dy}{dx}$: $x = t^4 - t^2 + t$, $y = \sqrt[3]{t}$.

Answer: $\frac{1}{3t^{2/3}\left(4t^3 - 2t + 1\right)}$ (hard)

30. Find $\frac{d^2y}{dx^2}$: $x = t^4 - t^2 + t$, $y = \sqrt[3]{t}$.

Answer: $\frac{-44t^3 + 10t - 2}{9t^{5/3}\left(4t^3 - 2t + 1\right)^3}$ (hard)

31. At what point does the curve $x = 1 - 2\cos^2 t$, $y = (\tan t)\left(1 - 2\cos^2 t\right)$ cross itself? Find the equations of both tangents at that point.

Answer: $(0, 0)$; $y = x$ and $y = -x$ (hard)

Chapter 9, Section 3
Arc Length and Surface Area

32. Find the length of the curve $x = 2t$, $y = 3t$, $0 \le t \le 1$.

A) $\sqrt{26}$ B) $\sqrt{60}$ C) $\sqrt{14}$ D) $\sqrt{28}$
E) $\sqrt{13}$ F) $\sqrt{15}$ G) $\sqrt{30}$ H) $\sqrt{52}$

Answer: $\sqrt{13}$ (easy)

33. Find the length of the curve $x = 2t^2 - 1$, $y = 4t^2 + 3$, $0 \le x \le 2$.

A) $4\sqrt{5}$ B) $8\sqrt{5}$ C) $8\sqrt{3}$ D) $2\sqrt{3}$
E) $2\sqrt{5}$ F) $4\sqrt{3}$ G) $16\sqrt{3}$ H) $16\sqrt{5}$

Answer: $8\sqrt{5}$ (medium)

34. Find the length of the curve $x = t^2$, $y = t^3$, $0 \le t \le \frac{1}{2}$.

A) 59/128   B) 61/128   C) 61/108   D) 61/256
E) 61/216   F) 59/256   G) 59/216   H) 59/108

Answer: 61/216 (hard)

35. Find the length of the curve $x = \cos^2 t$, $y = \sin^2 t$, $0 \le t \le \pi$.

A) $\pi/2$ B) $4\sqrt{2}$ C) $\pi/4$ D) $1/\sqrt{2}$
E) $2\sqrt{2}$ F) π G) 2π H) $\sqrt{2}$

Answer: $2\sqrt{2}$ (medium)

36. Find the length of the curve $x = \ln \cos t$, $y = t$, $0 \le t \le \pi/4$.

A) $\ln\left(2\sqrt{2}+1\right)$ B) $\ln\left(\sqrt{2}+2\right)$ C) $\ln\left(2\sqrt{2}+2\right)$
D) $\ln\left(\sqrt{2}+1\right)$ E) $\ln\left(2\sqrt{3}+1\right)$ F) $\ln\left(\sqrt{3}+2\right)$
G) $\ln\left(2\sqrt{3}+2\right)$ H) $\ln\left(\sqrt{3}+1\right)$

Answer: $\ln\left(\sqrt{2}+1\right)$ (medium)

37. Find the area of the surface obtained by rotating the curve $x = \sin t$, $y = \sin^2 t$ about the y-axis.

A) $4\pi\left(\sqrt{125/16}+1\right)/3$ B) $\pi\left(\sqrt{125}+1\right)/3$
C) $4\pi\left(\sqrt{125/64}+1\right)/3$ D) $\pi\left(\sqrt{125}-1\right)/3$
E) $2\pi\left(\sqrt{125/64}-1\right)/3$ F) $4\pi\left(\sqrt{125/16}-1\right)/3$
G) $2\pi\left(\sqrt{125/16}-1\right)/3$ H) $2\pi\left(\sqrt{125/64}+1\right)/3$

Answer: $\pi\left(\sqrt{125}-1\right)/3$ (hard)

38. Give an integral representing the length of the parametric curve $x = t^3$, $y = t^4$, $0 \le t \le 1$.

A) $\int_0^1 \left(t^3 + t^4\right) dt$ B) $\int_0^1 \sqrt{t^3 + t^4} \, dt$

C) $\int_0^1 \sqrt{1 + 3t^2} \, dt$ D) $\int_0^1 \sqrt{t^2 + 4t^3} \, dt$

E) $\int_0^1 \sqrt{9t^4 + 16t^6} \, dt$ F) $\int_0^1 \sqrt{4t^4 + 9t^6} \, dt$

G) $\int_0^1 \sqrt{t^5 + t^7} \, dt$ H) $\int_0^1 \sqrt{8t^6 + 6t^8} \, dt$

Answer: $\int_0^1 \sqrt{9t^4 + 16t^6} \, dt$ (easy)

39. Find the length of the curve with parametric equations $x = t^3$, $y = t^2$, $0 \le t \le 1$.

A) $\frac{13\sqrt{13}-1}{81}$ B) $\frac{13\sqrt{13}-8}{27}$ C) $\frac{2\left(6\sqrt{6}-1\right)}{27}$

D) $\frac{5\left(6\sqrt{6}-1\right)}{18}$ E) $\frac{2\sqrt{2}-1}{18}$ F) $\frac{2\left(5\sqrt{5}-2\sqrt{2}\right)}{9}$

G) $\frac{4\left(10\sqrt{10}-1\right)}{9}$ H) $\frac{15\sqrt{15}-27}{2}$

Answer: $\frac{13\sqrt{13}-8}{27}$ (hard)

40. Find the total length of the astroid $x = a \cos^3 \theta$, $y = a \sin^3 \theta$.

A) a B) $2a$ C) $3a$ D) $4a$
E) $5a$ F) $6a$ G) $7a$ H) $8a$

Answer: $6a$ (hard)

41. Find the length of the curve with parametric equations $x = \cos t + t \sin t$, $y = \sin t - t \cos t$, $0 \le t \le \pi$.

A) π B) π^2 C) $\pi/2$ D) $\pi^2/2$
E) $\pi/4$ F) $\pi^2/4$ G) $\pi/8$ H) $\pi^2/8$

Answer: $\pi^2/2$ (medium)

42. Find the length of the curve with parametric equations $x = \cos t$, $y = \sin t$, $0 \le t \le \pi/4$.

A) 1 B) 2 C) 3 D) $\pi/8$
E) $\pi/4$ F) $\pi/2$ G) $3\pi/4$ H) π

Answer: $\pi/4$ (easy)

43. Write the definite integral representing the length of the curve with parametric equations $x = f(t)$, $y = g(t)$, $a \le t \le b$.

A) $\int_a^b 2\pi t\, f(t)\, dt$ B) $\int_a^b \pi\, [f(t)]^2\, dt$

C) $\int_a^b \left(1 + [f'(t)]^2\right) dt$ D) $\int_a^b [1 + f'(t)]^2\, dt$

E) $\int_a^b \sqrt{1 + [f'(t)]^2}\, dt$ F) $\int_a^b \sqrt{1 + [g'(t)]^2}\, dt$

G) $\int_a^b \sqrt{[f'(t)]^2 + [g'(t)]^2}\, dt$ H) $\int_a^b [f'(t) + g'(t)]^2\, dt$

Answer: $\int_a^b \sqrt{[f'(t)]^2 + [g'(t)]^2}\, dt$ (easy)

44. What is the maximum curvature on the curve given by $y = x^2$?

Answer: $\kappa(0) = 2$ (hard)

45. Find the distance traveled by a particle with position (x, y) as t varies in the given time interval. Compare with the length of the curve.
$$x = \cos^2 t, \quad y = \cos t, 0 \le t \le 4\pi$$

Answer: distance $= 4\sqrt{5} + 2 \ln\left(\sqrt{5} + 2\right)$; $L = \sqrt{5} + \frac{1}{2} \ln\left(\sqrt{5} + 2\right)$ (hard)

46. Find the area of the surface obtained by rotating the given curve about the x-axis.
$$x = t^3, \quad y = t^2, 0 \le t \le 1$$

Answer: $2\pi\left(247\sqrt{13} + 64\right)/1215$ (medium)

47. Find the area of the surface obtained by rotating the given curve about the x-axis.
$$x = a\cos^3\theta, \ y = a\sin^3\theta, 0 \leq \theta \leq \tfrac{\pi}{2}$$

Answer: $\frac{6\pi a^2}{5}$ (medium)

48. Find the surface area generated by rotating the given curve about the y-axis.
$$x = e^t - t, \ y = 4e^{t/2}, 0 \leq t \leq 1$$

Answer: $\pi\left(e^2 + 2e - 6\right)$ (medium)

49. Find the length of the curve represented by $x = \arcsin\tfrac{t}{2}$ and $y = \ln\sqrt{4 - t^2}, 0 \leq t \leq 1$.

Answer: $\ln\sqrt{3}$ (medium)

50. Find the circumference of the circle: $x = 2\cos t, \ y = 2\sin t$.

Answer: 4π (medium)

51. If $x = \cos 2t, \ y = \sin^2 t$, and (x, y) represents the position of a particle, find the distance the particle travels as t moves from 0 to $\tfrac{\pi}{2}$.

Answer: $\sqrt{5}$ (hard)

52. The involute of a circle of radius 1 is given parametrically by:
$$x = \cos t + t\sin t$$
$$y = \sin t - t\cos t$$
Find the length of the portion of the involute which is traced out as t increases from 0 to π.

Answer: $\frac{\pi^2}{2}$ (medium)

53. Compute the length of the curve given parametrically by $x = \tfrac{1}{3}t^3$ and $y = \tfrac{1}{2}t^2$ for $0 \leq t \leq 2$.

Answer: $\frac{5\sqrt{5}-1}{3}$ (medium)

54. Find the length of the curve given parametrically by $x = \tfrac{t^2}{2} + 7$ and $y = \tfrac{1}{3}\left(2t + 1\right)^{3/2}$ for $2 \leq t \leq 6$.

Answer: 20 (hard)

55. An arc is described by the parametric equations $x = 3t^3$ and $y = 2t^2$. Sketch the arc and calculate its length from (a) $t = 0$ to $t = 2$, and (b) $t = -3$ to $t = 0$.

Answer:

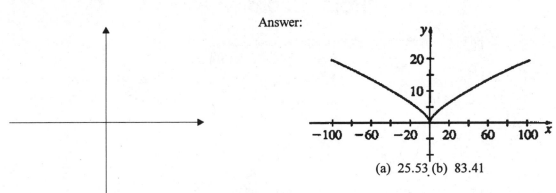

(a) 25.53 (b) 83.41

56. The equation of a curve in parametric form is
$$x = 5 \cos 3t$$
$$y = 4 \sin 3t$$
Find the arc length of the curve from $t = 0$ to $t = \frac{\pi}{8}$.

Answer: $\frac{3\pi}{2}$ (medium)

57. Find the length of the plane curve given parametrically by $x = t$ and $y = t^{2/3}$ between $t = 0$ and $t = 8$.

Answer: $\frac{8}{27}\left(10\sqrt{10} - 1\right)$ (medium)

58. A curve is written parametrically as $x = t^3$, $y = t^{9/2}$. Find the length of the curve from $t = 0$ to $t = 1$.

Answer: $\frac{8}{27}\left(\frac{13}{8}\sqrt{13} - 1\right)$ (medium)

59. Find the arc length of the curve defined by
$$x = t^3 + 1$$
$$y = 3t^2 + 2$$
for $0 \leq t \leq 1$.

Answer: $5\sqrt{5} - 8$ (medium)

60. The position of a particle $P(x, y)$ at time t is given by $x = \frac{1}{3}(2t + 3)^{3/2}$ and $y = \frac{t^2}{2} + t$. Find the arc length of the path the particle would travel from $t = 0$ to $t = 3$.

Answer: $\frac{21}{2}$ (hard)

Chapter 9, Section 4
Polar Coordinates

61.   Convert the polar coordinates $(3, 5\pi)$ to Cartesian coordinates.

A) $\left(-\sqrt{3}/2, -\sqrt{3}/2\right)$ B) $(3, 0)$ C) $(0, 3)$

D) $\left(\sqrt{3}/2, \sqrt{3}/2\right)$ E) $(-3, 0)$ F) $\left(\sqrt{3}/2, -\sqrt{3}/2\right)$

G) $(0, -3)$ H) $\left(-\sqrt{3}/2, \sqrt{3}/2\right)$

Answer: $(-3, 0)$ (easy)

62.   Convert the Cartesian coordinates $(1, 1)$ to polar coordinates.

A) $(1, \pi/4)$ B) $\left(\sqrt{2}, \pi/4\right)$ C) $\left(\sqrt{2}, \pi/2\right)$

D) $(1, 2\pi)$ E) $(1, \pi)$ F) $\left(\sqrt{2}, \pi\right)$

G) $(1, \pi/2)$ H) $\left(\sqrt{2}, 2\pi\right)$

Answer: $\left(\sqrt{2}, \pi/4\right)$ (easy)

63.   Which of the three sets of polar coordinates below represent the point whose rectangular coordinates are $(0, 1)$?

1) $(1, \pi/2)$

2) $(-1, 3\pi/2)$

3) $(1, 3\pi/2)$

A) none   B) 1   C) 2   D) 3

E) 1, 2   F) 1, 3   G) 2, 3   H) 1, 2, 3

Answer: 1, 2 (easy)

64.   Find a polar equation for the curve represented by the Cartesian equation $x^2 + (y - 1)^2 = 1$.

A) $r = \cos^2\theta$ B) $r = 2\sin^2\theta$ C) $r = \sin^2\theta$

D) $r = 2\sin\theta$ E) $r = 2\cos^2\theta$ F) $r = \cos\theta$

G) $r = \sin\theta$ H) $r = 2\cos\theta$

Answer: $r = 2\sin\theta$ (medium)

65.   Find a Cartesian equation for the curve represented by the polar equation
        $r\sin\theta + r^2\cos^2\theta + r^2 = 0$.

A) $y + 2y^2 + 2x^2 = 0$ B) $y^2 + x + x^2 = 0$ C) $x^2 + y + y^2 = 0$

D) $x + 2x^2 + 2y^2 = 0$ E) $x^2 + 2y + 2y^2 = 0$ F) $2x + 2x^2 + y^2 = 0$

G) $2y^2 + x + x^2 = 0$ H) $2x^2 + y + y^2 = 0$

Answer: $2x^2 + y + y^2 = 0$ (medium)

66. Find the smallest positive value of θ for which the curve $r = 1 + \cos \theta$ has a horizontal tangent.

A) $7\pi/6$ B) $2\pi/3$ C) $\pi/2$ D) $\pi/4$
E) $\pi/3$ F) $3\pi/4$ G) $\pi/6$ H) $5\pi/6$

Answer: $\pi/3$ (medium)

67. Express the polar equation $r = -4 \sin \theta$ in rectangular form.

Answer: $x^2 + (y + 2)^2 = 4$ (medium)

68. Let P have rectangular coordinates $(1, 1)$. Find a set of polar coordinates (r, θ) for P such that $r > 0, \ \theta < 0$.

Answer: $\left(\sqrt{2}, \frac{-7\pi}{4} \right)$ (medium)

69. Let P have rectangular coordinates $(1, 1)$. Find a set of polar coordinates (r, θ) for P such that $r < 0, \ \theta > 0$.

Answer: $\left(-\sqrt{2}, \frac{5\pi}{4} \right)$ (medium)

70. Let P have rectangular coordinates $(1, 1)$. Find a set of polar coordinates (r, θ) for P such that $r < 0, \ \theta < 0$.

Answer: $\left(-\sqrt{2}, \frac{-3\pi}{4} \right)$ (medium)

71. Find polar coordinates for the Cartesian point $\left(-2, 2\sqrt{3} \right)$.

Answer: $\left(4, \frac{2\pi}{3} \right)$ (easy)

72. Find Cartesian coordinates for the point whose polar coordinates are $\left(-3, \frac{3\pi}{4} \right)$.

Answer: $\left(\frac{3}{\sqrt{2}}, \frac{-3}{\sqrt{2}} \right)$ (easy)

73. Find polar coordinates for the Cartesian point $(0, -5)$.

Answer: $\left(5, \frac{3\pi}{2} \right)$ (easy)

74. Convert $x^3 + xy^2 - y^2 = 0$ to polar form and write r explicitly in terms of θ.

Answer: $r = \frac{\sin^2 \theta}{\cos \theta}$ or $r = \sin \theta \tan \theta$ (medium)

Chapter 9, Section 5
Areas and Lengths in Polar Coordinates

75. Find the area of the region bounded by the curve $r = 4$ and lying in the sector $0 \le \theta \le \pi/2$.

    A) 8π B) 4π C) 2π D) $\pi/2$
    E) π F) 16π G) 12π H) 3π

    Answer: 4π (easy)

76. Find the area of the region bounded by the curve $r = 4\theta$ and lying in the sector $0 \le \theta \le \pi/2$.

    A) $\pi^2/12$ B) $\pi^2/24$ C) $\pi^2/6$ D) $\pi^3/3$
    E) $\pi^2/3$ F) $\pi^3/6$ G) $\pi^3/24$ H) $\pi^3/12$

    Answer: $\pi^3/3$ (medium)

77. Find the area of the region bounded by the curve $r = \sin \theta$.

    A) 4π B) $3\pi/2$ C) 2π D) $\pi/2$
    E) $\pi/4$ F) $\pi/6$ G) π H) $\pi/3$

    Answer: $\pi/4$ (medium)

78. Find the area of the region inside the curve $r = 4 \sin \theta$ but not inside the curve $r = 2 \sin \theta$.

    A) 12π B) π C) 4π D) $\pi/2$
    E) 2π F) 6π G) 8π H) 3π

    Answer: 3π (medium)

79. Find the area of the region that lies inside both the curves $r = 4 \sin \theta$ and $r = 4 \cos \theta$.

    A) $2\pi - 2$ B) $2\pi + 4$ C) $\pi - 2$ D) $\pi - 1$ ·
    E) $\pi + 1$ F) $\pi + 2$ G) $2\pi + 2$ H) $2\pi - 4$

    Answer: $2\pi - 4$ (hard)

80. Find the length of the curve $r = 4 \sin \theta$.

    A) 2π B) 4π C) 6π D) $\pi/2$
    E) π F) 8π G) 12π H) 16π

    Answer: 4π (easy)

81.   Find the length of the curve $r = e^{\theta}, 0 \le \theta \le 2\pi$.

A) $e^{\pi} + 1$ B) $e^{2\pi} + 1$ C) $e^{2\pi} - 1$
D) $\sqrt{2}\,(e^{\pi} - 1)$ E) $\sqrt{2}\,(e^{2\pi} - 1)$ F) $\sqrt{2}\,(e^{2\pi} + 1)$
G) $e^{\pi} - 1$ H) $\sqrt{2}\,(e^{\pi} + 1)$

Answer: $\sqrt{2}\,(e^{2\pi} - 1)$ (medium)

82.   Find the area enclosed by one loop of the curve $r^2 = 2\sin\theta$.

A) 1/2   B) 1   C) 3/2   D) 2
E) 5/2   F) 3   G) 7/2   H) 4

Answer: $1/2$ (medium)

83.   Write the definite integral representing the length of the polar curve $r = f(\theta)\,, a \le \theta \le b$.

A) $\int_a^b r\,\frac{dr}{d\theta}\,d\theta$ B) $\int_a^b \left(r + \frac{dr}{d\theta}\right) d\theta$ C) $\int_a^b r^2\,\frac{d^2r}{d\theta^2}\,d\theta$

D) $\int_a^b \left(r^2 + \frac{d^2r}{d\theta^2}\right) d\theta$ E) $\int_a^b \sqrt{1 + \frac{d^2r}{d\theta^2}}\,d\theta$ F) $\int_a^b \sqrt{r^2 + \left(\frac{dr}{d\theta}\right)^2}\,d\theta$

G) $\int_a^b \sqrt{1 + r^2}\,d\theta$ H) $\int_a^b \sqrt{1 + \theta^2}\,d\theta$

Answer: $\int_a^b \sqrt{r^2 + \left(\frac{dr}{d\theta}\right)^2}\,d\theta$ (easy)

84.   Find the area of the region that lies inside the circle $r = 3\cos\theta$ and outside the cardioid $r = 1 + \cos\theta$.

A) $\pi/3$ B) $\pi/2$ C) $2\pi/3$ D) π
E) $4\pi/3$ F) $3\pi/2$ G) $5\pi/3$ H) 2π

Answer: π (hard)

85.   Find the area of the region inside the polar curve given by $r = 2 - 2\sin\theta$ and outside the polar curve given by $r = 3$.

Answer: $\frac{9\sqrt{3}}{2} - \pi$ (medium)

86.   Sketch the graph of $r = 2(\sin\theta + \cos\theta)$. Find the area of the region enclosed by the curve.

Answer:

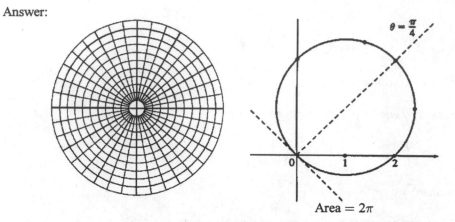

Area $= 2\pi$

87.   Sketch the graphs of the circle $r = 6\cos\theta$ and the cardioid $r = 2 + 2\cos\theta$ on the same coordinate system. Find the area of the region that is inside the circle and outside the cardioid.

Answer:

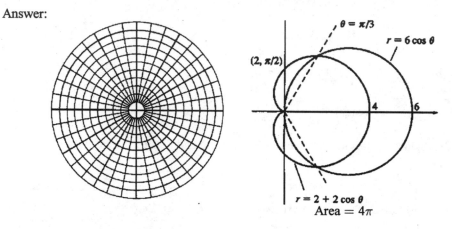

Area $= 4\pi$

88.   Find the total area outside $r = 1$ and inside $r = 2\sin 3\theta$.

Answer: $\frac{\sqrt{3}}{2} - \frac{\pi}{3}$ (medium)

89.   Find the area outside $r = 2$ but inside $r = 4\cos\theta$.

Answer: $\frac{4\pi}{3} + 2\sqrt{3}$ (medium)

90. Sketched below is the propeller (with equation $r = 2 \sin 3\theta$) to be mounted atop the beanies which will soon be required headgear for all mathematics, physics, and chemistry majors. As the proud wearer walks, the propeller will spin causing the words "mathematics," physics," and "chemistry" printed on the blades to blur and blend signifying the unity of pure science. Find the area of ONE BLADE of the propeller.

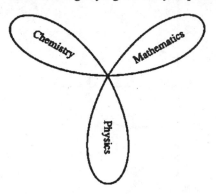

Answer: Area $= \frac{\pi}{3}$ (medium)

91. Find the area of the region R inside the circle $r = \sin \theta$ and outside the cardioid $r = 1 + \cos \theta$.

Answer: $\frac{4-\pi}{4}$ (hard)

92. Calculate the total area enclosed by the leaves of $r = 5 \cos 3\theta$.

Answer: $\frac{25\pi}{4}$ (medium)

93. Sketch the bifolium $r = a \sin \theta \cos^2\theta$. Find the total area enclosed.

Answer:

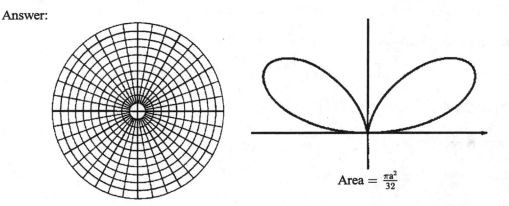

Area $= \frac{\pi a^2}{32}$

94. Sketch the graph and compute the area enclosed by the graph of the polar equation
$$r = 2 + \cos 2\theta$$

Answer:

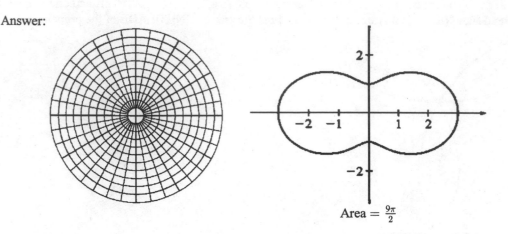

Area $= \frac{9\pi}{2}$

95. Find the area of the region inside the circle $r = 3$ and outside the spiral $r = \theta$, between the values of θ where $\theta = 0$ and where the two graphs intersect.

Answer: Area $= 9$ (medium)

96. Find the area inside the curve $r = 4\cos 2\theta$ and outside the curve $r = 2$.

Answer: $4\sqrt{3} + \frac{8\pi}{3}$ (medium)

97. Find the points of intersection of $r = 3\cos\theta$ and $r = 3 - 3\cos\theta$.

Answer: $\left(\frac{3}{2}, \frac{\pi}{3}\right)$, $\left(\frac{3}{2}, \frac{5\pi}{3}\right)$, $(0, 0)$ (medium)

98. Find all points of intersection of the curve $r = 2 - 4\sin\theta$ with the curve $r = 2\sin\theta$.

Answer: $(0, 0)$, $\left(0, \frac{\pi}{6}\right)$, $\left(\frac{2}{3}, \sin^{-1}(1/3)\right)$, $\left(\frac{2}{3}, \pi - \sin^{-1}(1/3)\right)$ (hard)

99. Find the length of the curve $r = \sin^3\left(\frac{\theta}{3}\right)$.

Answer: $\pi + \frac{3\sqrt{3}}{8}$ (medium)

100. Find the arc length of the curve $r = 3\sin\theta$.

Answer: 3π (medium)

Chapter 9, Section 6
Conic Sections

101. Give the y-coordinate of the focus of the parabola $y = x^2$.

A) 2   B) 4   C) $-1/4$ D) $-1/2$
E) 1/2   F) -4 G) 1/4   H) -2

Answer: 1/4 (easy)

102. Find the distance between focus and directrix of the parabola $y = x^2$.

A) 2   B) 8   C) 16   D) 1/8
E) 1/2   F) 1   G) 4   H) 1/4

Answer: 1/2 (medium)

103. Find the distance between the two foci of the ellipse $\frac{x^2}{4} + \frac{y^2}{8} = 1$.

A) 2   B) $2\sqrt{2}$ C) 8   D) $\sqrt{2}$
E) 4   F) $4\sqrt{2}$ G) 1   H) $8\sqrt{2}$

Answer: 4 (medium)

104. Find the distance between the two foci of the hyperbola $x^2 - y^2 = 8$.

A) 2   B) 8   C) $2\sqrt{2}$ D) 4
E) 1   F) $4\sqrt{2}$ G) $\sqrt{2}$ H) $8\sqrt{2}$

Answer: 8 (medium)

105. Find the focus of the parabola $2y^2 - 3y = 4x + 5$.

A) $(-33/32, 3/4)$ B) $(-33/32, 3/8)$ C) $(49/8, -5/4)$
D) $(49/4, -5/8)$ E) $(-33/32, -3/4)$ F) $(-33/32, -3/8)$
G) $(49/8, 5/4)$ H) $(49/4, 5/8)$

Answer: $(-33/32, 3/4)$ (hard)

106. An ellipse has foci located at $(-1, 0)$ and $(1, 0)$ and vertices located at $(-2, 0)$ and $(2, 0)$. How long is the vertical axis?

A) 2   B) 6   C) $2\sqrt{2}$ D) $4\sqrt{2}$
E) 3   F) $2\sqrt{3}$ G) 4   H) $4\sqrt{3}$

Answer: $2\sqrt{3}$ (medium)

107. A hyperbola has asymptotes $y = \pm x/2$ and vertices $(-1, 0)$ and $(1, 0)$. Find the distance between its foci.

A) $2\sqrt{3}$ B) $\sqrt{3}$ C) $\sqrt{5}$ D) $\sqrt{5}/4$
E) $\sqrt{5}/2$ F) $\sqrt{3}/4$ G) $\sqrt{3}/2$ H) $2\sqrt{5}$

Answer: $\sqrt{5}$ (medium)

108. Find an equation for the ellipse which has foci at the points $(2, 2)$ and $(2, -4)$, and is tangent to the line $y = 4$.

Answer: $\frac{(x-2)^2}{16} + \frac{(y+1)^2}{25} = 1$ (medium)

109. Sketch and discuss $4x^2 - 8x + 3y^2 + 6y + 7 = 0$.

Answer:

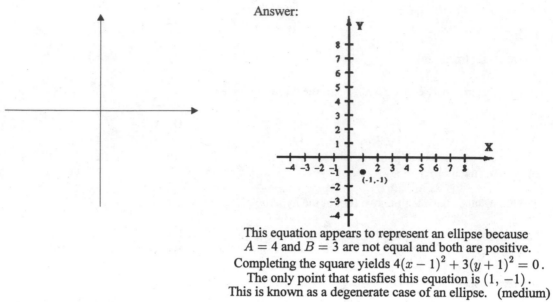

This equation appears to represent an ellipse because $A = 4$ and $B = 3$ are not equal and both are positive. Completing the square yields $4(x - 1)^2 + 3(y + 1)^2 = 0$. The only point that satisfies this equation is $(1, -1)$. This is known as a degenerate case of an ellipse. (medium)

110. Use the definition of the ellipse to find the equation of the locus of a point the sum of whose distances from $(-3, -4)$ and $(3, 4)$ is 12.

Answer: $27x^2 - 24xy + 2y^2 = 396$ (medium)

111. Consider the ellipse given by $25x^2 + 4y^2 + 150x - 40y + 225 = 0$. Find the center, the vertices, and the foci of the ellipse.

Answer: center: $(-3, 5)$; vertices: $(-3, 0)$ and $(-3, 10)$; foci: $\left(-3, 5 + \sqrt{21}\right)$ and $\left(-3, 5 - \sqrt{21}\right)$

(medium)

112. Find an equation of the conic which has foci at the points $(3, 4)$ and $(3, 8)$, and has vertices at the points $(3, 3)$ and $(3, 9)$.

Answer: $\frac{(x-3)^2}{5} + \frac{(y-6)^2}{9} = 1$ (medium)

113. Use the definition of a parabola to find the equation of the parabola with focus $(-1, 3)$ and directrix $x = 5$.

Answer: $(y - 3)^2 = -12(x - 2)$ (easy)

114. Find the area bounded by the parabola $x^2 = 4py$ and the line $y = p$.

Answer: $\frac{8p^2}{3}$ (easy)

115. Sketch the following conic: $x^2 - 4x - y^2 - 6y = 4$.

Answer: (easy)

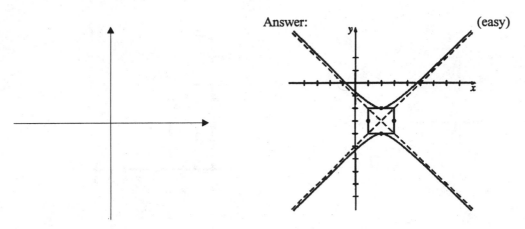

116. Given the hyperbola $4x^2 + 16x - 3y^2 + 18y + 1 = 0$, name the center, vertices and equations of the asymptotes.

Answer: center: $(-2, 3)$; vertices: $(-2, 5)$ and $(-2, 1)$; asymptotes: $y = 3 \pm \frac{\sqrt{3}}{2}(x + 2)$ (medium)

117. Identify the following as a circle, parabola, ellipse, or hyperbola: $5x^2 + y^2 - 3x - 15 = 0$.

Answer: ellipse (easy)

118. Identify the following as a circle, parabola, ellipse, or hyperbola: $3x^2 - 2y + 5x + 1 = 0$.

Answer: parabola (easy)

119. Identify the following as a circle, parabola, ellipse, or hyperbola: $x + 3y + 2x^2 - 2y^2 = 0$.

Answer: hyperbola (easy)

120. Identify the following as a circle, parabola, ellipse, or hyperbola: $3 - 2x^2 + 2x - 2y^2 + 4y = 0$.

Answer: circle (easy)

121. Sketch the graph of $4x^2 - 8x + y^2 - 4y = 8$.

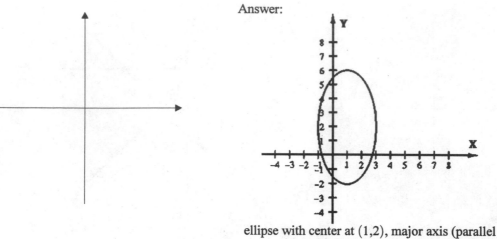

Answer:

ellipse with center at $(1,2)$, major axis (parallel to y-axis) 8 units, minor axis 4 units (medium)

122. The vertical face of a dam is the lower half of an ellipse whose major axis is 60 feet long and forms the top of the dam. The minor axis is 40 feet long. Find the force exerted on the face of the dam if the water level is at the top of the dam.

Answer: $8000p$ lbs. where p lb/ft^3 is the weight density of the liquid. (hard)

Chapter 9, Section 7
Conic Sections in Polar Coordinates

123. An ellipse has axes of lengths 1 and 3. Find its eccentricity.

A) 3
B) $\sqrt{8}/3$
C) $\sqrt{3}$
D) 2/3
E) $\sqrt{3}/4$
F) $\sqrt{3}/2$
G) $\sqrt{2}$
H) 2

Answer: $\sqrt{8}/3$ (medium)

124. An ellipse has eccentricity equal to $1/2$. Find the ratio of its major axis length $2a$ to its minor axis length $2b$.

A) $3/\sqrt{2}$
B) $\sqrt{6}$
C) $\sqrt{2}$
D) $2/\sqrt{3}$
E) $3\sqrt{2}$
F) $\sqrt{3}$
G) $2\sqrt{3}$
H) $2\sqrt{2}$

Answer: $2/\sqrt{3}$ (hard)

125. Find the eccentricity of the ellipse whose polar equation is $r = \frac{1}{2-\cos\theta}$.

A) 1/4
B) 2
C) 1/2
D) 1/10
E) 1
F) 1/8
G) 1/6
H) 1/12

Answer: 1/2 (easy)

126. Find the major axis length $2a$ of the ellipse whose polar equation is $r = \frac{1}{2-\cos\theta}$.

A) 5/2   B) 2   C) 3/4   D) 3
E) 8/3   F) 4/3   G) 2/3   H) 3/2

Answer: 4/3 (medium)

127. Find the distance from vertex to focus for the parabola whose polar equation is $r = \frac{4}{1-\cos\theta}$.

A) 3   B) 2   C) 8   D) 1
E) 4   F) 1/4   G) 1/3   H) 1/2

Answer: 2 (medium)

128. Find the distance between the vertices of the hyperbola whose polar equation is $r = \frac{4}{1-2\cos\theta}$.

A) 8/3   B) 2   C) 6   D) 4
E) 4/3   F) 3   G) 2/3   H) 16/3

Answer: 8/3 (medium)

129. Find the eccentricity of the hyperbola whose polar equation is $r = \frac{4}{1-2\cos\theta}$.

A) 4   B) 8/3   C) 2   D) 4/3
E) 3   F) 6   G) 2/3   H) 16/3

Answer: 2 (easy)

130. Write the equation of the ellipse with eccentricity $\frac{2}{3}$ and foci $(-5, 4)$ and $(7, 4)$.

Answer: $\frac{(x-1)^2}{81} + \frac{(y-4)^2}{45} = 1$

131. Sketch the graph of $r = 3\cos\left(\theta - \frac{\pi}{4}\right)$.

Answer:

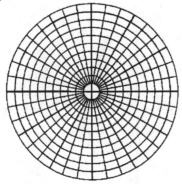
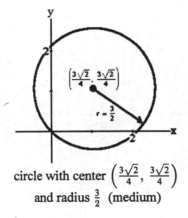

circle with center $\left(\frac{3\sqrt{2}}{4}, \frac{3\sqrt{2}}{4}\right)$
and radius $\frac{3}{2}$ (medium)

132. Sketch the graph of $r = a \cos \theta + a \sin \theta$.

Answer:

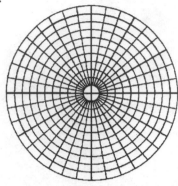

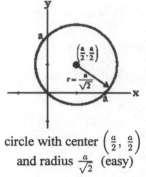

circle with center $\left(\frac{a}{2}, \frac{a}{2}\right)$
and radius $\frac{a}{\sqrt{2}}$ (easy)

133. Identify and sketch the conic $r = \frac{10}{3 - 2 \sin \theta}$.

Answer:

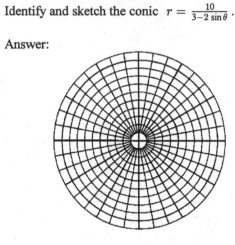

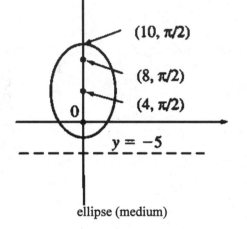

ellipse (medium)

134. Identify and sketch the conic $r = \frac{6}{1 + 5 \cos \theta}$.

Answer:

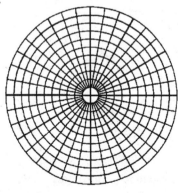

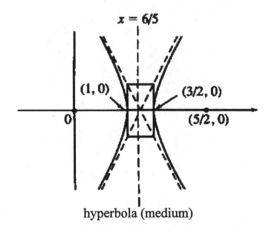

hyperbola (medium)

135. Identify and sketch the conic $r = \frac{1}{1 - \sin\theta}$.

Answer:

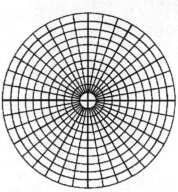

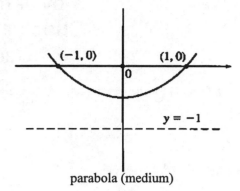

parabola (medium)

Calculus, 3rd Edition
by James Stewart
Chapter 10, Section 1
Sequences

1   Find a formula for the general term a_n of the sequence $\left\{1, -\frac{1}{2}, \frac{1}{4}, -\frac{1}{8}, \cdots\right\}$.

A) 2^{1-n} B) 2^{n-1} C) $(-2)^n$ D) $(-2)^{n-1}$
E) $(-1)^{2n}$ F) $(-2)^{1-n}$ G) $(-2)^{2n}$ H) 2^{-n}

Answer: $(-2)^{1-n}$ (easy)

2.   Find a formula for the general term a_n of the sequence $\{1, 6, 120, 5040, \ldots\}$.

A) $3^n(n+1)!$ B) $3^n\,n!$ C) $(n+1)!$ D) $(n+2)!$
E) $(2n)!$ F) $n!$ G) $(2n-1)!$ H) $2^n\,n!$

Answer: $(2n-1)!$ (medium)

3.   Determine the limit of the sequence $a_n = (n!)^{-1}$.

A) divergent   B) $\ln 2$ C) e^2 D) e
E) 1 F) $\ln 3$ G) $e - 1$ H) 0

Answer: 0 (easy)

4.   Determine the limit of the sequence $a_n = \dfrac{\sqrt{n+1}-\sqrt{n}}{\sqrt{n+1}+\sqrt{n}}$.

A) $1/4$ B) $\sqrt{2}$ C) 4 D) $1/\sqrt{2}$
E) 0 F) divergent   G) 2 H) $1/2$

Answer: 0 (medium)

5.   Determine the limit of the sequence $a_n = (n+1)!/n!$.

A) 2 B) 1 C) $1/3$ D) $1/2$
E) divergent F) 3 G) e H) 0

Answer: divergent (easy)

6.   Find the limit of the sequence $a_n = e^n/n!$.

A) $(e^2-1)/e$ B) $\sqrt{e}$ C) e D) e^2
E) 0 F) $(e-1)/e$ G) divergent   H) 1

Answer: 0 (medium)

7. Find the limit of the sequence $\left\{ \sqrt{3}, \sqrt{3\sqrt{3}}, \sqrt{3\sqrt{3\sqrt{3}}}, \ldots \right\}$.

A) 1   B) e^3 C) $e^{3/2}$ D) 3

E) 1/3   F) $e^{\sqrt{3}}$ G) π H) divergent

Answer: 3 (hard)

8. If $a_1 = 1$ and $a_{n+1} = \sqrt{1 + a_n}$ for $n \geq 1$, and $\lim_{n \to \infty} a_n = L$ is assumed to exist, then what must L be?

A) $\sqrt{2}$ B) $\sqrt{3}$ C) $\sqrt{5}$ D) $\sqrt{7}$

E) $\left(1 + \sqrt{2}\right)/2$ F) $\left(2 + \sqrt{3}\right)/4$ G) $\left(1 + \sqrt{5}\right)/2$ H) $\left(3 + \sqrt{7}\right)/2$

Answer: $\left(1 + \sqrt{5}\right)/2$ (hard)

9. Determine the limit of the sequence $a_n = (-1)^n / \sqrt{n}$.

A) -1 B) 0   C) 1/2   D) 1

E) $\sqrt{2}$ F) 2   G) e H) divergent

Answer: 0 (medium)

10. Determine the limit of the sequence $a_n = (-2)^n / n$.

A) -2 B) 0   C) $\ln 2$ D) $\sqrt{2}$

E) e^2 F) $-1/2$ G) 1   H) divergent

Answer: divergent (medium)

11. Determine the limit of the sequence $a_n = \frac{5 \cos n}{n}$.

A) 0   B) 1   C) 2   D) 3

E) 4   F) 5   G) 6   H) divergent

Answer: 0 (medium)

12. Determine the limit of the sequence $a_n = 2^n / n!$.

A) 0   B) 1   C) 2   D) 3

E) 4   F) 5   G) 6   H) divergent

Answer: 0 (medium)

13. State the precise condition on r for the sequence $a_n = r^n$ to have a finite limit.

A) $r < 1$ B) $-1 < r < 1$ C) $-1 \leq r < 1$ D) $-1 < r \leq 1$

E) $-1 \leq r \leq 1$ F) $-1 < r$ G) $r \leq 1$ H) $-1 \leq r$

Answer: $-1 < r \leq 1$ (medium)

14. Determine the limit of the sequence $a_n = [\ln(n+1) - \ln(n)]$.

A) $1/e$ B) 1   C) 2   D) 0
E) e F) 1/4   G) $\ln 2$ H) divergent

Answer: 0 (medium)

15. Determine the limit of the sequence $a_n = \frac{n!}{(n+3)!}$.

A) 0   B) 1   C) 2   D) e
E) 3   F) 1/2   G) 1/3   H) divergent

Answer: 0 (medium)

16. Determine the limit of the sequence $a_n = \frac{\sin n}{\sqrt{n}}$.

A) 0   B) 1   C) 2   D) 3
E) 4   F) 5   G) $\sqrt{e}$ H) divergent

Answer: 0 (medium)

17. If $a_1 = 1$ and $a_{n+1} = 3 - (1/a_n)$ for $n \geq 1$, find the limit of the sequence a_n.

A) 2   B) $\sqrt{2}$ C) $\sqrt{3}$ D) $\sqrt{5}$
E) $\left(2 + \sqrt{3}\right)/4$ F) $\left(3 + \sqrt{5}\right)/2$ G) $\left(5 + \sqrt{7}\right)/2$ H) $\left(5 + 2\sqrt{2}\right)/3$

Answer: $\left(3 + \sqrt{5}\right)/2$ (hard)

18. If $\frac{3n-1}{n+1} < x_n < \frac{3n^2+6n+2}{n^2+2n+1}$ for all positive integers n, then

A) $\lim_{n \to \infty} x_n = L$ where $-1 \leq L \leq 2$ B) $\lim_{n \to \infty} x_n = 3$
C) $\{x_n\}$ must be divergent   D) $\{x_n\}$ is monotonic
E) $\{x_n\}$ is bounded but may be divergent

Answer: $\lim_{n \to \infty} x_n = 3$ (medium)

19. Show, using the definition of the limit of a sequence, that $\lim_{n \to \infty} \frac{3}{n} = 0$.

Answer: We wish to show that for every $\epsilon > 0$ there is a positive integer N such that is $n > N$,
$\left|\frac{3}{n} - 0\right| < \epsilon$. Suppose $\epsilon > 0$. $\frac{3}{\epsilon} > 0$. By the theorem of Archimedes there is a positive
integer N such that $N > \frac{3}{\epsilon}$. Now if $n > N$, $n > N > \frac{3}{\epsilon}$; whence, by elementary algebra
we have $\frac{1}{n} < \frac{\epsilon}{3}$. So if $n > N$ then $\left|\frac{3}{n} - 0\right| = \frac{3}{n} = 3\left(\frac{1}{n}\right) < 3\left(\frac{\epsilon}{3}\right) = \epsilon$. Hence by the
definition of limit, $\lim_{n \to \infty} \frac{3}{n} = 0$. (hard)

20. The sequence defined by $x_n = \frac{(n+1)(n+3)}{n^2}$ is

    A) decreasing   B) increasing   C) non-monotonic
    D) divergent   E) bounded above but not bounded below

    Answer: decreasing (medium)

21. Consider the recursive sequence defined by $x_1 = 1$; $x_{n+1} = \frac{x_n^2+2}{2x_n}$, $n > 1$.
Evaluate the first three terms of this sequence.

    Answer: $x_1 = 1$; $x_2 = \frac{3}{2}$; $x_3 = \frac{17}{12}$ (easy)

22. Consider the recursive sequence defined by $x_1 = 1$; $x_{n+1} = \frac{x_n^2+2}{2x_n}$, $n > 1$. You may assume the sequence to be monotonic (after the first term) and bounded and hence convergent. Find its limit.

    Answer: $L = \sqrt{2}$ (medium)

23. Write the first five terms of the sequence: $a_n = \frac{4n-3}{3n+4}$.

    Answer: $\left\{ \frac{1}{7}, \frac{1}{2}, \frac{9}{13}, \frac{13}{16}, \frac{17}{19}, \ldots \right\}$ (easy)

24. Write the first five terms of the sequence: $a_n = \left\{ \frac{(-7)^{n+1}}{n!} \right\}$.

    Answer: $\left\{ 49, -\frac{343}{2}, \frac{2401}{6}, -\frac{16807}{24}, \frac{117649}{120}, \ldots \right\}$ (easy)

25. Find a formula for the general term a_n of $\left\{ \frac{1}{2}, \frac{1}{4}, \frac{1}{6}, \frac{1}{8}, \ldots \right\}$ assuming the pattern of the first few terms continues.

    Answer: $a_n = \frac{1}{2n}$ (easy)

26. Find a formula for the general term a_n of $\left\{ \frac{3}{2}, -\frac{9}{4}, \frac{27}{8}, -\frac{81}{16}, \ldots \right\}$ assuming the pattern of the first few terms continues.

    Answer: $a_n = (-1)^{n+1} \left(\frac{3}{2} \right)^n$ (medium)

27. Determine whether $a_n = 4\sqrt{n}$ converges or diverges. If it converges, find the limit.

    Answer: diverges (easy)

28. Determine whether $a_n = \sin(n\pi/2)$ converges or diverges. If it converges, find the limit.

    Answer: diverges (medium)

29. Determine whether $\left\{ \frac{n!}{(n+2)!} \right\}$ converges or diverges. If it converges, find the limit.

    Answer: converges to 0 (medium)

30. Determine whether $a_n = \frac{n \cos n}{n^2+1}$ converges or diverges. If it converges, find the limit.

    Answer: converges to 0 (medium)

31. Determine whether $a_n = \frac{1}{5^n}$ is increasing, decreasing, or not monotonic.

Answer: decreasing (easy)

32. Determine whether $a_n = \frac{3n+4}{2n+5}$ is increasing, decreasing, or not monotonic.

Answer: increasing (medium)

33. Determine whether $a_n = 3 + (-1)^n/n$ is increasing, decreasing, or not monotonic.

Answer: not monotonic (medium)

34. Determine whether $a_n = \frac{\sqrt{n+1}}{5n+3}$ is increasing, decreasing, or not monotonic.

Answer: decreasing (hard)

Chapter 10, Section 2
Series

35. Find the sum of the series $1 + \frac{1}{3} + \frac{1}{9} + \frac{1}{27} + \cdots$.

A) 7/4   B) 11/6   C) 3/2   D) 4/3
E) 5/3   F) 7/6   G) 5/4   H) divergent

Answer: 3/2 (easy)

36. Find the sum of the series $2 + \frac{1}{2} + \frac{1}{8} + \frac{1}{32} + \cdots$.

A) 15/7   B) 8/3   C) 7/3   D) 13/6
E) 16/7   F) 5/2   G) 17/6   H) divergent

Answer: 8/3 (medium)

37. Find the sum of the series $\sum_{n=1}^{\infty} \frac{1}{n(n+2)}$.

A) 3/4   B) 1/2   C) 3/5   D) 9/10
E) 7/10   F) 4/5   G) 2/3   H) divergent

Answer: 3/4 (hard)

38. Express the number $1.363636\ldots$ as a ratio of integers.

A) 17/13   B) 31/19   C) 30/19   D) 15/13
E) 17/11   F) 22/17   G) 15/11   H) 21/17

Answer: 15/11 (medium)

39. Find the values of x for which the series $\sum_{n=1}^{\infty} (x-1)^n$ converges.

A) $0 < x \le 2$ B) $-2 \le x < 0$ C) $-2 < x \le 0$
D) $0 \le x < 2$ E) $-2 < x < 0$ F) $0 < x < 2$
G) $0 \le x \le 2$ H) $-2 \le x \le 0$

Answer: $0 < x < 2$ (medium)

40. A rubber ball is dropped from a height of 10 feet and bounces to 3/4 its height after each fall. If it continues to bounce until it comes to rest, find the total distance in feet it travels.

A) 55   B) 70   C) 40   D) 65
E) 35   F) 45   G) 50   H) 60

Answer: 70 (medium)

41. Find the sum of the series $\sum_{n=1}^{\infty} \frac{(-1)^{n-1}}{2^n}$.

A) 1/3   B) 1/2   C) 3/5   D) 1
E) 3/2   F) 2   G) 3   H) divergent

Answer: 1/3 (medium)

42. Find the sum of the series $\sum_{n=1}^{\infty} (-1)^{n+1} \frac{2^n}{3^n}$.

A) 1/3   B) 1/2   C) 3/5   D) 1
E) 3/2   F) 2/5   G) 3   H) divergent

Answer: 2/5 (medium)

43. Find the sum of the series $\sum_{n=0}^{\infty} \frac{1}{2^n}$.

A) -1 B) 0   C) 1/2   D) 1
E) 2   F) 3/2   G) 4/3   H) 3

Answer: 2 (easy)

44. Find the sum of the series $\sum_{n=1}^{\infty} \frac{(-2)^{n+3}}{5^{n-2}}$.

A) 400   B) 400/3   C) 80   D) 400/7
E) 400/9   F) 400/11   G) 400/13   H) divergent

Answer: 400/7 (hard)

45. Find the sum of the series $\sum_{n=1}^{\infty} \frac{(-3)^{n-1}}{4^n}$.

A) $-3/4$ B) $-1/4$ C) $-1/7$ D) $1/7$
E) $1/4$ F) $3/4$ G) 0 H) divergent

Answer: 1/7 (medium)

46. Find the sum of the series $\sum_{n=1}^{\infty} \frac{2^n}{3^{n-1}}$.

A) $4/3$ B) $5/3$ C) 2 D) 3
E) 4 F) 5 G) 6 H) divergent

Answer: 6 (medium)

47. Find the sum of the series $\sum_{n=4}^{\infty} \frac{3}{n(n-1)}$.

A) $1/4$ B) $1/3$ C) $1/2$ D) $2/3$
E) $3/4$ F) 1 G) 2 H) divergent

Answer: 1 (medium)

48. Find the sum of the following series: $\sum_{n=1}^{\infty} \frac{2^n}{5^{n+1}}$

Answer: $\frac{2}{15}$ (medium)

49. $\frac{2}{9} - \frac{4}{27} + \cdots + \frac{(-1)^{n+1} \cdot 2^n}{3^{n+1}} + \cdots$ is equal to

A) $2/15$ B) $1/5$ C) $1/6$ D) $21/110$ E) $1/7$

Answer: 2/15 (medium)

50. Find the value of $\sum_{n=2}^{\infty} \frac{3^n + 5^n}{15^n}$

Answer: $S = \frac{13}{60}$ (medium)

51. Determine whether the series $1 - \frac{1}{2} + \frac{1}{4} - \frac{1}{8} + \cdots$ is convergent or divergent. If it is convergent, find its sum.

Answer: converges with sum $\frac{2}{3}$ (medium)

52. Determine whether the series $\frac{1}{2^6} + \frac{1}{2^8} + \frac{1}{2^{10}} + \frac{1}{2^{12}} + \cdots$ is convergent or divergent. If it is convergent, find its sum.

Answer: converges with sum $\frac{1}{48}$ (medium)

53. Determine whether the series $-\frac{81}{100} + \frac{9}{10} - 1 + \frac{10}{9} - \cdots$ is convergent or divergent. If it is convergent, find its sum.

Answer: diverges (medium)

54. Determine whether the series $\sum_{n=1}^{\infty} \frac{1}{e^{2n}}$ is convergent or divergent. If it is convergent, find its sum.

Answer: converges to $\frac{1}{e^2-1}$ (medium)

55. Determine whether the series $\sum_{n=0}^{\infty} \frac{4^{n+1}}{5^n}$ is convergent or divergent. If it is convergent, find its sum.

Answer: converges to 20 (medium)

56. Determine whether the series $\sum_{n=1}^{\infty} (-1)^{n-1} \frac{3^{2n}}{2^{3n+1}}$ is convergent or divergent. If it is convergent, find its sum.

Answer: diverges (medium)

57. Determine whether the series $\sum_{n=1}^{\infty} \frac{n^2}{3(n+1)(n+2)}$ is convergent or divergent. If it is convergent, find its sum.

Answer: diverges by the Test for Divergence (medium)

Chapter 10, Section 3
The Integral Test

58. Find the sum of the series $\sum_{n=1}^{\infty} \frac{1}{\sqrt{n}}$.

A) 20/3   B) e^2 C) 3   D) 20/7
E) 2   F) 10/7   G) 10/3   H) divergent

Answer: divergent (easy)

59. If we use the integral test to show that the series $\sum_{n=1}^{\infty} \frac{1}{n^2}$ converges, we obtain an improper integral with a finite value. What is that value?

A) 2/3   B) 7/6   C) 3/2   D) 1/2
E) 5/6   F) 4/3   G) 3/4   H) 1

Answer: 1 (easy)

60. If we use the integral test to show that the series $\sum_{n=1}^{\infty} \frac{1}{n(n+1)}$ converges, we obtain an improper integral with a finite value. What is that value?

A) e B) $\ln 2$ C) $\sqrt{3}$ D) $\sqrt{2}$
E) $e - 1$ F) $1/e$ G) $\ln 3$ H) 1

Answer: $\ln 2$ (hard)

61. Which of the three series below converge?

1) $\sum_{n=1}^{\infty} \frac{1}{n}$ 2) $\sum_{n=1}^{\infty} \frac{1}{n^{1.1}}$ 3) $\sum_{n=1}^{\infty} \frac{1}{n^{0.9}}$

A) 1, 2   B) 1   C) none   D) 3
E) 2   F) 2, 3   G) 1, 2, 3   H) 1, 3

Answer: 2 (easy)

62. Which of the three series below converge?

1) $\sum_{i=2}^{\infty} \frac{1}{n \ln n}$ 2) $\sum_{i=2}^{\infty} \frac{1}{n(\ln n)^2}$ 3) $\sum_{i=2}^{\infty} \frac{1}{n(\ln n)^3}$

A) 2   B) 1, 2, 3   C) 1, 3   D) 2, 3
E) 3   F) none   G) 1, 2   H) 1

Answer: 2, 3 (medium)

63. According to the proof of the integral test, the sum of the series $\sum_{n=1}^{\infty} \frac{1}{n^{1.001}}$ must lie between what two values?

A) 101, 102   B) 102, 103   C) 999, 1000
D) 1001, 1002   E) 1002, 1003   F) 1000, 1001
G) 99, 100   H) 100, 101

Answer: 1000, 1001 (hard)

64. What is the value of p that marks the boundary between convergence and divergence of the series $\sum_{n=2}^{\infty} \frac{1}{n(\ln n)^p}$?

A) $1/2$ B) $1/3$ C) diverges for all p
D) $\ln 2$ E) 1 F) $\ln 3$
G) converges for all p H) $1/e$

Answer: 1 (medium)

65. Which of three series below converge?

1) $\sum_{n=1}^{\infty} \frac{1}{n^4}$ 2) $\sum_{n=1}^{\infty} \frac{n^2}{2n^2+1}$ 3) $\sum_{n=1}^{\infty} \left(\sqrt{2}\right)^n$

A) none   B) 1   C) 2   D) 3
E) 1, 2   F) 1, 3   G) 2, 3   H) 1, 2, 3

Answer: 1 (easy)

66. The series $\sum_{n=1}^{\infty} \frac{1}{n^\alpha}$ converges if and only if

A) $\alpha < 1$ B) $-1 < \alpha < 1$ C) $\alpha \le 1$
D) $\alpha > 1$ E) $\alpha \ge 1$ F) $\alpha < -1$
G) $\alpha < -1$ H) $-1 < \alpha < 1$

Answer: $\alpha > 1$ (medium)

67. Which of the three series below converge?

1) $\sum_{n=1}^{\infty} \frac{n}{n+1}$ 2) $\sum_{n=1}^{\infty} \frac{\pi^n}{3^n}$ 3) $\sum_{n=1}^{\infty} \frac{1}{n\sqrt{n}}$

A) none   B) 1   C) 2   D) 3
E) 1, 2   F) 1, 3   G) 2, 3   H) 1, 2, 3

Answer: 3 (easy)

68. Use the integral test to determine if the following series converges or diverges:

$$\sum_{n=1}^{\infty} \frac{n}{(n^2+1)^2}$$

Answer: the integral has a value of $\frac{1}{4}$, which, since it is finite, the series converges (easy)

69. Use the integral test to show that the series $\sum_{k=2}^{\infty} \frac{1}{k(\ln k)^p}$ converges is $p > 1$ and diverges if $p \le 1$. [Hint: Consider two cases $p = 1$ and $p \ne 1$.]

Answer: Suppose that $p = 1$. Using the integral test with $\int_2^\infty \frac{dx}{x \ln k}$ gives

$$\lim_{l \to +\infty} \left(\ln(\ln x) \right)_2^1 = \infty \text{ and the series diverges. If } p \ne 1, \text{ then using the integral test}$$

with $\int_2^\infty \frac{dx}{x(\ln x)^p}$ gives $\lim_{l \to \infty} \left(\frac{(\ln x)^{1-p}}{1-p} \right)_2^1$. Since $\ln x \to \infty$ as $x \to \infty$, the

convergence of the series depends on whether $\ln x$ is in the numerator or denominator of the limit above. If $p > 1$, the $\ln x$ is in the denominator and the series converges. If $p > 1$, the $\ln x$ is in the numerator and the series diverges. So we have convergence if $p > 1$ and divergence if $p \le 1$. (hard)

70. Use the integral test to determine whether $\sum_{n=2}^{\infty} \frac{1}{n(\log n)^4}$ converges or diverges.

Answer: converges (medium)

71. Determine whether or not the following infinite series converges: $\sum_{k=2}^{\infty} \frac{1}{k(\ln k)^2}$

Answer: converges (medium)

72. Determine whether the following series converges or diverges. $\sum\limits_{n=1}^{\infty} 3ne^{-n^2}$

Answer: converges (medium)

Chapter 10, Section 4
The Comparison Tests

73. Which of the following three tests will establish that the series $\sum\limits_{n=1}^{\infty} \frac{3}{n(n+2)}$ converges?

      1) Comparison test with $\sum\limits_{n=1}^{\infty} 3n^{-2}$

      2) Limit comparison test with $\sum\limits_{n=1}^{\infty} n^{-2}$

      3) Comparison test with $\sum\limits_{n=1}^{\infty} 3n^{-1}$

A) none   B) 1   C) 2   D) 3
E) 1, 2   F) 1, 3   G) 2, 3   H) 1, 2, 3

Answer: 1 , 2 (medium)

74. Which of the following three tests will establish that the series $\sum\limits_{n=1}^{\infty} \frac{n}{\sqrt{2n^5+1}}$ converges?

      1) Comparison test with $\sum\limits_{n=1}^{\infty} n^{-5/2}$

      2) Comparison test with $\sum\limits_{n=1}^{\infty} n^{-3/2}$

      3) Comparison test with $\sum\limits_{n=1}^{\infty} n^{-1/2}$

A) none   B) 1   C) 2   D) 3
E) 1, 2   F) 1, 3   G) 2, 3   H) 1, 2, 3

Answer: 2 (easy)

75. Which of the following three tests will establish that the series $\sum\limits_{n=1}^{\infty} \frac{n}{\sqrt{7n^3+46}}$ diverges?

      1) Limit comparison test with $\sum\limits_{n=1}^{\infty} n^{-1}$ 2) Comparison test with $\sum\limits_{n=1}^{\infty} n^{-1}$

      3) Comparison test with $\sum\limits_{n=1}^{\infty} n^{-1/2}$

A) none   B) 1   C) 2   D) 3
E) 1, 2   F) 1, 3   G) 2, 3   H) 1, 2, 3

Answer: 1 (hard)

76. Which of the following series converge?

1) $\sum_{n=1}^{\infty} \frac{1}{n^2+\sqrt{n}}$ 2) $\sum_{n=1}^{\infty} \frac{\sqrt{n}}{n^2+\ln n}$ 3) $\sum_{n=1}^{\infty} \frac{n}{\sqrt{n^3+2n^2}}$

A) none   B) 1   C) 2   D) 3
E) 1, 2   F) 1, 3   G) 2, 3   H) 1, 2, 3

Answer: 1, 2 (medium)

77. Which of the following series converge?

1) $\sum_{n=1}^{\infty} n^{-n}$ 2) $\sum_{n=1}^{\infty} e^{100-n}$ 3) $\sum_{n=1}^{\infty} \frac{n^n}{n!}$

A) none   B) 1   C) 2   D) 3
E) 1, 2   F) 1, 3   G) 2, 3   H) 1, 2, 3

Answer: 1, 2 (medium)

78. Which of the following series converge?

1) $\sum_{n=1}^{\infty} \frac{1}{\ln(n+1)}$ 2) $\sum_{n=1}^{\infty} \frac{1}{[\ln(n+1)]^2}$ 3) $\sum_{n=1}^{\infty} \frac{1}{[\ln(n+1)]^3}$

A) none   B) 1   C) 2   D) 3
E) 1, 2   F) 1, 3   G) 2, 3   H) 1, 2, 3

Answer: none (medium)

79. Which of the following series converge?

1) $\sum_{n=1}^{\infty} \frac{1}{e^n}$ 2) $\sum_{n=1}^{\infty} \frac{1}{\sqrt{e^n}}$ 3) $\sum_{n=1}^{\infty} \frac{1}{\sqrt[3]{e^n}}$

A) none   B) 1   C) 2   D) 3
E) 1, 2   F) 1, 3   G) 2, 3   H) 1, 2, 3

Answer: 1, 2, 3 (easy)

80. Which of the following series converge?

1) $\sum_{n=1}^{\infty} \frac{3^{2n}}{2^{3n}}$ 2) $\sum_{n=1}^{\infty} \frac{1}{(n+1)^3}$ 3) $\sum_{n=1}^{\infty} \frac{n+1}{\sqrt{n^3+2}}$

A) none   B) 1   C) 2   D) 3
E) 1, 2   F) 1, 3   G) 2, 3   H) 1, 2, 3

Answer: 2 (medium)

81. Which of the following series converge?

$$1) \sum_{n=1}^{\infty} (-1)^n \qquad 2) \sum_{n=1}^{\infty} 2^n \qquad 3) \sum_{n=1}^{\infty} \frac{1}{2+n^3}$$

A) none
B) 1
C) 2
D) 3
E) 1, 2
F) 1, 3
G) 2, 3
H) 1, 2, 3

Answer: 3 (easy)

82. Which of the following series converge?

$$1) \sum_{n=1}^{\infty} \frac{n}{\sqrt{n^3+n^2}} \qquad 2) \sum_{n=2}^{\infty} \frac{n}{n\sqrt{n-1}} \qquad 3) \sum_{n=1}^{\infty} \frac{1}{n^2+n+1}$$

A) none
B) 1
C) 2
D) 3
E) 1, 2
F) 1, 3
G) 2, 3
H) 1, 2, 3

Answer: 3 (medium)

83. Determine whether $\sum_{n=1}^{\infty} \frac{\cos n + 3^n}{n^2 + 5^n}$ is convergent or divergent.

Answer: convergent (medium)

84. Determine whether the series $\sum_{n=0}^{\infty} \frac{1 + \sin^2 n}{5^n}$ converges.

Answer: converges (medium)

85. Consider the two series: a) $\sum_{k=2}^{\infty} \frac{\ln k}{k}$ and b) $\sum_{k=2}^{\infty} \frac{1}{k \ln k}$. Suppose you compare (a) and (b) to the series $\sum_{k=1}^{\infty} \frac{1}{k}$. What (if anything) can you conclude about the convergence or divergence of (a) and (b) using ONLY this comparison test?

Answer: $\sum_{k=1}^{\infty} \frac{1}{k}$ diverges to ∞. Since $\ln k > 1$ for $k \geq 3$, we have a) $\frac{\ln k}{k} > \frac{1}{k}$ and

b) $\frac{1}{k \ln k} < \frac{1}{k}$. From a) we conclude that $\sum_{k=2}^{\infty} \frac{\ln k}{k}$ also diverges to ∞. b) nothing

can be concluded from b) above. The comparison test yields no useful information

about the series $\sum_{k=2}^{\infty} \frac{1}{k \ln k}$. (hard)

86. For the series below, tell whether or not it converges, and indicate what test you used. If the test involves a limit, give the limit. If the test involves a comparison, give the comparison.

$$\sum_{n=2}^{\infty} \frac{n^{1/n}}{\ln(n)}$$

Answer: It diverges by the comparison test, since $\sum_{n=2}^{\infty} \frac{1}{n}$ diverges, so does the given series. (hard)

Chapter 10, Section 5
Alternating Series

87. Which of the following are alternating series?

   1) $\sum\limits_{n=1}^{\infty} \cos n$ 2) $\sum\limits_{n=1}^{\infty} \cos n\pi$ 3) $\sum\limits_{n=1}^{\infty} \sin n\pi$

   A) none   B) 1   C) 2   D) 3
   E) 1, 2   F) 1, 3   G) 2, 3   H) 1, 2, 3

   Answer: 2 (easy)

88. Which of the following series converge?

   1) $\sum\limits_{n=1}^{\infty} \frac{(-1)^n}{\ln(n+1)}$ 2) $\sum\limits_{n=1}^{\infty} (-1)^n \ln(n+1)$ 3) $1 - \frac{1}{2} + \frac{2}{3} - \frac{3}{4} + \frac{4}{5} - \frac{5}{6} + \cdots$

   A) none   B) 1   C) 2   D) 3
   E) 1, 2   F) 1, 3   G) 2, 3   H) 1, 2, 3

   Answer: 1 (medium)

89. If we add the first 100 terms of the alternating series $1 - \frac{1}{2} + \frac{1}{3} - \frac{1}{4} + \frac{1}{5} - \cdots$, how close can we determine the partial sum s_{100} to be to the sum s of the series?

   A) $s_{100} > s$, with $s_{100} - s < 1/101$ B) $s_{100} > s$, with $s_{100} - s < 1/e^{100}$
   C) $s_{100} > s$, with $s_{100} - s < 1/100$ D) $s_{100} < s$, with $s - s_{100} < 1/e^{101}$
   E) $s_{100} > s$, with $s_{100} - s < 1/e^{101}$ F) $s_{100} < s$, with $s - s_{100} < 1/101$
   G) $s_{100} < s$, with $s - s_{100} < 1/100$ H) $s_{100} < s$, with $s - s_{100} < 1/e^{100}$

   Answer: $s_{100} < s$, with $s - s_{100} < 1/100$ (medium)

90. How many terms of the alternating series $\sum\limits_{n=1}^{\infty} (-1)^{n+1} n^{-2}$ must we add in order to be sure that the partial sum s_n is within 0.0001 of the true sum s?

   A) 10   B) 300   C) 30000   D) 30
   E) 3   F) 10000   G) 100   H) 1000

   Answer: 100 (medium)

91. Which of the following series converge?

   1) $\sum\limits_{n=1}^{\infty} \frac{n}{n+1}$ 2) $\sum\limits_{n=1}^{\infty} \frac{\sqrt{n+1}}{n^2+2}$ 3) $\sum\limits_{n=1}^{\infty} \frac{(-1)^{n-1}}{\sqrt{n+1}}$

   A) none   B) 1   C) 2   D) 3
   E) 1, 2   F) 1, 3   G) 2, 3   H) 1, 2, 3

   Answer: 2, 3 (medium)

92. Which of the following series converge?

   1) $\sum_{n=1}^{\infty} \frac{1}{n}$ 2) $\sum_{n=1}^{\infty} \frac{1}{n^2}$ 3) $\sum_{n=1}^{\infty} \frac{(-1)^n}{n}$

   A) none   B) 1   C) 2   D) 3
   E) 1, 2   F) 1, 3   G) 2, 3   H) 1, 2, 3

   Answer: 2, 3 (easy)

93. Which one of the following series diverges?

   A) $\sum_{n=1}^{\infty} \left(\frac{3}{\pi}\right)^n$ B) $\sum_{n=2}^{\infty} \frac{1}{\sqrt{n^3+1}}$ C) $\sum_{n=4}^{\infty} \frac{(-1)^n}{\ln n}$

   D) $\sum_{n=2}^{\infty} \frac{3}{n \ln n}$ E) $\sum_{n=1}^{\infty} \left(\frac{1}{n} - \frac{1}{n+1}\right)$ F) $\sum_{n=1}^{\infty} \left(\frac{2}{e}\right)^n$

   G) $\sum_{n=1}^{\infty} \frac{3}{n^2 \ln n}$ H) $\sum_{n=1}^{\infty} 3n^{-3/2}$

   Answer: $\sum_{n=2}^{\infty} \frac{3}{n \ln n}$ (hard)

94. Test the following series for convergence or divergence: $-5 - \frac{5}{2} + \frac{5}{5} - \frac{5}{8} + \frac{5}{11} - \frac{5}{14} + \cdots$

   Answer: converges by the Alternating Series Test (easy)

95. Test the following series for convergence or divergence: $\frac{1}{\ln 2} - \frac{1}{\ln 3} + \frac{1}{\ln 4} - \frac{1}{\ln 5} + \frac{1}{\ln 6} - \cdots$

   Answer: converges by the Alternating Series Test (easy)

96. Test the following series for convergence or divergence: $\sum_{n=1}^{\infty} \frac{(-1)^n}{\sqrt{n+3}}$

   Answer: converges by the Alternating Series Test (medium)

97. Test the following series for convergence or divergence: $\sum_{n=2}^{\infty} \frac{(-1)^{n-1}}{n \ln n}$

   Answer: converges by the Alternating Series Test (medium)

98. Test the following series for convergence or divergence: $\sum_{n=1}^{\infty} (-1)^n \frac{n^2}{n^2+1}$

   Answer: diverges by the Divergence Test (medium)

99. Test the following series for convergence or divergence: $\sum_{n=1}^{\infty} (-1)^{n+1} \frac{n}{2^n}$

   Answer: converges by the Alternating Series Test (medium)

100. Test the following series for convergence or divergence: $\sum_{n=1}^{\infty} (-1)^{n-1} \frac{\ln n}{n}$

Answer: converges by the Alternating Series Test (medium)

101. Test the following series for convergence or divergence: $\sum_{n=1}^{\infty} \frac{\sin\left(\frac{n\pi}{2}\right)}{n!}$

Answer: converges (medium)

102. Test the following series for convergence or divergence: $\sum_{n=1}^{\infty} (-1)^{n-1} \frac{(n+9)(n+10)}{n(n+1)}$

Answer: diverges (medium)

103. Test the following series for convergence or divergence: $\sum_{n=1}^{\infty} (-1)^n \cos\left(\frac{\pi}{n}\right)$

Answer: diverges (medium)

104. Test the following series for convergence or divergence: $\sum_{n=1}^{\infty} \frac{(-1)^n}{|n-10\pi|}$

Answer: converges (medium)

105. Approximate the sum $\sum_{n=1}^{\infty} \frac{(-1)^{n+1}}{n^4}$ with error < 0.001.

Answer: 0.948 (medium)

106. Approximate the sum $\sum_{n=0}^{\infty} \frac{(-1)^n n}{4^n}$ with error < 0.002.

Answer: -0.161 (medium)

Chapter 10, Section 6
Absolute Convergence and the Ratio and Root Tests

107. Examine the two series below for absolute convergence (A), conditional convergence (C), or divergence (D).

1) $\sum_{n=1}^{\infty} (-1)^n$ 2) $\sum_{n=1}^{\infty} (-1)^{n-1} n^{-1}$

A) 1A, 2A   B) 1A, 2C   C) 1A, 2D   D) 1C, 2A
E) 1C, 2C   F) 1C, 2D   G) 1D, 2A   H) 1D, 2C

Answer: 1D, 2C (easy)

108. Examine the two series below for absolute convergence (A), conditional convergence (C), or divergence (D).

1) $\sum_{n=1}^{\infty} (-1)^{n-1} n^{-1}$ 2) $\sum_{n=1}^{\infty} (-1)^{n-1} n^{-2}$

A) 1A, 2A   B) 1A, 2C   C) 1A, 2D   D) 1C, 2A
E) 1C, 2C   F) 1C, 2D   G) 1D, 2A   H) 1D, 2C

Answer: 1C, 2A (easy)

109. Which of the following series will, when rearranged, converge to different values?

1) $\sum_{n=1}^{\infty} n^{-1}$ 2) $\sum_{n=1}^{\infty} (-1)^{n-1} n^{-1}$ 3) $\sum_{n=1}^{\infty} (-1)^{n-1} n^{-2}$

A) none   B) 1   C) 2   D) 3
E) 1, 2   F) 1, 3   G) 2, 3   H) 1, 2, 3

Answer: 2 (medium)

110. Which of the following series are conditionally convergent?

1) $\sum_{n=1}^{\infty} (-e)^{-n}$ 2) $\sum_{n=1}^{\infty} (-1)^{-n} n^{-1}$ 3) $\sum_{n=1}^{\infty} (-1)^{-n} n^{-2}$

A) none   B) 1   C) 2   D) 3
E) 1, 2   F) 1, 3   G) 2, 3   H) 1, 2, 3

Answer: 2 (easy)

111. Examine the two series below for absolute convergence (A), conditional convergence (C), or divergence (D).

1) $\sum_{n=1}^{\infty} (-1)^{n-1} \frac{(n+2)3^n}{2^{2n+1}}$ 2) $\sum_{n=1}^{\infty} (-1)^{n-1} \frac{(n+3)2^{2n}}{3^{n+100}}$

A) 1A, 2A   B) 1A, 2C   C) 1A, 2D   D) 1C, 2A
E) 1C, 2C   F) 1C, 2D   G) 1D, 2A   H) 1D, 2C

Answer: 1A, 2D (medium)

112. Examine the two series below for absolute convergence (A), conditional convergence (C), or divergence (D).

1) $\sum_{n=1}^{\infty} \frac{(-1)^{n-1}}{\ln(n+1)}$ 2) $\sum_{n=1}^{\infty} \frac{(-1)^{n-1}}{(\ln(n+1))^2}$

A) 1A, 2A   B) 1A, 2C   C) 1A, 2D   D) 1C, 2A
E) 1C, 2C   F) 1C, 2D   G) 1D, 2A   H) 1D, 2C

Answer: 1C, 2C (medium)

113. Examine the two series below for absolute convergence (A), conditional convergence (C), or divergence (D).

1) $\sum\limits_{n=1}^{\infty} (-1)^{n-1} \frac{n+1}{\ln(n+1)}$ 2) $\sum\limits_{n=1}^{\infty} (-1)^{n-1} \frac{\ln(n+1)}{n+1}$

A) 1A, 2A   B) 1A, 2C   C) 1A, 2D   D) 1C, 2A
E) 1C, 2C   F) 1C, 2D   G) 1D, 2A   H) 1D, 2C

Answer: 1D, 2C (medium)

114. Which of the following series converge?

1) $\sum\limits_{n=1}^{\infty} \left(\frac{n}{2+3n}\right)^n$ 2) $\sum\limits_{n=2}^{\infty} \frac{n+1}{\sqrt{n^4-1}}$ 3) $\sum\limits_{n=1}^{\infty} \frac{1}{1+n^2}$

A) none   B) 1   C) 2   D) 3
E) 1, 2   F) 1, 3   G) 2, 3   H) 1, 2, 3

Answer: 1, 3 (medium)

115. Which of the following series are *conditionally* convergent?

1) $\sum\limits_{n=1}^{\infty} \frac{(-1)^n}{n^2}$ 2) $\sum\limits_{n=1}^{\infty} \frac{(-1)^{n-1}}{\sqrt{n}}$ 3) $\sum\limits_{n=1}^{\infty} \frac{\cos n}{2^n}$

A) none   B) 1   C) 2   D) 3
E) 1, 2   F) 1, 3   G) 2, 3   H) 1, 2, 3

Answer: 2 (medium)

116. Which of the following series are *conditionally* convergent?

1) $\sum\limits_{n=1}^{\infty} (-1)^{n+1} \frac{n+2}{n^2+1}$ 2) $\sum\limits_{n=1}^{\infty} \frac{(-1)^n}{n^4}$ 3) $\sum\limits_{n=1}^{\infty} \frac{\sin n\pi}{\pi^n}$

A) none   B) 1   C) 2   D) 3
E) 1, 2   F) 1, 3   G) 2, 3   H) 1, 2, 3

Answer: 1 (medium)

117. Which of the following series diverge?

1) $\sum\limits_{n=1}^{\infty} \frac{n+2}{n^2+1}$ 2) $\sum\limits_{n=1}^{\infty} \frac{n!}{2^n}$ 3) $\sum\limits_{n=1}^{\infty} \left(\frac{2n-1}{n+3}\right)^n$

A) none   B) 1   C) 2   D) 3
E) 1, 2   F) 1, 3   G) 2, 3   H) 1, 2, 3

Answer: 1, 2, 3 (hard)

118. Which of the following series are absolutely convergent?

1) $\sum\limits_{n=1}^{\infty} \frac{(-1)^n}{n^2}$ 2) $\sum\limits_{n=1}^{\infty} \frac{(-1)^n}{n}$ 3) $\sum\limits_{n=1}^{\infty} \frac{1}{n^3}$

A) none   B) 1   C) 2   D) 3
E) 1, 2   F) 1, 3   G) 2, 3   H) 1, 2, 3

Answer: 1, 3 (easy)

119. Which of the following series can be shown to be convergent *using the Ratio Test*?

1) $\displaystyle\sum_{n=1}^{\infty} \frac{1}{n^2}$ 2) $\displaystyle\sum_{n=1}^{\infty} \frac{n}{3^n}$ 3) $\displaystyle\sum_{n=1}^{\infty} \frac{2^n}{\sqrt{n}}$

A) none   B) 1   C) 2   D) 3

E) 1, 2   F) 1, 3   G) 2, 3   H) 1, 2, 3

Answer: 2 (medium)

120. Which *one* of the following series is divergent?

A) $\displaystyle\sum_{n=1}^{\infty} \left(\frac{2}{3}\right)^n$ B) $\displaystyle\sum_{n=1}^{\infty} \frac{1}{n^2+1}$ C) $\displaystyle\sum_{n=1}^{\infty} \frac{1}{n5^n}$

D) $\displaystyle\sum_{n=2}^{\infty} \frac{n}{n^2-1}$ E) $\displaystyle\sum_{n=1}^{\infty} \frac{n^3}{n^5+2}$ F) $\displaystyle\sum_{n=1}^{\infty} \frac{2^n}{n!}$

G) $\displaystyle\sum_{n=1}^{\infty} \frac{\pi}{n^2}$ H) $\displaystyle\sum_{n=1}^{\infty} (-1)^{n-1}\, \pi/n$

Answer: $\displaystyle\sum_{n=2}^{\infty} \frac{n}{n^2-1}$ (hard)

121. Determine whether the given series is conditionally convergent, absolutely convergent or divergent.

$$\sum_{n=1}^{\infty} \frac{(-1)^{n+1}}{\sqrt{n}}$$

Answer: conditionally convergent (easy)

122. Determine whether the given series is conditionally convergent, absolutely convergent or divergent.

$$\sum_{k=2}^{\infty} \frac{(-1)^{k+1}}{\ln k}$$

Answer: converges conditionally (medium)

123. Determine whether the given series is conditionally convergent, absolutely convergent or divergent.

$$\sum_{n=1}^{\infty} \frac{(-1)^{n+1} n}{n^2+1}$$

Answer: converges conditionally (medium)

124. Does the series $\displaystyle\sum_{n=1}^{\infty} \frac{2^{3n}}{5^n}$ converge or diverge? Justify.

Answer: $\dfrac{a_{n+1}}{a_n} = \dfrac{2^{3(n+1)}}{5^{n+1}} \cdot \dfrac{5^n}{2^{3n}} = \dfrac{2^{3n}\cdot 8 \cdot 5^n}{5^n \cdot 5 \cdot 2^{3n}} = \dfrac{8}{5} > 1$. Therefore by the ratio test this series

diverges. Or use the fact that it is a geometric series. (medium)

125. Test for convergence: $\displaystyle\sum_{n=1}^{\infty} \frac{3^n}{n!}$.

Answer: the series converges (medium)

126. Test for convergence: $\sum\limits_{n=0}^{\infty} \frac{n!}{3^n}$.

Answer: the series diverges (medium)

127. Establish the convergence or divergence of the series $\sum\limits_{n=1}^{\infty} \frac{(n+3)!-n!}{2^n}$.

Answer: divergent (medium)

128. Which of the following series is convergent but not absolutely convergent?

A) $\sum\limits_{n=1}^{\infty} \frac{1}{n}$ B) $\sum\limits_{n=1}^{\infty} \frac{\sin n}{n^2}$ C) $\sum\limits_{n=1}^{\infty} \frac{(-1)^n}{\sqrt{n}}$ D) $\sum\limits_{n=1}^{\infty} \frac{3^n}{2^n+\sqrt{n}}$ E) $\sum\limits_{n=1}^{\infty} \frac{1-2n}{n+1}$

Answer: (c) is convergent by the alternating series test but not absolutely convergent

since $\sum\limits_{0}^{\infty} \left| \frac{(-1)^n}{\sqrt{n}} \right| = \sum\limits_{n=1}^{\infty} \frac{1}{n^{1/2}}$ is a divergent p-series. (medium)

129. Determine if the following infinite series converges absolutely, converges conditionally, or diverges:
$\sum\limits_{k=1}^{\infty} \frac{(-1)^k k}{k^2+1}$

Answer: Since this is an alternating series, and $\lim\limits_{k \to \infty} \frac{k}{k^2+1} = 0$, then the series must

converge. $\sum\limits_{k=1}^{\infty} \left| \frac{(-1)^k k}{k^2+1} \right| = \sum\limits_{k=1}^{\infty} \frac{k}{k^2+1}$ diverges since it is asymptotically proportional to

a divergent series, the harmonic series: $\lim\limits_{k \to \infty} \frac{\frac{k}{k^2+1}}{\frac{1}{k}} = \lim\limits_{k \to \infty} \frac{k^2}{k^2+1} = 1$. Therefore, the

given series converges conditionally. (medium)

Chapter 10, Section 7
Strategy for Testing Series

130. Use the Ratio Test to examine the two series below, stating: absolute convergence (A), divergence (D), or Ratio Test inconclusive (I).

1) $\sum\limits_{n=1}^{\infty} n^{-100}$ 2) $\sum\limits_{n=1}^{\infty} 100^{-n}$

A) 1A, 2A   B) 1A, 2D   C) 1A, 2I   D) 1D, 2A
E) 1D, 2D   F) 1D, 2I   G) 1I, 2A   H) 1I, 2D

Answer: 1I, 2A (easy)

131. Use the Ratio Test to examine the two series below, stating: absolute convergence (A), divergence (D), or Ratio Test inconclusive (I).

1) $\sum_{n=1}^{\infty} (-1)^{n-1} \frac{2^{2n+1}}{5^n}$ 2) $\sum_{n=1}^{\infty} (-1)^{n-1} \frac{5^n}{2^{2n+1}}$

A) 1A, 2A   B) 1A, 2D   C) 1A, 2I   D) 1D, 2A
E) 1D, 2D   F) 1D, 2I   G) 1I, 2A   H) 1I, 2D

Answer: 1A, 2D (medium)

132. For which of the following series will the Test for Divergence establish divergence?

1) $\sum_{n=1}^{\infty} (-1)^n$ 2) $\sum_{n=1}^{\infty} n^{-1}$ 3) $\sum_{n=1}^{\infty} \frac{n+1}{2n}$

A) none   B) 1   C) 2   D) 3
E) 1, 2   F) 1, 3   G) 2, 3   H) 1, 2, 3

Answer: 1, 3 (medium)

133. For which of the following series will the Ratio Test fail to give a definite answer (i.e., be inconclusive)?

1) $\sum_{n=1}^{\infty} (99/100)^n$ 2) $\sum_{n=1}^{\infty} (100/99)^n$ 3) $\sum_{n=1}^{\infty} n^{-100}$

A) none   B) 1   C) 2   D) 3
E) 1, 2   F) 1, 3   G) 2, 3   H) 1, 2, 3

Answer: 3 (medium)

134. Tell which of the following three series can be compared with geometric series to establish convergence.

1) $\sum_{n=1}^{\infty} \frac{1}{2+3^n}$ 2) $\sum_{n=1}^{\infty} \frac{n}{n^3+4}$ 3) $\sum_{n=1}^{\infty} (-1)^{n-1} \frac{n^2}{3^n}$

A) none   B) 1   C) 2   D) 3
E) 1, 2   F) 1, 3   G) 2, 3   H) 1, 2, 3

Answer: 1, 3 (hard)

135. Tell which of the following three series cannot be found convergent by the ratio test but can be found convergent by comparison with a p-series.

1) $\sum_{n=1}^{\infty} \frac{1}{2+3^n}$ 2) $\sum_{n=1}^{\infty} \frac{n}{n^3+4}$ 3) $\sum_{n=1}^{\infty} (-1)^{n-1} \frac{n^2}{3^n}$

A) none   B) 1   C) 2   D) 3
E) 1, 2   F) 1, 3   G) 2, 3   H) 1, 2, 3

Answer: 2 (hard)

136.   Which *one* of the following series diverges?

A) $\sum\limits_{n=1}^{\infty} \frac{1}{n(2n+1)}$

B) $\sum\limits_{n=1}^{\infty} \frac{2n}{n+1}$

C) $\sum\limits_{n=1}^{\infty} \frac{1}{(n+1)(n+3)}$

D) $\sum\limits_{n=1}^{\infty} \frac{1}{3^n}$

E) $\sum\limits_{n=1}^{\infty} \frac{n-2}{n2^n}$

F) $\sum\limits_{n=1}^{\infty} \frac{2n}{n!}$

G) $\sum\limits_{n=1}^{\infty} \frac{n^{100}}{n!}$

H) $\sum\limits_{n=1}^{\infty} \frac{n^{100}}{2^n}$

Answer: $\sum\limits_{n=1}^{\infty} \frac{2n}{n+1}$ (hard)

137.   Which of the following series converge?

1) $\sum\limits_{n=1}^{\infty} \frac{1}{1+n^3}$

2) $\sum\limits_{n=1}^{\infty} \frac{(-1)^n}{\sqrt[3]{n}}$

3) $\sum\limits_{n=1}^{\infty} \left(\frac{3n+1}{2n+1}\right)^n$

A) none   B) 1   C) 2   D) 3
E) 1, 2   F) 1, 3   G) 2, 3   H) 1, 2, 3

Answer: 1, 2 (medium)

138.   Which of the following series converge?

1) $\sum\limits_{n=1}^{\infty} n^{-0.9}$

2) $\sum\limits_{n=1}^{\infty} \frac{3^n}{n+5^n}$

3) $\sum\limits_{n=1}^{\infty} \frac{n}{1+4n}$

A) none   B) 1   C) 2   D) 3
E) 1, 2   F) 1, 3   G) 2, 3   H) 1, 2, 3

Answer: 2 (medium)

139.   Analyze the following series for convergence vs. divergence: $\sum\limits_{n=1}^{\infty} \cos\left(\frac{1}{n^2}\right)$.

Answer: diverges (medium)

140.   Analyze the following series for convergence vs. divergence: $\sum\limits_{n=1}^{\infty} \frac{1}{e^n}$.

Answer: converges (easy)

141.   Analyze the following series for convergence vs. divergence: $\sum\limits_{n=1}^{\infty} \frac{3^n}{n!}$.

Answer: converges (medium)

142.   Analyze the following series for convergence vs. divergence: $\sum\limits_{n=1}^{\infty} \frac{\sin n}{n^2}$.

Answer: converges (absolutely) (medium)

143. Analyze the following series for convergence vs. divergence: $\sum\limits_{n=1}^{\infty} \frac{n}{5n^2+\sqrt{n}}$.

Answer: diverges (medium)

144. Analyze the following series for convergence vs. divergence: $\sum\limits_{n=1}^{\infty} \frac{(-1)^n}{n}$.

Answer: converges (easy)

Chapter 10, Section 8
Power Series

145. Find the radius of convergence of $\sum\limits_{n=0}^{\infty} 3x^n$.

A) 2   B) 1/2   C) 6   D) 1/6
E) 3   F) 1   G) 1/3   H) 0

Answer: 1 (easy)

146. Find the radius of convergence of $\sum\limits_{n=0}^{\infty} (3x)^n$.

A) 3   B) 0   C) 2   D) 1/6
E) 6   F) 1/3   G) 1   H) 1/2

Answer: 1/3 (easy)

147. Find the interval of convergence of $\sum\limits_{n=0}^{\infty} \frac{x^n}{3n+1}$.

A) $[-3,3]$ B) $(-1,1)$ C) $(-3,3)$ D) $[-1,1]$
E) $(-1,1]$ F) $(-3,3]$ G) $[-3,3)$ H) $[-1,1)$

Answer: $[-1,1)$ (medium)

148. Find the interval of convergence of $\sum\limits_{n=0}^{\infty} \frac{(-3x)^n}{3n+1}$.

A) $(-1/3,1/3)$ B) $(-1/3,1/3]$ C) $[-1/3,1/3)$ D) $[-1/3,1/3]$
E) $(-3,3)$ F) $(-3,3]$ G) $[-3,3)$ H) $[-3,3]$

Answer: $(-1/3,1/3]$ (medium)

149. Find the interval of convergence of $\sum\limits_{n=0}^{\infty} \frac{x^n}{2n^2}$.

A) $[-1,1]$ B) $(-1,1]$ C) $(-1,1)$ D) $[-1,1)$
E) $[-2,2]$ F) $(-2,2]$ G) $(-2,2)$ H) $[-2,2)$

Answer: $[-1,1]$ (medium)

150. Find the radius of convergence of $\sum\limits_{n=0}^{\infty} \frac{(2n)!}{n!} x^n$.

A) 2   B) $1/e$ C) 1   D) 0
E) $2e$ F) e G) $1/2$ H) $1/(2e)$

Answer: 0 (hard)

151. Find the radius of convergence of $\sum\limits_{n=0}^{\infty} x^n/n!$.

A) $1/e$ B) ∞ C) 2   D) 0
E) $1/(2e)$ F) $1/2$ G) e H) $2e$

Answer: ∞ (easy)

152. Find the radius of convergence of $\sum\limits_{n=0}^{\infty} \frac{4^n}{n!} (x-2)^n$.

A) 0   B) $1/4$ C) $1/2$ D) 1
E) 2   F) 4   G) 8   H) ∞

Answer: ∞ (medium)

153. Find the radius of convergence of $\sum\limits_{n=1}^{\infty} \frac{(x+3)^n}{\sqrt{n}\, 2^n}$.

A) $1/2$ B) 1   C) 2   D) 3
E) 4   F) 5   G) 6   H) ∞

Answer: 2 (medium)

154. Find the interval of convergence of $\sum\limits_{n=1}^{\infty} \frac{(x+3)^n}{\sqrt{n}\, 2^n}$.

A) $(-1, 2)$ B) $(-2, 2]$ C) $[-3, 3)$ D) $[-3, 3]$
E) $(-5, -1)$ F) $[-5, -1)$ G) $(-1, 3]$ H) $[-1, 3]$

Answer: $[-5, -1)$ (medium)

155. Find the radius of convergence of $\sum\limits_{n=1}^{\infty} \frac{(x+2)^n}{n^2 3^n}$.

A) 0   B) 1   C) 2   D) 3
E) 4   F) 5   G) 6   H) ∞

Answer: 3 (medium)

156. Find the interval of convergence of $\sum\limits_{n=1}^{\infty} \frac{(x+2)^n}{n^2 3^n}$.

A) $[-5, 1]$ B) $(-3, 3)$ C) $[-2, 3)$ D) $(-\infty, \infty)$

E) $(-5, 1)$ F) $[-1, 5)$ G) $(-3, 2]$ H) $[-2/3 , 2/3]$

Answer: $[-5, 1]$ (hard)

157. Find the radius of convergence of $\sum\limits_{n=0}^{\infty} \frac{n}{4^n} (x + 3)^n$.

A) 0   B) 1   C) 2   D) 3

E) 4   F) 5   G) 6   H) ∞

Answer: 4 (easy)

158. Find the interval of convergence of $\sum\limits_{n=0}^{\infty} \frac{n}{4^n} (x + 3)^n$.

A) $(-3, 3)$ B) $[-3, 3)$ C) $[-3, 3]$ D) $(-3, 3]$

E) $(-7, 1)$ F) $[-7, 1)$ G) $[-7, 1]$ H) $(-7, 1]$

Answer: $(-7, 1)$ (medium)

159. Find the interval of convergence of $\sum\limits_{n=1}^{\infty} \frac{x^n}{n^2}$.

A) $(-\infty, \infty)$ B) $(-1, 1)$ C) $(-1, 1]$ D) $[-1, 1)$

E) $[-1, 1]$ F) $(-4, 4)$ G) $(-4, 4]$ H) $[-4, 4)$

Answer: $[-1, 1]$ (medium)

160. Find the radius of convergence of $\sum\limits_{n=1}^{\infty} (-1)^n \sqrt{n}\, 4^n (x - 6)^n$.

A) 0   B) 2   C) 4   D) 6

E) $1/2$ F) $1/4$ G) $1/6$ H) ∞

Answer: $1/4$ (medium)

161. Find the interval of convergence of $\sum\limits_{n=1}^{\infty} \frac{x^n}{n}$.

A) $(-1, 1)$ B) $(-1, 1]$ C) $[-1, 1)$ D) $[-1, 1]$

E) $(-e, e)$ F) $(-e, e]$ G) $[-e, e)$ H) $[-e, e]$

Answer: $[-1, 1)$ (medium)

162. Find the radius of convergence of $\sum\limits_{n=0}^{\infty} \frac{(-1)^n \, x^{2n+1}}{2n+1}$.

A) 1   B) 1/2   C) 2   D) 0
E) ∞ F) 1/4   G) 4   H) 8

Answer: 1 (medium)

163. Find the radius of convergence of $\sum\limits_{n=1}^{\infty} \frac{(-1)^n \, (x+2)^n}{\sqrt{n} \, 3^n}$.

A) 0   B) 1   C) 2   D) 3
E) 4   F) 5   G) 6   H) ∞

Answer: 3 (medium)

164. Find the interval of convergence of $\sum\limits_{n=1}^{\infty} \frac{(-1)^n \, (x+2)^n}{\sqrt{n} \, 3^n}$.

A) $(-\infty, \infty)$ B) $(-5, 1]$ C) $[-5, 1)$ D) $[-5, 1]$
E) $(-4, 0]$ F) $[-4, 0)$ G) $[-4, 0]$ H) $(-3, -1)$

Answer: $(-5, 1]$ (medium)

165. Find the radius of convergence of $\sum\limits_{n=1}^{\infty} \frac{(x-2)^n}{n3^n}$.

A) 0   B) 1   C) 2   D) 3
E) 4   F) 5   G) 6   H) ∞

Answer: 3 (medium)

166. Find the interval of convergence of $\sum\limits_{n=1}^{\infty} \frac{(x-2)^n}{n3^n}$.

A) $(1, 3)$ B) $[1, 3)$ C) $(2, 4]$ D) $[2, 4]$
E) $(-1, 5)$ F) $[-1, 5)$ G) $(-2, 6]$ H) $(-\infty, \infty)$

Answer: $[-1, 5)$ (medium)

167. Find the radius of convergence of $\sum\limits_{n=0}^{\infty} \frac{(-3)^n \, (x-1)^n}{\sqrt{n+1}}$.

A) 0   B) 1/3   C) 1/2   D) 1
E) 2   F) 3   G) 4   H) ∞

Answer: 1/3 (medium)

168. Find the interval of convergence of $\sum\limits_{n=0}^{\infty} \frac{(-3)^n (x-1)^n}{\sqrt{n+1}}$.

A) $(2/3, 4/3]$ B) $[2/3, 4/3)$ C) $(1/2, 3/2)$ D) $[1/2, 3/2]$
E) $(0, 2]$ F) $[0, 2)$ G) $(-1, 3)$ H) $[-2, 4]$

Answer: $(2/3, 4/3]$ (hard)

169. Find the interval of convergence of the power series $\sum\limits_{k=0}^{\infty} \frac{(-1)^k k^2}{5^k} (x-2)^k$.

Answer: $(-3, 7)$ (medium)

170. Find the interval of convergence for $\sum\limits_{n=1}^{\infty} \frac{x^n}{4n^2}$.

Answer: $[-1, 1]$ (easy)

171. Find the interval of convergence for $\sum\limits_{n=1}^{\infty} \frac{x^n}{n2^n}$.

Answer: $[-2, 2)$ (easy)

172. Find the interval of convergence of the power series $\sum\limits_{n=1}^{\infty} \frac{(-1)^n (x-2)^n}{\sqrt[3]{n}}$.

Answer: $(1, 3]$ (medium)

173. Consider the power series $\sum\limits_{k=1}^{\infty} \frac{(-1)^k}{k} x^k$.

(a) Find the radius of convergence.

(b) Determine what happens at the end points (absolute or conditional convergence, or divergence.)

Answer: (a) $r = 1$; (b) for $x = 1$, converges conditionally; for $x = -1$, diverges (medium)

174. Which of the following is impossible for the convergence set of the power series $\sum\limits_{n=0}^{\infty} a_n (x-3)^n$?

A) $0 < x < 6$ B) $1 \leq x < 5$ C) $2 \leq x \leq 5$ D) $2 \leq x \leq 4$
E) $-1 < x \leq 7$

Answer: $2 \leq x \leq 5$ (medium)

175. Find the radius of convergence of the series $\sum\limits_{n=1}^{\infty} \frac{3^n (x-2)^{2n+1}}{n!}$.

Answer: $r = \infty$; i.e., the series converges for all real x. (medium)

176. Find the interval of convergence for $\sum\limits_{n=0}^{\infty} x^n$.

Answer: $(-1, 1)$ (easy)

177. Find the interval of convergence for $\sum\limits_{k=0}^{\infty} \left(\frac{e^k}{k+1} \right) x^k$.

Answer: $\frac{-1}{e} \leq x \leq \frac{1}{e}$

178. Find the interval of convergence for $\sum\limits_{k=1}^{\infty} \frac{x^k}{2^k k^2}$.

Answer: $[-2, 2]$ (medium)

179. Find the interval of convergence for $\sum\limits_{k=1}^{\infty} \frac{(-1)^k (x-3)^k}{5^k (k+1)}$.

Answer: $(-2, 8]$ (medium)

Chapter 10, Section 9
Representation of Functions as Power Series

180. Find a power series representation for the function $f(x) = \frac{1-x}{1+x}$ and give its interval of convergence.

Answer: $1 - 2 \sum\limits_{n=0}^{\infty} (-1)^n x^{n+1}$, interval of convergence $|x| < 1$ (medium)

181. Find a power series representation for $f(x) = \frac{x}{x+5}$ and find its interval of convergence.

Answer: $\sum\limits_{n=0}^{\infty} (-1)^n (\frac{x}{5})^{n+1}$, interval of convergence $|x| < 5$ (medium)

182. Express the function $f(x) = \frac{5x+7}{x^2+2x-3}$ as the sum of a power series by first using partial fractions.

Answer: $\frac{2}{3} \sum\limits_{n=0}^{\infty} (-1)^n (\frac{x}{3})^n - 3 \sum\limits_{n=0}^{\infty} x^n$ (medium)

183. Find a power series representation for the function $f(x) = \ln \sqrt{1-x}$ and determine the radius of convergence.

Answer: $-\frac{1}{2} \sum\limits_{n=0}^{\infty} \frac{x^{n+1}}{n+1}$, radius of convergence 1 (medium)

184. Find a power series representation for $f(x) = \arctan(3x)$ and determine its radius of convergence.

Answer: $3 \sum\limits_{n=0}^{\infty} \frac{(-9)^n x^{2n+1}}{2n+1}$, radius of convergence $\frac{1}{3}$ (medium)

185. Evaluate $\int \frac{1}{1+x^5}\,dx$ as a power series.

Answer: $C + \sum\limits_{n=0}^{\infty} \frac{(-1)^n x^{5n+1}}{5n+1}$ (easy)

186. Approximate the definite integral $\int_0^1 e^{-x^2}\,dx$ accurate to six decimal places.

Answer: 0.746824 (medium)

187. Approximate the definite integral $\int_0^{1/2} \frac{\ln(1+x)}{x}\,dx$ accurate to six decimal places.

Answer: 0.448414 (medium)

188. a) Show that the function $f(x) = \sum\limits_{n=0}^{\infty} \frac{(8x)^n}{n!}$ is a solution to the differential equation $\frac{dy}{dx} = 8y$.
    b) Show that $f(x) = e^{8x}$.

Answer: a) $\frac{d}{dx} \sum\limits_{n=0}^{\infty} \frac{(8x)^n}{n!} = \sum\limits_{n=0}^{\infty} \frac{d}{dx}\left(\frac{(8x)^n}{n!}\right) = \sum\limits_{n=1}^{\infty} \frac{8^n n x^{n-1}}{n!}$

$\qquad = \sum\limits_{n=1}^{\infty} 8^n \frac{x^{n-1}}{(n-1)!} = 8 \sum\limits_{n=1}^{\infty} \frac{(8x)^{n-1}}{(n-1)!}$

$\qquad = 8 \sum\limits_{n=1}^{\infty} \frac{(8x)^n}{n!} = 8y$

b) $e^y = \sum\limits_{n=0}^{\infty} \frac{y^n}{n!}$; letting $y = 8x$, we have that $e^{8x} = \sum\limits_{n=0}^{\infty} \frac{(8x)^n}{n!} = f(x)$ (medium)

189. Find the sum of the series $\sum\limits_{n=1}^{\infty} \frac{n^2}{3^n}$.

Answer: 1.5 (hard)

190. Find the sum of the series $\sum\limits_{n=2}^{\infty} (n-1)x^n \qquad |x| < 1$.

Answer: $\frac{x^2}{(1-x)^2}$ (medium)

Chapter 10, Section 10
Taylor and Maclaurin Series

191. Find the coefficient of x^2 in the Maclaurin series for $f(x) = \frac{1}{x+2}$.

A) 1   B) 1/8   C) 1/2   D) $-1/4$
E) $-1/2$ F) -1 G) 1/4   H) $-1/8$

Answer: 1/8 (medium)

192. Find the coefficient of x^3 in the Maclaurin series for $f(x) = \sin 2x$.

A) $-2/3$ B) $-4/3$ C) $4/3$ D) $-8/3$
E) $2/3$ F) $8/3$ G) $-1/3$ H) $1/3$

Answer: $-4/3$ (medium)

193. Find the radius of convergence of the Maclaurin series for $f(x) = \frac{1}{4+x^2}$.

A) 1 B) $1/8$ C) ∞ D) $1/4$
E) $1/2$ F) 4 G) 8 H) 2

Answer: 2 (medium)

194. Find the coefficient of x^2 in the Maclaurin series for e^{x-1}.

A) e B) $1/e$ C) $1/(2e)$ D) 2
E) $1/2$ F) 0 G) 1 H) $e/2$

Answer: $1/(2e)$ (hard)

195. Find the coefficient of x^2 in the Maclaurin series for $f(x) = e^{-x^2}$.

A) $1/4$ B) -1 C) $1/2$ D) -2
E) 1 F) $-1/4$ G) $-1/2$ H) 2

Answer: -1 (easy)

196. Find the coefficient of x^5 in the Maclaurin series for $f(x) = \int \cos\left(x^2\right) dx$. (Note: the series is unique except for the constant of integration.)

A) $-1/10$ B) $1/15$ C) $-1/5$ D) $2/5$
E) $-2/5$ F) $-1/15$ G) $1/5$ H) $1/10$

Answer: $-1/10$ (medium)

197. Find a series representation of $\int \frac{e^x}{x} dx$.

A) $\sum_{n=0}^{\infty} \frac{x^n}{(n+1)!} + C$ B) $\sum_{n=0}^{\infty} \frac{x^{n+1}}{n!} + C$

C) $\sum_{n=0}^{\infty} \frac{x^{n+1}}{(n+1)!} + C$ D) $\sum_{n=1}^{\infty} \frac{(-1)^n}{n} x^n + C$

E) $\ln|x| + \sum_{n=1}^{\infty} \frac{x^n}{n \cdot n!} + C$ F) $\ln|x| + \sum_{n=1}^{\infty} \frac{x^n}{(n+1)!} + C$

G) $\ln|x| + \sum_{n=1}^{\infty} \frac{n+1}{n!} x^n + C$ H) $\ln|x| + \sum_{n=1}^{\infty} \frac{(-1)^n}{n!} x^n + C$

Answer: $\ln|x| + \sum_{n=1}^{\infty} \frac{x^n}{n \cdot n!} + C$ (medium)

198. Find the terms in the Maclaurin series for the function $f(x) = \ln(1 + x)$, as far as the term in x^3.

A) $1 - x + x^2 - x^3$

B) $x - x^2 + x^3$

C) $1 - x + \frac{1}{2}x^2 - \frac{1}{6}x^3$

D) $x - \frac{1}{2}x^2 + \frac{1}{3}x^3$

E) $1 + \frac{1}{2}x + \frac{2}{3}x^2 + \frac{5}{6}x^3$

F) $x + \frac{1}{2}x^2 + \frac{1}{6}x^3$

G) $1 + \frac{x}{2} + \frac{1}{6}x^2 + \frac{1}{24}x^3$

H) $x - \frac{1}{24}x^2 + \frac{1}{120}x^3$

Answer: $x - \frac{1}{2}x^2 + \frac{1}{3}x^3$ (medium)

199. Find the terms in the Maclaurin series for the function $f(x) = e^{-x}$, as far as the term in x^3.

A) $1 - x + \frac{1}{2}x^2 - \frac{1}{6}x^3$

B) $1 + x + \frac{1}{2}x^2 - \frac{1}{6}x^3$

C) $1 - x + x^2 - x^3$

D) $1 + x + x^2 + x^3$

E) $1 - x + \frac{1}{2}x^2 - \frac{1}{3}x^3$

F) $1 + x + \frac{1}{2}x^2 + \frac{1}{3}x^3$

G) $-x + x^3$

H) $x - x^3$

Answer: $1 - x + \frac{1}{2}x^2 - \frac{1}{6}x^3$ (easy)

200. Find the first four terms in the Maclaurin series for $f(x) = xe^{-x}$.

A) $x - x^2 + x^3 - x^4$

B) $x - \frac{1}{2}x^2 + \frac{1}{3}x^3 - \frac{1}{4}x^4$

C) $x - x^2 + \frac{1}{2}x^3 - \frac{1}{6}x^4$

D) $x - 2x^2 + 3x^3 - 4x^4$

E) $x + \frac{1}{2}x^2 + \frac{1}{6}x^3 + \frac{1}{24}x^4$

F) $x + x^2 + \frac{1}{3}x^3 + \frac{1}{8}x^4$

G) $x + x^2 + \frac{1}{2}x^3 + \frac{1}{6}x^4$

H) $\frac{1}{2}x - \frac{1}{6}x^2 + \frac{1}{24}x^3 - \frac{1}{120}x^4$

Answer: $x - x^2 + \frac{1}{2}x^3 - \frac{1}{6}x^4$ (medium)

201. Use a Maclaurin series to approximate $\int_0^1 e^{-t^2}\, dt$ with an accuracy of 0.01.

Answer: 0.7428571 (medium)

202. In terms of powers of x, the power series for $\frac{1}{1-x} = \sum\limits_{n=0}^{\infty} x^n$. Find the power series for $\frac{1}{(1-x)^2}$ in terms of powers of x.

Answer: $\sum\limits_{n=1}^{\infty} n x^{n-1}$ (easy)

203. Find the Taylor series for $x \cos x$ about the origin.

Answer: $\sum\limits_{n=0}^{\infty} \frac{(-1)^n x^{2n+1}}{(2n)!}$ (hard)

204. Give the Taylor series expansion of $f(x) = \sin x$ about the point $c = \frac{\pi}{4}$.

Answer: $\frac{\sqrt{2}}{2} + \frac{\sqrt{2}}{2}\left(x - \frac{\pi}{4}\right) - \frac{\sqrt{2}}{2} \cdot \frac{1}{2!}\left(x - \frac{\pi}{4}\right)^2 - \frac{\sqrt{2}}{2} \cdot \frac{1}{3!}\left(x - \frac{\pi}{4}\right)^3 + \cdots$ (medium)

205. Find the Taylor series for $y = \ln x$ at 2.

Answer: $\ln 2 + \sum\limits_{n=1}^{\infty} \frac{(-1)^{n-1}}{n}\left(\frac{x-2}{2}\right)^n$ (medium)

206. Find the Taylor polynomial of degree 4 at 0 for the function defined by $f(x) = \ln(1+x)$. Then compute the value of $\ln(1.1)$ accurate to as many decimal places as the polynomial of degree 4 allows.

Answer: $\ln(1+x) = x - \frac{1}{2}x^2 + \frac{1}{3}x^3 - \frac{1}{4}x^4$; $\ln(1.1) = .095$, accurate to three decimal places

(medium)

The following three questions pertain to the Taylor series about $x = 0$ for $f(x) = e^x$.

207. Derive the Taylor series about $x = 0$ for $f(x) = e^x$.

Answer: $\displaystyle\sum_{k=0}^{\infty} \frac{x^k}{k!}$ (easy)

208. Use the result of the last question to obtain the series expansion for e^{-x^2}.

Answer: $1 - x^2 + \frac{x^4}{2!} - \frac{x^6}{3!} + \frac{x^8}{4!} - \cdots$ (medium)

209. Use the result of the last question to obtain $\int_0^1 e^{-x^2}\, dx$ to two decimal place accuracy.

Answer: .74 (medium)

210. Find a Taylor series of degree 4 about $x = 0$ for $f(x) = \log \sec x$.

Answer: $\frac{x^2}{2} + \frac{x^4}{12}$ (medium)

211. Find the Maclaurin series expansion with $n = 5$ for $f(x) = 2^x$. Use this expansion to approximate $2^{.1}$.

Answer: $1 + (\ln 2)\, x + \frac{(\ln 2)^2\, x^2}{2!} + \frac{(\ln 2)^3\, x^3}{3!} + \frac{(\ln 2)^4\, x^4}{4!} + \frac{(\ln 2)^5\, x^5}{5!} + \cdots$; $2^{.1} \doteq 1.0718$ (hard)

212. Find the Maclaurin series expansion for $f(x) = \ln(1 - x)$ and determine the interval of convergence.

Answer: $\displaystyle\sum_{n=1}^{\infty} -\frac{1}{n}x^n$; converges for all x such that $-1 \le x < 1$. (medium)

213. If the Maclaurin series for $f(x)$ is $1 - 9x + 16x^2 - 25x^3 + \cdots$, then $f^3(0)$ is equal to

A) -25 B) $-25/6$ C) -150 D) $-25/3$
E) -75

Answer: -150 (medium)

214. Find the Taylor series of degree 5 about $x = 0$ for $y = \tan^2 x$.

Answer: $x^2 + \frac{2}{3}x^4 + \cdots$ (medium)

Chapter 10, Section 11
The Binomial Series

215. Find the coefficient of x^3 in the binomial series for $(1+x)^5$.

   A) 3   B) 6   C) 15   D) 20
   E) 10   F) 5   G) 16   H) 12

   Answer: 10 (easy)

216. Find the coefficient of x in the binomial series for $\sqrt{1+x}$.

   A) 2   B) -1 C) 1   D) $-1/2$
   E) 1/2   F) $-\sqrt{2}$ G) -2 H) $\sqrt{2}$

   Answer: 1/2 (easy)

217. Find the coefficient of x^3 in the binomial series for $\sqrt{1+x}$.

   A) $-1/2$ B) $-1/4$ C) 1/8   D) 1/2
   E) $-1/8$ F) $-1/16$ G) 1/16   H) 1/4

   Answer: 1/16 (medium)

218. Find the coefficient of x^3 in the binomial series for $\frac{1}{(1+x)^4}$.

   A) 6   B) 20   C) -6 D) -10
   E) -20 F) -12 G) 10   H) 12

   Answer: -20 (medium)

219. Use the binomial series to expand the function $\sqrt{4+x}$ as a power series. Give the coefficient of x^2 in that series.

   A) $-1/8$ B) $-1/32$ C) $-1/64$ D) 1/8
   E) 1/32   F) $-1/16$ G) 1/64   H) 1/16

   Answer: $-1/64$ (medium)

220. How many coefficients in the binomial series (expansion) of $(1+x)^7$ are divisible by 7?

   A) 0   B) 5   C) 7   D) 3
   E) 2   F) 6   G) 1   H) 4

   Answer: 6 (medium)

221. Find the terms in the power series expansion for the function $f(x) = \frac{1}{\sqrt{1+x^2}}$, as far as the term in x^3.

    A) $1 - x + x^2 - x^3$ B) $x - \frac{1}{2}x^2 + \frac{1}{3}x^3$ C) $1 - x + \frac{1}{2}x^2 - \frac{1}{6}x^3$

    D) $1 - x^2$ E) $1 + x^2$ F) $1 - \frac{1}{2}x + \frac{1}{24}x^2 - \frac{1}{120}x^3$

    G) $1 - \frac{1}{2}x^2$ H) $x + \frac{1}{6}x^3$

Answer: $1 - \frac{1}{2}x^2$ (medium)

222. Find the terms of the Maclaurin (binomial) series for $\frac{1}{\sqrt{1-x}}$, as far as the term in x^3.

    A) $1 - x + x^2 - x^3$ B) $1 - \frac{1}{2}x + \frac{1}{4}x^2 + \frac{1}{8}x^3$ C) $1 + \frac{1}{2}x + \frac{3}{8}x^2 + \frac{5}{16}x^3$

    D) $1 - \frac{1}{2}x + \frac{3}{4}x^2 - \frac{5}{8}x^3$ E) $1 + \frac{1}{2}x + \frac{1}{4}x^2 + \frac{1}{6}x^3$ F) $1 - \frac{1}{2}x + \frac{1}{6}x^2 + \frac{1}{24}x^3$

    G) $1 + \frac{1}{2}x + \frac{3}{4}x^2 + \frac{15}{16}x^3$ H) $1 - \frac{1}{2}x + \frac{3}{8}x^2 + \frac{7}{24}x^3$

Answer: $1 + \frac{1}{2}x + \frac{3}{8}x^2 + \frac{5}{16}x^3$ (medium)

223. Find the terms of the Maclaurin (binomial) series for $f(x) = \frac{1}{\sqrt{1+2x}}$, as far as the term in x^3.

    A) $1 - x + x^2 - x^3$ B) $1 + x - \frac{1}{2}x^2 + \frac{1}{3}x^3$ C) $1 - x + \frac{3}{2}x^2 - \frac{5}{2}x^3$

    D) $1 + x + 3x^2 + 5x^3$ E) $1 - x + \frac{3}{2}x^2 - \frac{7}{3}x^3$ F) $1 + x + \frac{1}{2}x^2 + \frac{7}{3}x^3$

    G) $1 - x + \frac{5}{2}x^2 - \frac{7}{3}x^3$ H) $1 + x + \frac{7}{2}x^2 + \frac{11}{3}x^3$

Answer: $1 - x + \frac{3}{2}x^2 - \frac{5}{2}x^3$ (hard)

224. Express $\frac{1}{\sqrt{1+x}}$ as a power series in x and from the result obtain a binomial series for $\frac{1}{\sqrt{1-x^2}}$.

Answer: $1 - \frac{1}{2}x + \sum_{n=2}^{\infty} \frac{(-1)^n \cdot 1 \cdot 3 \cdot 5 \cdots (2n-1)\, x^n}{2^n \cdot n!}$; $1 + \frac{1}{2}x^2 + \sum_{0}^{\infty} \frac{1 \cdot 3 \cdot 5 \cdots (2n-1)\, x^{2n}}{2^n \cdot n!}$ (hard)

225. Use the binomial series formula to obtain the Maclaurin series for $f(x) = (1+x)^{1/3}$.

Answer: $1 + \frac{1}{3}x + \sum_{n=2}^{\infty} \frac{(-1)^{n+1} \cdot 2 \cdot 5 \cdot 8 \cdots (3n-4)\, x^n}{3^n \cdot n!}$, for $|x| < 1$ (hard)

226. Find a power series representation for $(b+x)^{3/2}$ where b is a perfect square, and state the radius of convergence in terms of b.

Answer: $b^{3/2} + \frac{3b^{1/2}x}{2} + 3\sum_{n=2}^{\infty} \frac{(-1)^n \cdot 1 \cdot 3 \cdot 5 \cdots (2n-5)\, x^n b^{(3-2n)/2}}{2^n \cdot n!}$; $r = b$ (hard)

227. Use the binomial series to expand $\frac{1}{(1+x)^3}$ as a power series. State the radius of convergence.

Answer: $1 + \sum_{n=1}^{\infty} \frac{(-1)^n\, 3 \cdot 4 \cdot 5 \cdots (n+2)\, x^n}{n!}$ with $R = 1$ (medium)

228. Use the binomial series to expand $\sqrt[3]{1+x^2}$ as a power series. State the radius of convergence.

Answer: $1 + \frac{x^2}{3} + \sum_{n=2}^{\infty} \frac{(-1)^{n-1} \, 2\cdot 5\cdot 8 \cdots (3n-4) \, x^{2n}}{3^n \, n!}$ with $R = 1$ (medium)

229. Use the binomial series to expand $\frac{1}{\sqrt{2+x}}$ as a power series. State the radius of convergence.

Answer: $\frac{\sqrt{2}}{2}\left[1 + \sum_{n=1}^{\infty} \frac{(-1)^n \, 1\cdot 3\cdot 5 \cdots (2n-1) \, x^n}{2^{2n} \, n!}\right]$ with $\left|\frac{x}{2}\right| < 1$ so $|x| < 2$ and $R = 2$. (hard)

230. Use the binomial series to expand $(4+x)^{3/2}$ as a power series. State the radius of convergence.

Answer: $8 + 3x + \sum_{n=2}^{\infty} \frac{(3)\,(1)\,(-1)\cdots(5-2n)\,x^n}{8^{n-1} \, n!}$ with $\left|\frac{x}{4}\right| < 1$ so $|x| < 4$ and $R = 4$. (hard)

231. Use the binomial series to expand $\frac{x^2}{\sqrt{1-x^3}}$ as a power series. State the radius of convergence.

Answer: $x^2 + \sum_{n=1}^{\infty} \frac{1\cdot 3\cdot 5 \cdots (2n-1)\,x^{3n+2}}{2^n \, n!}$ with $R = 1$ (hard)

232. Use the binomial series to expand $\sqrt[5]{x-1}$ as a power series. State the radius of convergence.

Answer: $-1 + \frac{x}{5} + \sum_{n=2}^{\infty} \frac{4\cdot 9 \cdots (5n-6)\,x^n}{5^n \, n!}$ with $R = 1$ (hard)

Chapter 10, Section 12
Applications of Taylor Polynomials

233. According to Taylor's Formula, what is the maximum error possible in the use of the sum $\sum_{n=0}^{4} x^n/n!$ to approximate e^x in the interval $-1 \le x \le 1$?

A) $e/240$ B) $e/48$ C) $e/480$ D) $e/24$
E) $e/20$ F) $e/120$ G) $e/12$ H) $e/60$

Answer: $e/120$ (medium)

234. Find the coefficient of $(x-2)^2$ in the Taylor polynomial $T_2(x)$ for the function x^3 at the number 2.

A) 3   B) 0   C) 1   D) 6
E) 2   F) 5   G) 8   H) 4

Answer: 6 (medium)

235. What is the smallest value of n that will guarantee (according to Taylor's Formula) that the Taylor polynomial T_n at the number 0 will be within 0.0001 of e^x for $0 \leq x \leq 1$?

A) 4   B) 5   C) 8   D) 6
E) 7   F) 2   G) 3   H) 9

Answer: 7 (hard)

236. Find the fourth degree Taylor's polynomial of the function $f(x) = xe^x$ at the number $a = 0$.

Answer: $x + x^2 + \frac{x^3}{2} + \frac{x^4}{6}$ (medium)

237. Find the Taylor polynomial $T_3(x)$ for the function $f(x) = \frac{5x}{2+4x}$ at the point $x_0 = 0$.

Answer: $T_3(x) = \frac{15}{48} x^3 - \frac{5}{16} x^2 + \frac{5}{4} x$ (medium)

238. Use a Taylor polynomial of degree 5 to approximate the function $f(x) = \sin x$.

Answer: $x - \frac{1}{6} x^3 + \frac{1}{120} x^5$ (easy)

239. Write the fourth degree Taylor polynomial centered about the origin for the function $f(x) = e^{-2x}$.

Answer: $T_4(x) = 1 - 2x - 2x^2 - \frac{4}{3} x^3 + \frac{2}{3} x^4$ (medium)

240. Find the Taylor polynomial, $T_3(x)$, for $f(x) = xe^x$.

Answer: $T_3(x) = 0 + x + x^2 + \frac{1}{2} x^3$ (easy)

241. Find the second degree Taylor polynomial for $f(x) = \sqrt{x}$, centered about $a = 100$. Also obtain a bound for the error in using this polynomial to approximate $\sqrt{100.1}$.

Answer: $T_2(x) = 10 + \frac{1}{20} (x - 100) - \frac{1}{8000} (x - 100)^2$; $|\text{error}| \leq 6 \times 10^{-10}$ (hard)

242. $\boxed{C}$ Find an approximation for $\sin(.1)$ accurate to 6 decimal places (the .1 is in radians).

Answer: 0.099833 (medium)

243. Give the 4th degree Taylor polynomial for $f(x) = \sqrt{x}$ about the point $x = 4$. Using this polynomial, approximate $\sqrt{4.2}$. Give the maximum error for this approximation.

Answer: $T_4(x) = 2 + \frac{x-4}{4} + \frac{(x-4)^2}{64} + \frac{(x-4)^3}{512} - \frac{5(x-4)^4}{16384} + R_4$; $\sqrt{4.2} \doteq 2.049390137$;

$R_4 \doteq 0.0000000171$ (hard)

244. $\boxed{C}$ Use the 3rd degree Taylor polynomial of $f(x) = \sqrt{x}$ about $x = 4$ to approximate $\sqrt{6}$. Use the remainder term to give an upper bound for the error in the above approximation.

Answer: $\sqrt{6} \doteq T_3(6) = 2 + \frac{2}{4} - \frac{2^2}{64} + \frac{2^3}{512} = 2.453125$; $|\text{error}| \leq 0.005$ (hard)

245. $\boxed{C}$ Find the third degree Taylor polynomial, with remainder, centered at $x = 1$ for $f(x) = \ln x$. Use this result to approximate $\ln(1.2)$ and estimate the accuracy of this approximation.

Answer: $T_3(x) = (x-1) - \frac{1}{2!}(x-1)^2 + \frac{2}{3!}(x-1)^3$, $R_3(x) = \frac{-(x-1)^4}{4c^4}$ where c is some

number between 1 and x; $\ln(1.2) \doteq 0.18266$ with $R_3(1.2) \leq 0.0004$.

The approximation is accurate to 3 decimal places. (hard)

246. Write the Taylor polynomial at 0 of degree 4 for $f(x) = \ln(1+x)$.

Answer: $x - \frac{1}{2}x^2 + \frac{1}{3}x^3 - \frac{1}{4}x^4$ (medium)

247. $\boxed{G}$ Estimate the range of values of x for which the approximation $\frac{1}{x} = 1 - (x-1) + (x-1)^2$ is accurate to within 0.01

A) $[0.68, 1.41]$ B) $[0.61, 1.54]$ C) $[0.995, 1.005]$ D) $[1.51, 2.59]$
E) $[0.95, 1.05]$ F) $[0.80, 1.23]$ G) $[0.980, 1.023]$ H) $[0.89, 1.14]$

Answer: $[0.80, 1.23]$ (medium)

248. $\boxed{G}$ Estimate the range of values of x for which the approximation $\ln x = \ln 2 + \frac{1}{2}(x-2) - \frac{1}{8}(x-2)^2$ is accurate to within 0.01.

A) $[1.08, 3.20]$ B) $[1.80, 2.20]$ C) $[0.89, 3.56]$ D) $[1.43, 2.66]$
E) $[0.45, 1.78]$ F) $[0.71, 1.33]$ G) $[1.90, 2.10]$ H) $[1.99, 2.01]$

Answer: $[1.43, 2.66]$ (medium)

249. $\boxed{G}$ Estimate the range of values of x for which the approximation $\sqrt{x^2+3} = 2 + \frac{1}{2}(x-1) + \frac{3}{16}(x-1)^2$ is accurate to within 0.0002.

Answer: $[0.84, 1.16]$ (medium)

250. $\boxed{G}$ Estimate the range of values of x for which the approximation $e^x \cos x = 1 + x - \frac{1}{3}x^3$ is accurate to within 0.001

Answer: $[-0.282, 0.274]$ (medium)

Calculus, 3rd Edition
by James Stewart
Appendix A
Numbers, Inequalities, and Absolute Values

1. The solution set of the inequality $|x - 1| < 12$ is of the form $(a, 13)$. Find the value of a.

    A) -12 B) -9 C) -11 D) -6
    E) -7 F) -13 G) -10 H) -8

    Answer: -11 (easy)

2. The solution set of the inequality $|2 - x| \geq 10$ is of the form $(-\infty, -8] \cup [a, \infty)$. Find the value of a.

    A) -7 B) 11 C) -4 D) 8
    E) 12 F) -6 G) 9 H) 10

    Answer: 12 (easy)

3. The solution set of the inequality $|3x - 2| \geq 7$ is of the form $(-\infty, a] \cup [3, \infty)$. Find the value of a.

    A) $-7/5$ B) $-7/2$ C) $-5/7$ D) $-5/2$
    E) $-2/5$ F) $-5/3$ G) $-2/7$ H) $-7/3$

    Answer: $-5/3$ (medium)

4. The solution set of the inequality $x^2 - 2x \leq 15$ is of the form $[a, 5]$. Find the value of a.

    A) 2 B) -4 C) 0 D) -3
    E) -5 F) -1 G) -2 H) 1

    Answer: -3 (medium)

5. The solution set of the inequality $x^2 + x - 1 \geq 0$ is an interval of the form $[a, b]$. Find the value of $b - a$ (that is, the length of the interval).

    A) $\sqrt{2}$ B) 3 C) 2 D) $3/2$
    E) $5/2$ F) $\sqrt{3}/2$ G) $\sqrt{3}$ H) $\sqrt{5}$

    Answer: $\sqrt{5}$ (medium)

6. The solution set of the inequality $|x+1| + |x - 2| \leq 5$ is an interval of the form $[a, b]$. Find the value of $b - a$ (that is, the length of the interval).

    A) 6 B) 1 C) 7 D) 8
    E) 3 F) 2 G) 4 H) 5

    Answer: 5 (hard)

7. Find the smaller of the two roots of the equation $\left|\frac{4x-2}{x+1}\right| = 1$.

A) 1   B) $\frac{1}{3}$ C) $\frac{2}{3}$ D) -1

E) $-\frac{2}{3}$ F) $-\frac{1}{3}$ G) $\frac{1}{5}$ H) $-\frac{1}{5}$

Answer: $-\frac{1}{5}$ (hard)

8. Given $|x-4| = |2x+1|$ find the values of x.

Answer: $1, -5$ (medium)

9. The solution set of the inequality $|x+1| + |x-2| \leq |5-x|$ is an interval of the form $[a, b]$. Find the value of $b - a$ (that is, the length of the interval).

A) 6   B) 1   C) 7   D) 8

E) 3   F) 2   G) 4   H) 5

Answer: 6   (hard)

10. The solution set of the inequality $|x+1| - |3-x| \geq |x-2|$ is an interval of the form $[a, b]$. Find the value of $b - a$ (that is, the length of the interval).

A) 4   B) 3   C) $4\frac{1}{3}$ D) $4\frac{2}{3}$

E) $3\frac{2}{3}$ F) 2   G) $3\frac{1}{3}$ H) $3\frac{1}{2}$

Answer: $4\frac{2}{3}$ (hard)

Calculus, 3rd Edition
by James Stewart
Appendix B
Coordinate Geometry and Lines

1. Find the slope of the line through the two points $(1, 3)$ and $(7, 13)$.

   A) 5/3   B) −4/7   C) −7/4   D) 4/7

   E) −3/5   F) 7/4   G) 3/5   H) −5/3

   Answer: 5/3 (easy)

2. Find the y-intercept of the line through the two points $(4, 9)$ and $(18, 2)$.

   A) 9.5   B) 9   C) 12   D) 10.5

   E) 11   F) 11.5   G) 10   H) 12.5

   Answer: 11 (medium)

3. Find the y-intercept of the line passing through the point $(6, 5)$ and perpendicular to the line $y = 2x + 17$.

   A) 6   B) 10   C) 12   D) 8

   E) 0   F) 2   G) −2   H) 4

   Answer: 8 (medium)

4. Find the slope of the line that has y-intercept equal to 3.5 and passes through the point $(3, 5)$.

   A) −2/3   B) 3/2   C) −2   D) 2/3

   E) 2   F) 1/2   G) −3/2   H) −1/2

   Answer: 1/2 (easy)

5. Find the angle of inclination, in degrees, of the line through the two points $\left(0, \sqrt{3}\right)$ and $(1, 0)$.

   A) 45   B) 30   C) 60   D) 90

   E) 120   F) 180   G) 150   H) 135

   Answer: 120 (easy)

6. Find the x-coordinate of the point of intersection of the two lines $y = 2x + 13$ and $y = 4x - 49$.

   A) −18   B) 18   C) −62   D) −36

   E) 31   F) 36   G) −31   H) 62

   Answer: 31 (medium)

7. Find the y-intercept of the perpendicular bisector of the line segment joining the two points $(3, 2)$ and $(6, 3)$.

A) -16
B) 8
C) 9
D) 16
E) 12
F) -8
G) -12
H) -9

Answer: 16 (hard)

8. Find the distance between the two points $(0, 7)$ and $(3, 3)$.

A) $\sqrt{4}$
B) 4
C) $\sqrt{5}$
D) $\sqrt{2}$
E) 3
F) $\sqrt{3}$
G) 5
H) 2

Answer: 5 (easy)

9. Find the distance between the two points $(0, 1)$ and $(2, 0)$.

A) $\sqrt{4}$
B) $\sqrt{2}$
C) 3
D) 4
E) 2
F) 5
G) $\sqrt{3}$
H) $\sqrt{5}$

Answer: $\sqrt{5}$ (easy)

10. Find the point on the x-axis that is equidistant from $(1, 1)$ and $(2, 2)$.

A) $(1.5, 0)$
B) $(-1.5, 0)$
C) $(2, 0)$
D) $(-2.5, 0)$
E) $(-3, 0)$
F) $(3, 0)$
G) $(2.5, 0)$
H) $(-2, 0)$

Answer: $(3, 0)$ (medium)

11. Find the x-coordinate of the midpoint of the line segment joining the points $(35, 29)$ and $(-117, 22)$.

A) $51/2$
B) -41
C) $-51/2$
D) $-7/2$
E) 76
F) -76
G) $7/2$
H) 41

Answer: -41 (medium)

12. Find the equation of the perpendicular bisector of the segment joining the points $(-4, 0)$ and $(8, 6)$.

A) $2x + y = 7$
B) $x + y = 7$
C) $x + 2y = 7$
D) $x + y = 3$
E) $2x + y = 3$
F) $x + 2y = 3$
G) $x - 2y = 4$
H) $2x - y = 4$

Answer: $2x + y = 7$ (medium)

13. Given the points $A(6, -7)$, $B(-3, -1)$, and $C(2, -2)$ use slopes to show that ABC is a right triangle.

Answer: $m_{AB} = \frac{-3-(-7)}{11-6} = \frac{4}{5}$ and $m_{AC} = \frac{-2-(-7)}{2-6} = -\frac{5}{4}$. Thus $m_{AB} \cdot m_{AC} = -1$

and so AB is perpendicular to AC and $\triangle ABC$ must be a right triangle. (medium)

14. Show that $A(1, 1)$, $B(11, 3)$, $C(10, 8)$, and $D(0, 6)$ are vertices of a rectangle.

Answer: The slopes of the four sides are: $m_{AB} = \frac{3-1}{11-1} = \frac{1}{5}$, $m_{BC} = \frac{8-3}{10-11} = -5$, $m_{CD} = \frac{6-8}{0-10} = \frac{1}{5}$, and $m_{DA} = \frac{1-6}{1-0} = -5$. Hence $AB \parallel CD$, $BC \parallel DA$, $AB \perp BC$, $BC \perp CD$, $CD \perp DA$, and $DA \perp AB$, and so $ABCD$ is a rectangle.

(medium)

15. Show that the lines $3x - 5y + 19 = 0$ and $10x + 6y - 50 = 0$ are perpendicular and find their point of intersection.

Answer: $3x - 5y + 19 = 0 \Leftrightarrow 5y = 3x + 19 \Leftrightarrow y = \frac{3}{5}x + \frac{19}{5} \Rightarrow m_1 = \frac{3}{5}$ and $10x + 6y - 50 = 0 \Leftrightarrow 6y = -10x + 50 \Leftrightarrow y = -\frac{5}{3}x + \frac{25}{3} \Rightarrow m_2 = -\frac{5}{3}$.
Since $m_1 m_2 = \frac{3}{5}\left(-\frac{5}{3}\right) = -1$ the two lines are perpendicular. To find the point of intersection:
$\frac{3}{5}x + \frac{19}{5} = -\frac{5}{3}x + \frac{25}{3} \Leftrightarrow 9x + 57 = -25x + 125 \Leftrightarrow 34x = 68 \Leftrightarrow x = 2 \Rightarrow y = \frac{3}{5}(2) + \frac{19}{5} = \frac{25}{5} = 5$. Thus, the point of intersection is $(2, 5)$. (medium)

Calculus, 3rd Edition
by James Stewart
Appendix C
Graphs of Second-Degree Equations

1. Find the y-coordinate of the vertex of the parabola $y + 3 = x^2$.

    A) $-4/9$ B) $-9/4$ C) $9/4$ D) $-3/2$
    E) $3/2$ F) $4/9$ G) 3 H) -3

    Answer: -3 (easy)

2. Find the x-coordinate of the vertex of the parabola $y = x^2 + x$.

    A) -4 B) $-1/4$ C) $-1/2$ D) $1/2$
    E) 4 F) -2 G) 2 H) $1/4$

    Answer: $-1/2$ (medium)

3. Find the positive x-intercept of the ellipse $4x^2 + 9y^2 = 36$.

    A) 3 B) 6 C) 8 D) 4
    E) 9 F) 12 G) 2 H) 8

    Answer: 3 (medium)

4. Find the x-coordinate of the center of the ellipse $2x^2 + 6x + y^2 = 0$.

    A) 3 B) $-3/2$ C) $3/2$ D) 2
    E) $1/2$ F) -3 G) -2 H) $-1/2$

    Answer: $-3/2$ (medium)

5. Find the slope of the positive-sloped asymptote of the hyperbola $\frac{x^2}{2^2} - \frac{y^2}{3^2} = 4$.

    A) $3/2$ B) $1/2$ C) $1/3$ D) $2/3$
    E) 2 F) 3 G) $4/9$ H) $9/4$

    Answer: $3/2$ (medium)

6. For what value of the number c is the hyperbola $4x^2 - cy^2 = 144$ an equilateral hyperbola?

    A) 12 B) 72 C) 1 D) 6
    E) 9 F) 36 G) 4 H) 576

    Answer: 4 (medium)

7. Find the x-coordinate of the point or points farthest to the right in the region bounded by the curves $y = 3x$, $x = y^2$.

A) 9 B) $\sqrt{3}/3$ C) 1/27 D) 1/9
E) $\sqrt{3}$ F) 3 G) 1/3 H) 27

Answer: 1/9 (medium)

8. Find the radius of the circle $x^2 + y^2 - 2x + 4y = 4$.

A) $\sqrt{3}$ B) 4 C) 3 D) $\sqrt{5}$
E) 5 F) 2 G) $\sqrt{2}$ H) 1

Answer: 3 (medium)

9. Find the x-coordinate of the center of the circle $x^2 + 3x + y^2 + 6y = 15$.

A) 5/2 B) 1/2 C) −1/2 D) −5/2
E) 3/2 F) −3 G) −3/2 H) 3

Answer: −3/2 (medium)

10. For what value of c does the equation $x^2 + 2x + y^2 + 4y = c$ represent not a circle but rather a single point?

A) 6 B) −4 C) −6 D) 5
E) 4 F) −3 G) 3 H) −5

Answer: −5 (medium)

Calculus, 3rd Edition
by James Stewart
Appendix D
Trigonometry

1.   Convert 140° to radians .

   Answer: $\frac{7\pi}{9}$ (easy)

2.   Convert −135° to radians .

   Answer: $-\frac{3\pi}{4}$ (easy)

3.   Convert $\frac{\pi}{18}$ to degrees .

   Answer: 10° (easy)

4.   Convert $\frac{5\pi}{8}$ to degrees .

   Answer: 112.5° (easy)

5.   If a circle has radius 5 m, what is the length of an arc subtended by a central arc of $\frac{4\pi}{7}$ rad?

   Answer: $\frac{20\pi}{7}$ m (easy)

6.   If a circle has radius 4 m, what angle is subtended at the center of the circle by an arc π m long?

   Answer: $\frac{\pi}{4}$ rad (easy)

7.   Use a trignometric identity to find the exact value of sin 15°.

   Answer: $\frac{\sqrt{6}}{4} - \frac{\sqrt{2}}{4}$ (medium)

8.   Use a trignometric identity to find the exact value of cos 75°.

   Answer: $\frac{\sqrt{6}}{4} - \frac{\sqrt{2}}{4}$ (medium)

9.   Find $\sin \theta$ if $\sec \theta = 5$, $\frac{3\pi}{4} < \theta < 2\pi$.

   Answer: $-\frac{2\sqrt{6}}{5}$ (medium)

10.   Find $\tan \theta$ if $\cos \theta = \frac{2}{3}, 0 < \theta < \frac{\pi}{4}$.

   Answer: $\frac{\sqrt{5}}{2}$ (medium)

11. Find all values of x in the interval $[0, 2\pi]$ that satisfy the equation $\sin^2 2x = 2\sin^2 x$.

Answer: $0,\ \frac{\pi}{4},\ \frac{3\pi}{4},\ \pi,\ \frac{5\pi}{4},\ \frac{7\pi}{4},\ 2\pi$ (medium)

Calculus, 3rd Edition
by James Stewart
Appendix H
Complex Numbers

1. Write the expression $(4 + 6i) + (7 - i)$ in the form $a + bi$.

   Answer: $11 + 5i$ (easy)

2. Write the expression $(3 - i)(6 + 2i)$ in the form $a + bi$.

   Answer: $20 + 0i$ (easy)

3. Write the expression $\frac{6-2i}{1-2i}$ in the form $a + bi$.

   Answer: $2 + 2i$ (easy)

4. Write the complex conjugate of $(3i - 1)(6 + i)$ in the form $a + bi$.

   Answer: $-9 - 17i$ (easy)

5. Write the number $e^{2+\frac{\pi}{4}i}$ in the form $a + bi$.

   Answer: $\frac{\sqrt{2}}{2} e^2 + \frac{\sqrt{2}}{2} e^2 i$ (easy)

6. Write the number $e^{\frac{\pi}{3}i}$ in the form $a + bi$.

   Answer: $\frac{1}{2} + \frac{\sqrt{3}}{2} i$ (easy)

7. Find all solutions of the equation $x^2 - 5x + 7 = 0$.

   Answer: $\frac{5}{2} + \frac{\sqrt{3}}{2} i, \frac{5}{2} - \frac{\sqrt{3}}{2} i$ (medium)

8. Find all solutions of the equation $x^4 - x^2 + 1 = 0$.

   Answer: $\frac{\sqrt{3}}{2} + \frac{1}{2} i, -\frac{\sqrt{3}}{2} - \frac{1}{2} i, \frac{1}{2} + \frac{\sqrt{3}}{2} i, -\frac{1}{2} - \frac{\sqrt{3}}{2} i$ (hard)

9. Find all solutions of the equation $x^3 + 8 = 0$.

   Answer: $1 + \sqrt{3} i, 1 - \sqrt{3} i, -2$ (medium)

10. Find $(1 + i)^{10}$ using De Moivre's Theorem.

    Answer: $32i$ (medium)

11. Write the number $\sqrt{3} + i$ in polar form with argument between 0 and 2π.,,

Answer: $2e^{\frac{\pi}{6}i}$ (easy)
+

Now symbolic computation and mathematical typesetting is as accessible as your Windows™-based word processor!

Scientific WorkPlace™ 2.0 for Windows

Producing publication-quality course materials, journal articles, research reports, or full-length books has never been so easy!

"Scientific WorkPlace is a heavy-duty mathematical word processor and typesetting system that is able to expand, simplify, and evaluate conventional mathematical expressions and compose them as elegant printed mathematics. It gives working mathematicians LaTeX without pain."
—Roger Horn, University of Utah

"The thing I like most about Scientific WorkPlace is its basic simplicity and ease of use. With an absolute minimum of effort, one can begin to do things that LaTeX and Maple can help with."
—Barbara Osofsky, Rutgers University

Easy access to a powerful computer algebra system *inside* your word-processing documents!

Scientific WorkPlace is a revolutionary program that gives you a "work place" environment—a single place to do all your work. It combines the ease of use of a technical word processor with the typesetting power of TeX and the numerical, symbolic, and graphic computational facilities of the **Maple**® V computer algebra system. All capabilities are included in the program—you don't need to *own* or *learn* TeX, LaTeX, or Maple to use *Scientific WorkPlace*—**everything for super productivity is included in one powerful tool for just $495.00!**

With *Scientific WorkPlace*, you can enter, solve, and graph mathematical problems right in your word-processing documents in seconds, with no clumsy cut-and-paste from equation editors or clipboards. Input mathematics as easily as you type in words. *Scientific WorkPlace* calculates answers quickly and accurately, then prints your work in impressive, professional-quality documents using TeX's internationally accepted mathematical typesetting standard. More than 200 document styles, AMS fonts, and a style editor are included.

Install *Scientific WorkPlace* and watch your productivity soar! You'll be creating professional-quality documents in a fraction of the time you would spend using any other program!

ORDER FORM

Yes! Please send me Scientific Workplace 2.0 for Windows

_____ copies (ISBN: 0-534-25596-5) @ $495.00 each   _____

(Residents of AL, AZ, CA, CO, CT, FL, GA, IL, IN, KS, KY, LA, MA, MD, MI, MN, MO, NC, NJ, NY, OH, PA, RI, SC, TN, TX, UT, VA, WA, WI must add appropriate sales tax)   Tax   _____

Payment Options   Handling _____
_____ Purchase Order enclosed. Please bill me.
_____ Check or Money Order enclosed.   Total   _____
_____ Charge my _____ VISA _____ MasterCard _____ American Express

Card Number _____ Expiration Date _____

Signature_____

Please ship to: (Billing and shipping address must be the same.)

Name_____

Department _____ School _____

Street Address _____

City _____ State_____ Zip+4_____

Office phone number (_____) _____

You can fax your response to us at 408-375-6414 or e-mail your order to: info@brookscole.com or detach, fold, secure, and mail with payment.

SECURE WITH TAPE

CUT ALONG DOTTED LINE

FOLD HERE

BUSINESS REPLY MAIL

FIRST CLASS   PERMIT NO. 358   PACIFIC GROVE, CA

POSTAGE WILL BE PAID BY ADDRESSEE

ATTN: _____ MARKETING _____

Brooks/Cole Publishing Company
511 Forest Lodge Road
Pacific Grove, California 93950-9968

NO POSTAGE
NECESSARY
IF MAILED
IN THE
UNITED STATES

FOLD HERE

EXP® Version 3.0
The Scientific Word Processor for Windows™
$318.00

WYSIWYG math editing and word processing
ideal for students and professionals in mathematics, science, and engineering!

No more hassles. No more headaches. With **EXP Version 3.0**, creating scientific or mathematical documents can be hassle-free, and even fun! As you type in your document, including mathematical equations or formulas, your work appears on the screen *as it will appear on the printed page*. All the mathematical symbols, spacing, and italics are correctly placed—no need for you to jump to a special math editing window.

If you are serious about including mathematical expressions in documents, then EXP Version 3.0 is the tool of choice. EXP Version 3.0 allows you to:

- mix mathematical notation and formulas freely with text and graphics
- handle the special requirements of typesetting chemical expressions
- use more than 500 special symbols
- typeset your mathematical text as small as 4 point or as large as 612 point, and print that text on any Windows-supported printer
- use any word-processing feature, including the automatic numbering facility, anywhere, even inside formulas
- use the find and replace command to find a math expression and replace it with a different one
- create "text libraries" to store pieces of text or mathematics to which you refer frequently

---

ORDER FORM

Yes! Please send me the Student Edition of EXP Version 3.0, The Scientific Word Processor for Windows (ISBN: 0-534-19608-X)
____ copies @ $318.00 each

(Residents of AL, AZ, CA, CO, CT, FL, GA, IL, IN, KS, KY, LA, MA, MD, MI, MN, MO, NC, NJ, NY, OH, PA, RI,SC, TN, TX, UT, VA, WA, WI must add appropriate sales tax)

Subtotal _____

Tax _____

Handling _____

Total _____

Payment Options
__Purchase Order enclosed. Please bill me.
__Check or Money Order enclosed.
__Charge my __VISA __MasterCard ___American Express
Card Number _____Expiration Date_____
Signature_____

Please ship to: (Billing and shipping address must be the same.)
Name_____
Department_____School_____
Street Address_____
City_____ State_____ Zip+4_____
Office phone number(____)_____
You can fax your response to us at 408-375-6414 or e-mail your order to: info@brookscole.com
or detach, fold, secure, and mail with payment.

SECURE WITH TAPE

CUT ALONG DOTTED LINE

FOLD HERE

NO POSTAGE
NECESSARY
IF MAILED
IN THE
UNITED STATES

BUSINESS REPLY MAIL

FIRST CLASS   PERMIT NO. 358   PACIFIC GROVE, CA

POSTAGE WILL BE PAID BY ADDRESSEE

ATTN: MARKETING

Brooks/Cole Publishing Company
511 Forest Lodge Road
Pacific Grove, California 93950-9968

FOLD HERE